ELECTROMECHANICAL ENERGY CONVERSION

McGRAW-HILL ELECTRICAL AND ELECTRONIC ENGINEERING SERIES

FREDERICK EMMONS TERMAN, *Consulting Editor*
W. W. HARMAN AND J. G. TRUXAL, *Associate Consulting Editors*

AHRENDT AND SAVANT · Servomechanism Practice
ANGELO · Electronic Circuits
ASELTINE · Transform Method in Linear System Analysis
ATWATER · Introduction to Microwave Theory
BAILEY AND GAULT · Alternating-current Machinery
BERANEK · Acoustics
BRENNER AND JAVID · Analysis of Electric Circuits
BRUNS AND SAUNDERS · Analysis of Feedback Control Systems
CAGE · Theory and Application of Industrial Electronics
CAUER · Synthesis of Linear Communication Networks
CHIRLIAN AND ZEMANIAN · Electronics
CLEMENT AND JOHNSON · Electrical Engineering Science
COTE AND OAKES · Linear Vacuum-tube and Transistor Circuits
CUCCIA · Harmonics, Sidebands, and Transients in Communication Engineering
CUNNINGHAM · Introduction to Nonlinear Analysis
EASTMAN · Fundamentals of Vacuum Tubes
EVANS · Control-system Dynamics
FEINSTEIN · Foundations of Information Theory
FITZGERALD AND HIGGINBOTHAM · Basic Electrical Engineering
FITZGERALD AND KINGSLEY · Electric Machinery
FRANK · Electrical Measurement Analysis
FRIEDLAND, WING, AND ASH · Principles of Linear Networks
GEPPERT · Basic Electron Tubes
GLASFORD · Fundamentals of Television Engineering
GREINER · Semiconductor Devices and Applications
HAMMOND · Electrical Engineering
HANCOCK · An Introduction to the Principles of Communication Theory
HAPPELL AND HESSELBERTH · Engineering Electronics
HARMAN · Fundamentals of Electronic Motion
HARMAN AND LYTLE · Electrical and Mechanical Networks
HARRINGTON · Introduction to Electromagnetic Engineering
HARRINGTON · Time-harmonic Electromagnetic Fields
HAYT · Engineering Electromagnetics
HILL · Electronics in Engineering
JOHNSON · Transmission Lines and Networks
KOENIG AND BLACKWELL · Electromechanical System Theory
KRAUS · Antennas
KRAUS · Electromagnetics
KUH AND PEDERSON · Principles of Circuit Synthesis
LEDLEY · Digital Computer and Control Engineering
LePAGE · Analysis of Alternating-current Circuits
LePAGE AND SEELY · General Network Analysis

ELECTROMECHANICAL
ENERGY CONVERSION

Samuel Seely, Ph.D.

Professor of Electrical Engineering
Case Institute of Technology

McGRAW-HILL BOOK COMPANY, INC. 1962

New York   San Francisco   Toronto   London

ELECTROMECHANICAL ENERGY CONVERSION

THE MAPLE PRESS COMPANY, YORK, PA.

Preface

There has been a growing recognition of the need for a presentation of general energy-conversion principles as part of the electrical-engineering student's scientific foundation. Several books have made considerable strides along these lines during the last decade. This book has been prepared to extend these general principles and to apply them to the description of the operation and performance of broad classes of devices.

Among the major topics which receive attention in this book are a formulation of the general principles of electromechanical energy conversion; energy transfer, a general study of coupled circuits with air and iron cores; energy conversion in incremental transducers; energy conversion in rotating machinery. Clearly, the objectives of the book are limited, since energy conversion in its broadest application goes far beyond the study of electromechanical devices.

One of the important features of the presentation is the development of very powerful general methods of analysis, usually following the presentation of a series of progressively more complicated problems of a given class, to provide the tools for general study. For example, dynamic problem analysis is formulated from an energy point of view through the application of Lagrange's equations. This approach has the advantage that the method is general and may be used to analyze problems beyond those of any given discipline of engineering. In fact, in mixed electromechanical transducers, with which we are concerned, the analysis by such a general method proves to be particularly convenient.

Another feature of the study is the presentation of alternative methods of approach to a given class of problems. Such presentations are made in the discussion of the transformer, where a network and a transformer emf analysis are given. Moreover, some discussion is also included to lend substance to the analysis of the transformer from an electromagnetic-field-theory point of view. An interesting and a more extensive parallel development is to be found in the discussion of rotating energy converters. Here a substantially network formulation is introduced, with the analysis proceeding from a study of the system as viewed through the electrical and mechanical ports. Following the analysis of a series of d-c machines of different types, the Kron primitive (generalized) machine is introduced as a suitable model for general study. This model is then employed to study a number of important types of a-c machinery. Later the study introduces the White-Woodson model, and this is initially examined from an electromagnetic-field-theory point of view so that the student will understand the important aspects of such an analysis. This analysis is carried sufficiently far to show that it yields essentially the same results as those deduced from the Kron model. In fact, one might almost say that these models are mathematical transformations of each other and that one is derivable from the other by appropriate transformations. In both cases the discussion is largely limited to the machines with balanced excitation, although in a few special examples the excitation is unbalanced. The more general discussion of unbalanced excitation is carried out for the general n-m-phase machine. Here the purpose is to show the general analytical method, rather than to exploit the results.

In the development of the text material, it has been assumed that the student has completed a program in network theory, including transient analysis, and that he has also completed work in electric- and magnetic-field theory up to an introductory level of Maxwell's equations.[1] It is for this reason that a discussion is ordinarily considered to be completed when the differential equations which describe the system under survey have been deduced or when an equivalent network has been found which represents the system. It is assumed that the student can carry out a detailed solution in any particular case.

Most of the material in this book has been classroom-tested, with very successful results. The experiences and efforts of the author's colleagues at Case Institute of Technology, Drs. R. D. Chenoweth and J. S. Meisel, in helping with the development of this material is gratefully acknowledged. Also, the "core-program" notes, prepared at the Massachusetts Institute of Technology and made available at the September, 1957, Workshop in Electrical Engineering Education through the kind offices of Dean Gordon S. Brown, are acknowledged for detail and direction. Particular acknowledgment is made of the notes and the subsequent book by Drs. D. C. White and H. H. Woodson, "Electromechanical Energy Conversion." Also, the availability of a portion of the notes, "Dynamic Circuit Analysis," by Prof. H. K. Messerle[2] is acknowledged. It is not possible to list the many other references to which the author turned. He expresses his gratitude to them all, because without them this work would not have been possible.

Samuel Seely

[1] The author's book, "Introduction to Electromagnetic Fields," McGraw-Hill Book Company, Inc., New York, 1958, was prepared to satisfy this need.

[2] Also, H. K. Messerle, Dynamic Circuit Analysis, *Trans. AIEE*, **59**: 567 (April, 1960).

Contents

CONTENTS

CONTENTS

1

Electrical Energy Processes

This chapter introduces the several electrical energy processes which are of importance to the electrical engineer. Our subsequent discussions will be limited principally to three processes: energy storage, energy transfer (the transformer), and electromechanical energy conversion of the incremental- and gross-motion types. Something is said about the scope of our study in order to establish the perspective for the work to follow.

1-1. Introduction. A number of very important classes of physical devices exist which involve different electrical energy processes. The energy processes of importance may be classified as (1) energy storage; (2) energy transfer; (3) energy transmission; (4) energy radiation; (5) energy conversion; (6) energy control. It is one of the purposes of this book to study the details of classes of devices which intimately involve (1), (2), and (5) of this list.

A second purpose follows from the fact that devices which involve many of these energy processes are included as part of larger systems. The complete performance of such systems, whether of the open-loop or closed-loop types, involves knowledge of the performance of each element of the system. Such performance characteristics are ordinarily specified as the output-input characteristics, and these may be given in terms of the appropriate differential equations relating the output response (mechanical or electrical) to the specified input excitation (electrical or mechanical). The output-input characteristic may be given in terms of the so-called "system function" of the device, a function of the complex variable s, which may be obtained through a Laplace or other appropriate transformation of the differential equation. The device may also be described in terms of its equivalent electrical circuit, although this is often just a secondary means for deducing the output-input characteristics. As a consequence, deducing the output-input characteristic of the devices under study will be one of the important objectives in our considerations. In many cases these system functions will be studied further to discuss the performance characteristics of the device.

The formal approach to our studies will be in terms of energy functions, in those cases where this is feasible. The desirability of such an approach stems from the fact that whatever the form of the energy, whether mechanical, electrical, chemical, nuclear, thermal, etc., energy has the same units in all systems. Moreover, energy is a scalar quantity, which therefore allows initially simpler concepts to be employed in the solution of problems which might involve energy in a number of forms simultaneously.

A definition or description of energy is extremely difficult. In its scientific aspects, energy is often defined as the capacity for performing work. The energy that matter possesses by virtue of its motion is called kinetic energy. Also, if matter possesses energy by virtue of its position, this energy is called potential energy. However, energy is associated with phenomena other than those involving the position or motion of matter. For example, as found in electromagnetic-field theory, potential energy is spatially distributed in both electric and magnetic fields.

An inherent complexity in the study of energy and energy processes arises from the fact that in field situations it is not always possible to specify clearly where the energy resides. For example, in the study of static and moving electric charges, and the consequent electric and magnetic fields which are produced thereby, it is not always possible to state that the energy resides in the charge. Nor is it possible to show that the energy resides in the electric and magnetic fields. In the description of radiation and propagation phenomena, one proceeds ordinarily from considerations of the time-varying fields, although these fields are produced by accelerated charges. It is important to retain an objective viewpoint of the situation and to deduce functions which describe the appropriate energy states of the system, but without too much concern for the philosophical question of the "more basic" description of the source of the energy states. For this reason alternative descriptions will often be discussed.

1-2. Energy Storage. Energy storage becomes intimately involved with almost all other energy processes, either through its direct role as the process under survey or in its intermediate position as the source of energy in other energy processes. For example, in the study of energy transfer, some consideration will be given to the energy supplied to the field by one set of windings (the input port) and the energy supplied by the field to a second set of windings (the output port). In the study of energy conversion, the relation between the mechanical forces and the energy storage will provide a starting point for further discussion.

1-3. Energy Transfer. Energy transfer as here contemplated will involve an electrical-energy-to-electrical-energy process, often with a change in the impedance level of the system. If one were to associate kinetic energy with the energy in magnetic form due to currents and potential energy with the energy in electric form due to potentials, then the energy-transfer devices would involve a change in the relative division between potential and kinetic energies. Energy is conserved in the process, of course.

While both electric and magnetic fields ordinarily exist in an energy-transfer device, one or the other field usually predominates. Such devices as vacuum tubes, semiconductors, crystal and capacitor microphones, and dielectric amplifiers are fundamentally electric-field devices. The principal magnetic-field devices include motors, generators, relays, magnetic amplifiers, transformers. The transformer, which will be studied in some detail, is predominantly a magnetic-field device. As will be found, the electric field associated with this device must be evaluated in order to provide a complete description of its operation.

Consider a two-winding transformer, the windings of which are fixed with respect to each other and also remain fixed with respect to the magnetic material making up the magnetic structure. The description of the operation of this device will be given from two alternative, though equivalent, viewpoints, both of which stem from the basic law of electromagnetic induction of Faraday. Relative to the external terminal pairs, or ports, the two descriptions are equivalent. One of these approaches may be termed the "network" viewpoint, the other being the "power," or "emf," viewpoint. Each viewpoint possesses some special merit, but neither viewpoint provides any direct clue to the fundamental process by which the energy is transferred from one winding to the other. Recourse to the Maxwell equations is had in order to discuss this feature of transformer operation.

1-4. Energy Conversion. It is quite possible to design a device which possesses features not unlike those of the transformer, but with provision for one or both windings to display motion with respect to the stationary magnetic structure. This device is here designated as an energy-conversion device. A very important class of practical devices allows for the motion of only one winding relative to the stationary magnetic structure. In the incremental-motion transducer the winding may undergo a small (incremental) motion about some position of equilibrium. This class of device includes the loudspeaker and the microphone. Gross-motion devices, such as the rotating machine, are those in which the motion of a portion of the device may be so large that additional factors in the analysis are required. Both classes of devices will be studied in some detail.

In the limited scope herein contemplated, energy-conversion devices will be those in which electrical energy is converted into mechanical, acoustical, or thermal energy. The inverse process of converting mechanical, acoustical, or thermal energy into electrical energy is equally important. Of these various conversion processes, the electromagnetic-energy-conversion process involving electrical-to-mechanical and mechanical-to-electrical energy will receive most of our attention.

It will be found that in practical applications many more magnetic-field (current-operated) devices exist than electric-field (voltage-operated) devices. This fact results not from the inability to devise more electric-field devices, which may be regarded as the dual of the magnetic-field devices, but principally because of the limitations of the electrical materials that are available. It is an unfortunate fact that electric-field materials which support the same stored energy densities that are possible with magnetic-field materials simply do not exist. Part of the reason is readily understood by comparing the expression for the energy densities in the electric and magnetic fields, $\frac{1}{2}\epsilon E^2$ and $\frac{1}{2}\mu H^2$, with ϵ of the order of 10^{-11} farad/m and μ of the order of 10^{-6} henry/m. Should new electrical materials be developed which do have high energy-density storage properties, it is certain that additional electric-field devices will be developed.

Two possible starting points exist in the study of energy-conversion devices, and both will receive attention. One approach proceeds from the principles of conservation of energy. Force relations may be deduced by an application of the principle of virtual work. The second procedure follows from expressions for the potential and kinetic energies, the force relations being deduced by means of Lagrange's equations, a method to be discussed in some detail in what follows. Once force relations have been obtained, they may be used to study the dynamic behavior of the device. It is often desirable to deduce equivalent electric circuits from the force equations by the principles of analogs. A feature of these analogs is that they will permit the application of techniques of solution and some of the basic system-behavior experience possessed by the electrical engineer in evaluating the performance and response of energy-conversion devices.

When considered from the point of view of the principle of conservation of energy, any energy-conversion process must be expressible in terms of an energy balance of the form

$$\text{Energy input} = \text{energy output} + \text{energy stored} + \text{energy lost} \quad (1\text{-}1)$$

Consider the electric motor, for example. In this device the input energy is electrical, the output energy is mechanical, the stored energy is both electrical and mechanical, and the energy lost is thermal and results from electrical losses in the conductors and in the iron members and frictional losses in the bearings and in the windage caused by the rotating assembly. The situation here discussed may be represented graphically, as in Fig. 1-1. Despite the different forms in which the energy exists, Eq. (1-1) must be satisfied in the energy-conversion process.

The distribution of the stored energy within the various portions of the machine will affect both the static and the dynamic characteristics of the machine. However, considerations of energy alone will not, in general, provide all the information that is necessary for a description of the operation of the device. Such factors as the features of the coupling field between the electrical and mechanical variables and the impedance levels of the device (as, for example, the voltage and current relationships or torque and speed relationships) are fundamental to the description of the performance and operation of the device, but these are not contained in the principle of conservation of energy.

When considered from the point of view of generalized coordinates and Lagrange's equations, the system is described in terms of its energy

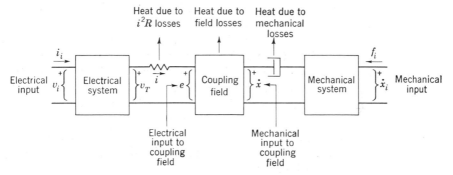

Fig. 1-1. General representation of electromechanical-energy-conversion device.

parameters, which must, of course, satisfy Eq. (1-1). This may be considered as a method alternative to and generally much more powerful and systematic than the principle of conservation of energy, since the effects of the coupling field and the impedance levels are taken into account in these equations. Because of their general and powerful character, the application of Lagrange's equations is widespread in the analysis of physical processes.

In the last analysis, of course, the description of the process of energy conversion must involve considerations of Coulomb's law of force between electric charges or of Ampère's law of force between currents, as these are the only available independent relationships between mechanical force and electrical quantities. The resulting coupling field will be electric or magnetic, but for energy conversion both an electric and a magnetic field, in accordance with Poynting, must be present. However, the converter is classified as magnetic when the physical structure is largely ferromagnetic; it is electric when the structure is an electric conductor with associated dielectric mediums.

1-5. Rotating Power Converters. Rotating power converters constitute a very important and a very complicated class of electromechanical devices. The complications arise from the fact that a series of windings exist which are fixed with respect to the stationary frame of the machine; a series of windings exist which are fixed with respect to the movable portions of the structure; and because of the character of the excitation of the windings in polyphase machines, the resulting fields which are produced thereby will be moving in the confined space of the air gap in which the fields exist, for reasons other than the physical motion of the mechanical structure. Thus, for example, relative to a point which is fixed in the air gap of the machine, there can be moving fields due to the stationary assembly of windings, there can be moving fields due to the rotating assembly of windings, and there will be the effects of the moving fields due to the motion of the rotating assembly. These fields exist in all classes and types of machines, and except for the particular constraints that might be imposed on certain of the field components by the special features of the machine, the machines possess much in common. It appears reasonable that a single unified model might exist which could provide the basis for the study of many types of rotating electrical machinery. Actually two generalized models will be discussed, and these are mathematically equivalent. One model is described in terms of an equivalent rotating network, and the other is described initially in terms of the **E** and **H** fields that are produced in the air gap of the machine by the currents in the windings.

The rotating-network model of the rotating machine is accomplished in terms of the "primitive" machine originally proposed by G. Kron.[1] With this single, basic generalized machine as the starting point, the essential aspect of the performance of most important types of machines can be deduced. Often it is necessary to supplement the basic machine with some special features of the material of the machine or with some special features of design. Basically, however, the analyses for all machines proceed along similar lines and are expressed in terms of the electrical equations at the electrical ports and the mechanical equation at the mechanical port. A fundamental need in this method is to be able to translate the important features of the actual machine into the language of the basic machine and then subsequently to refer the results back into the actual machine language. This proves to be a not too difficult procedure.

The White-Woodson[2] idealized rotating machine that is discussed from

---

[1] G. Kron, "The Application of Tensors to the Analysis of Rotating Electric Machinery," 2d ed., General Electric Company, Schenectady, N.Y., 1942.

[2] D. C. White and H. H. Woodson, "Electromechanical Energy Conversion," John Wiley & Sons, Inc., New York, 1959.

an electromagnetic-field-theory viewpoint differs from the rotating-network model only in the procedure by which one develops the important features of the machine model and its basic characteristics. Rather than postulate a primitive machine with a specification of self-inductances of windings and mutual inductances between windings, one begins by postulating an idealized machine model and then deducing the **E** and **H** fields that exist in the air gap of this model. From considerations of the fields, the energy flow along the air gap and the energy flow across the air gap follow by evaluating the appropriate Poynting vectors and integrating these over appropriately chosen surfaces. From considerations of the fields it is possible to calculate the energy storage and so the various inductances of the machine, from which the port conditions follow. Clearly, the study of this machine differs from that of the Kron machine in detail, and it is ultimately shown that one model is essentially a mathematically transformed version of the other.

2

Principles of Electromechanical
Energy Conversion

Many of the devices to be discussed in this book are described in terms of the electric and magnetic fields which have been generated in certain specified regions of space. This chapter, which is the starting point for this study, will review certain pertinent material of electromagnetic-field theory. Many of the important concepts will be presented with little comment, since it is supposed that the reader has become conversant with this material in previous studies. Those aspects of this work which are of especial importance in our subsequent discussions will receive more detailed attention.

2-1. Electromagnetic Principles.[1] The important electric- and magnetic-field vectors and their interrelationships are contained in Maxwell's equations (see Appendix B). These must be supplemented by force and energy relations in order to provide the required information for our subsequent studies. These relations will receive detailed attention below.

Some of the electromechanical devices to be considered are electric-field devices, and it will be necessary to use those principles of electric-field theory which relate mechanical force and motion to potential and charge or to quantities which are defined in terms of these. Since charged surfaces rather than point charges are involved in devices, the force relations in terms of energy storage will better meet our needs than the simple formulation of Coulomb's law in terms of point charges.

As has already been noted, the great majority of electromechanical devices are magnetic-field devices, and so the pair of principles that relate mechanical force and motion to emfs and current will be of especial interest. These principles are associated with the names Faraday and Ampère. We consider each:

---

[1] For more details, see S. Seely, "Introduction to Electromagnetic Fields," McGraw-Hill Book Company, Inc., New York, 1958.

1. Faraday's law in its usual representation includes two different processes, and these are often referred to by the terms "motional emf" and "transformer emf." Consider a wire that is moving with a velocity **v'** in a magnetic field **B**. The emf that is induced in the conductor is given by the expression

$$v = \int \mathbf{v'} \times \mathbf{B} \cdot d\mathbf{l} \qquad (2\text{-}1)$$

where $d\mathbf{l}$ denotes an element of length of the conductor. Refer to the special case illustrated in Fig. 2-1, with the closed external circuit assumed

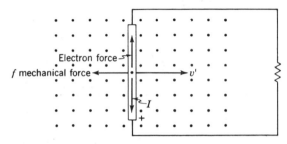

Fig. 2-1. A wire moving with velocity perpendicular to magnetic flux lines (B out of paper).

outside the magnetic field. Only the conductor moves, and the total integral of Eq. (2-1) becomes

$$v = \int_0^l \mathbf{v'} \times \mathbf{B} \cdot d\mathbf{l} \qquad (2\text{-}2)$$

But for the case illustrated $\mathbf{v'} \times \mathbf{B}$ is a constant along l, so that the integration may be effected simply, with the result

$$v = Blv' \qquad \text{volts} \qquad (2\text{-}3)$$

Of course, if **v'** is not perpendicular to **B**, the appropriate component dictated by the vector relation must be considered.

The second emf or electromotance-inducing process is that referred to as the "transformer emf"; it relates the emf that is set up in a circuit when the magnetic flux linking the circuit is changing in any manner with time. The explicit relation is

$$v = -\frac{d\psi}{dt} \qquad \text{volts} \qquad (2\text{-}4)$$

This expression specifies that the magnitude of the emf is proportional to the time rate of change of ψ, the flux linkages with the circuit. The minus sign takes account of the sense of the induced emf and is dictated by Lenz's law. It is noted that by proper interpretation Eq. (2-4) contains Eq. (2-1), and it is for this reason that the point form of Faraday's law in the Maxwell set contains the single term curl $\mathbf{E} = -\dot{\mathbf{B}}$.

2. A mechanical force is exerted on a conductor when it carries current in a magnetic field. Also, there is a mechanical force on iron (and certain other materials) in a magnetic field. A detailed discussion of this matter is given below.

In so far as the final motion of the energy converter is concerned, this depends not only upon the electrical aspects of the device but also upon the mechanical features. As noted in Chap. 1, it will often be found convenient to use Lagrange's equations to deduce the force equations of the total device.

2-2. Potential Energy of a System of Charged Conductors. The total potential energy of a system of charged bodies may be calculated in terms of their charges (volume charge density ρ and surface charge density σ) and potentials v by calculating the work done in bringing the charges from infinity until a specified charge distribution is attained. Such a calculation leads to the following expression,

$$W_e = \tfrac{1}{2} \int_\tau v\rho \, d\tau + \tfrac{1}{2} \int_A v\sigma \, dA \qquad \text{joules} \qquad (2\text{-}5)$$

where the first term on the right is the electrostatic potential energy associated with the volume distribution of charges and the second term is the potential energy associated with the surface charge distributions. When the integrands are subject to certain electric-field transformations, the equivalent form is the expression

$$W_e = \tfrac{1}{2} \int_{\substack{\text{all} \\ \text{space}}} \mathbf{E} \cdot \mathbf{D} \, d\tau \qquad \text{joules} \qquad (2\text{-}6)$$

A comparison of the two forms given by Eqs. (2-5) and (2-6) is interesting. Equation (2-5) seems to imply that the energy is distributed only in the region of charge density, whereas Eq. (2-6) seems to show that the energy resides wherever there is an electric field. In fact, Eq. (2-6) shows that the total energy in an electric field of whatever nature may be regarded as being distributed throughout the entire field with a density at any point equal to

$$w_e = \frac{\epsilon_0}{2} E^2 \qquad \text{joules/unit volume} \qquad (2\text{-}7)$$

Such a statement involves the assumption that electrostatic energy is something that can be spatially distributed. Clearly, while the foregoing equation can suggest such a hypothesis, it in no way demands it.

Consider the case of an array of conductors $(1, 2, \ldots , k)$ placed in an electric field. Suppose that the final charge on conductor k is Q_k and that its final potential is V_k. The total potential energy associated with this system of charged conductors is, from Eq. (2-5),

$$W_e = \frac{1}{2} \int_A v\sigma \, dA \qquad (2\text{-}8)$$

since only surface charges exist on the conductors. Since this expression is to be taken over the surfaces of the conductors, it may be written as

$$W_e = \sum_k \frac{1}{2} \int_{A_k} v\sigma \, dA \qquad (2\text{-}9)$$

But the potential over each conductor is constant. Therefore it follows that

$$W_e = \sum_k \frac{1}{2} V_k \int_{A_k} \sigma \, dA = \sum_k \frac{1}{2} V_k Q_k \qquad (2\text{-}10)$$

For a linear system Q_k is proportional to the v on each of the other conductors, namely,

$$Q_k = \sum_{s=1}^{n} C_{ks} v_s \qquad (2\text{-}11)$$

where C_{ks} is the mutual capacitance between conductors k and s and C_{kk} is the self-capacitance of circuit k. Combine this with Eq. (2-10), and so

$$W_e = \frac{1}{2} \sum_{k=1}^{n} \sum_{s=1}^{n} C_{sk} v_s v_k \qquad (2\text{-}12)$$

which is the general expression for energy storage, in terms of the capacitance coefficients. For the case of a single capacitor, this gives the well-known form

$$W_e = \frac{1}{2} C V^2 \qquad (2\text{-}13)$$

Attention is directed to the fact that in this development there is an implicit assumption that a linear relationship exists between the charge and the potential on each conductor. This follows directly from the manner of the development leading to Eq. (2-5) for the energy W_e. This is not a serious restriction in the electric-field case since electric hysteresis and saturation are generally small effects. Certain aspects of this non-linearity will be discussed below.

2-3. Forces between Charged Conductors. It is now desired to determine the force which the system of charged conductors exerts on the conductor k or on any particular group of conductors. The desired expression may be obtained by the application of the principle of virtual work. This principle, which is simply a restatement of the law of conservation of energy, states in this case that, if one of the conductors is given a small displacement consistent with the geometrical constraints on the system, then during this displacement the electrical energy change is such that

Sum of energy increments from all sources = mechanical work done by system on circuit or group of circuits displaced + sum of increments in electrical energy storage + sum of energy losses

In mathematical form this is written

$$\delta W_{\varepsilon} = \delta W_{\text{mech}} + \delta W_e + \text{losses (neglected)} \qquad (2\text{-}14)$$

To proceed, it is noted that the mechanical work done against the electrical force in the virtual displacement is expressed by the relation

$$\delta W_{\text{mech}} = f_r \, \delta r \qquad (2\text{-}15)$$

This suggests that we write, from Eq. (2-14),

$$f_r = \frac{\partial W_{\text{mech}}}{\partial r} - \frac{\partial W_e}{\partial r} \qquad (2\text{-}16)$$

It is now noted that the virtual displacement may be effected in two different ways, namely, at constant *charge* or at constant *potential*. It will be shown that the forces that result under virtual displacements of either type of constraint will be the same. The two alternatives will be examined.

Constant Charge. This case, which assumes that the virtual displacement is made at constant charge, implies that the sources which supplied the energy to establish the field have been removed. It follows directly from Eq. (2-16) that

$$f_r = - \left. \frac{\partial W_e}{\partial r} \right|_{Q_k = \text{const}} \qquad (2\text{-}17)$$

This expression shows that the force is the rate of decrease of stored electrical energy with displacement at constant charge. By combining this expression with Eq. (2-10), the resulting expression is

$$f_r = - \sum_{k=1}^{n} \tfrac{1}{2} Q_k \frac{\partial V_k}{\partial r} \qquad (2\text{-}18)$$

Constant Potential. If the potentials of the charged surfaces are maintained constant during the virtual displacement, then charges dQ_k are transferred during the time of the displacement. Under these circumstances each Q_k is a function of the displacement. The electrical energy supplied to the system is now

$$dW_{\text{mech}} = \sum_{k=1}^{n} V_k \, dQ_k \qquad (2\text{-}19)$$

If this expression is combined with Eqs. (2-10) and (2-16), the force equation becomes

$$f_r = \sum_{k=1}^{n} V_k \frac{\partial Q_k}{\partial r} - \sum_{k=1}^{n} \tfrac{1}{2} V_k \frac{\partial Q_k}{\partial r}$$

or
$$f_r = \sum_{k=1}^{n} \tfrac{1}{2} V_k \frac{\partial Q_k}{\partial r} \qquad (2\text{-}20)$$

This is a very interesting result, since it shows that, for a virtual displacement under conditions of constant potential, the work done is just equal to the energy stored.   Thus, to maintain constant potential as the geometry changes, the batteries must provide an amount of energy exactly equal to twice the work that is done by the external sources. Physically this means that in this process when the field does work on the kth charge not only must the battery supply this work but at the same

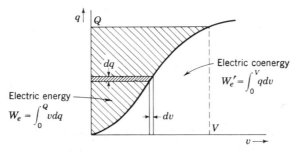

FIG. 2-2. To define the electric coenergy.

time it must supply a like additional amount of energy to the stored energy.   This situation is often referred to as the 50-50 rule.   A similar rule will be found to apply in the magnetic case.

The converse of the foregoing relates to the case when work is done on the charges by changing their disposition against the action of electrostatic forces.   In this case the energy returned to the sources (essentially by charging the batteries) is twice the amount of the mechanical work that is done, the second half being restored to the sources by a reduction in the stored magnetic energy.   It is noted that the 50-50 rule is not valid if the dielectric in which the conductors are immersed is subject to saturation.

Equation (2-20) may be combined with Eq. (2-10) to yield the form

$$f_r = \frac{\partial W_e}{\partial r} \bigg|_{V_k = \text{const}} \qquad (2\text{-}21)$$

This expression shows that the force is the rate of increase in stored electrical energy with displacement at constant potential.

There is some interest in examining the effects of saturation on the foregoing results.   This is most conveniently done by referring to Fig. 2-2.

This figure places saturation clearly in evidence, but electric hysteresis is neglected. In this graph the crosshatched area above the curve denotes the electric energy, according to Eq. (2-9). The area under the curve is known as the *electric coenergy*.[1] Without going into detailed calculations, the effect of saturation reflects itself in the form of the equations which describe the field. The expressions for force, which appear as a reasonable extension of our results, are the following: In terms of the voltages and charges

$$f_r = -\sum_{k=1}^{n} \int_0^{Q_k} \frac{\partial v_k}{\partial r} \, dq_k \qquad \text{joules/m} \qquad (2\text{-}22a)$$

and

$$f_r = \sum_{k=1}^{n} \int_0^{V_k} \frac{\partial q_k}{\partial r} \, dv_k \qquad \text{joules/m} \qquad (2\text{-}22b)$$

In terms of electric energy and coenergy these may be written

$$f_r = -\left. \frac{\partial W_e}{\partial r} \right|_{Q_k = \text{const}} \qquad (2\text{-}23a)$$

and

$$f_r = \left. \frac{\partial W'_e}{\partial r} \right|_{V_k = \text{const}} \qquad (2\text{-}23b)$$

Clearly, when the medium is linear, the forces are the same and Eq. (2-23b) agrees with Eq. (2-21).

Example 2-3.1. The force tending to draw the dielectric into the parallel-plate

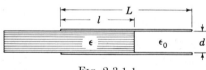

FIG. 2-3.1-1

capacitor illustrated in the accompanying figure is to be evaluated under the two cases discussed above. In one case, the capacitor will remain connected to the source of potential; in the second case, the capacitor will have been charged to the potential V and then disconnected from the source. Neglect fringing in both cases, although actually the general results are independent of this condition.

Solution. (*a*) *Constant Potential.* In this case it is required to evaluate Eq. (2-23b); thus we must determine

$$f_l = \left. \frac{\partial W'_e}{\partial l} \right|_{V = \text{const}}$$

where W'_e is the coenergy of the system. By Eq. (2-16) for the linear case

$$W'_e = W_e = \tfrac{1}{2}CV^2$$

Thus

$$f_l = \tfrac{1}{2}V^2 \frac{\partial C}{\partial l}$$

[1] O. K. Mawardi, On the Concept of Coenergy, *J. Franklin Inst.*, **264**: 313 (1957).

An application of the techniques of electrostatics permits one to find the capacitance C, which is the following:

$$C = \frac{L}{d} [\epsilon l + \epsilon_0 (L - l)]$$

The force expression is thus

$$f_l = \tfrac{1}{2} V^2 \frac{L}{d} (\epsilon - \epsilon_0)$$

(b) *Constant Charge.* The required expression for the force is given by Eq. (2-23a),

$$f_l = -\left. \frac{\partial W_e}{\partial l} \right|_{Q = \text{const}}$$

where

$$W_e = \frac{Q_2}{2C}$$

It follows therefore that

$$f_l = -\frac{Q^2}{2} \left(-\frac{1}{C^2} \frac{\partial C}{\partial l} \right) = \tfrac{1}{2} V^2 \frac{\partial C}{\partial l}$$

This is the same expression for the force as above, as it must be, since no motion has occurred. For a finite displacement of the dielectric the total work may be different in the two cases.

2-4. Potential Energy in a System of Rigid Currents. We begin our discussion by considering a single circuit carrying a constant current I to be placed in a magnetic field of fixed external sources. Owing to the mechanical force of magnetic origin that acts on the system, it will be supposed that the circuit is displaced, rotated, or deformed by an infinitesimal amount. This virtual displacement is denoted $\delta \mathbf{r}$. The work done by the circuit against the force in the virtual displacement must be supplied by the current source and is given by the expression

$$d(\delta W) = \delta \mathbf{r} \cdot d\mathbf{f} \qquad (2\text{-}24)$$

But Ampère's law for the force on a current in a magnetic field is

$$d\mathbf{f} = I \, d\mathbf{l} \times \mathbf{B} \qquad (2\text{-}25)$$

Thus

$$d(\delta W) = I \, \delta \mathbf{r} \cdot d\mathbf{l} \times \mathbf{B} \qquad (2\text{-}26)$$

The combination of the dot and cross products of the three vectors in Eq. (2-26) is called the scalar triple product. It is a property of the scalar triple product, as may be shown by carrying out the specified vector operations, that this quantity is unchanged by the cyclic interchange of the vectors. Therefore, Eq. (2-26) may be written as

$$d(\delta W) = I \mathbf{B} \cdot \delta \mathbf{r} \times d\mathbf{l}$$

However, the cross product of two vectors specifies the area (one vector times the normal component of the second vector), which is in the direction of unit normal perpendicular to the area (and is in the direction of advance of a right-hand screw in turning from the first to the second vector through an angle 90° or less). Therefore $\mathbf{B} \cdot (\delta \mathbf{r} \times d\mathbf{l})$ is an element of magnetic flux linkages swept out by $d\mathbf{l}$ in its motion. For the entire circuit, the increment of flux linkages $d\psi$ due to the displacement is

$$\oint \mathbf{B} \cdot \delta\mathbf{r} \times d\mathbf{l} = \delta\psi \tag{2-27}$$

Therefore from Eq. (2-26) the total work done by the system during the displacement is

$$\delta W = I \oint \mathbf{B} \cdot \delta\mathbf{r} \times d\mathbf{l}$$

which may then be written in the simple, though very important, form

$$\delta W = I \, \delta\psi \tag{2-28}$$

If it is now assumed that the external sources and the current I are maintained constant in the virtual displacement, then the work done by the mechanical forces is compensated by a decrease in a potential-energy function U. We may then write

$$\delta U = -\delta W = -I \, \delta\psi \tag{2-29}$$

This implies that the potential energy of the rigid current in the magnetic field is

$$U = -I\psi \tag{2-30}$$

If $d\mathbf{r}$ is a real rather than a virtual displacement, then work must be done to keep the current constant. Now, because of the change in flux linkages, an emf will be induced,

$$V = -\frac{d\psi}{dt}$$

where dt is the time required to effect the displacement. But this induced emf must be counterbalanced by an equal and opposite applied voltage V_i. The work done by the applied voltage on the circuit during this time interval is

$$V_i I \, dt = I \, d\psi \tag{2-31}$$

This expression may be interpreted to show that the work done by the mechanical forces in a small displacement of a linear circuit is exactly compensated by the energy supplied by the source to maintain the current constant. The total work on the circuit is zero.

Let us now evaluate the energy that is being supplied during the process of building up the currents in the system of n rigid currents. This may be done by considering the energy that is supplied to all currents I_k as they are increased from zero to their final values, or, equivalently, as the flux-linking current I_k is increased from zero to its final value Ψ_k. It will be supposed that the wires are of infinitesimal thickness so that Ψ is exactly defined for each circuit.

Now suppose that an external emf V_{ki} which is generated by chemical or mechanical means is connected to the typical circuit k which has a resistance R_k associated with it. If at any instant the current in the circuit is i_k and if the magnetic flux threading the circuit is ψ_k, then variations in current are accompanied by variations in flux linkages. If V_k is the emf induced by a variation in ψ_k, then

$$V_k + V_{ki} = R_k i_k \qquad (2\text{-}32)$$

or
$$V_{ki} = R_k i_k + \frac{d\psi_k}{dt} \qquad (2\text{-}33)$$

The power expended by the impressed source V_{ki} is $V_{ki} i_k$, and the work done on the kth circuit in the interval dt is

$$dW_k = R_k i_k^2\, dt + i_k\, d\psi_k \qquad (2\text{-}34)$$

Of this work the amount $R_k i_k^2\, dt$ is dissipated as heat, while $i_k\, d\psi_k$ is stored as magnetic energy. Thus a variation in the magnetic energy of the n current filaments is related to the increments in fluxes by

$$W = \sum_{k=1}^{n} \int_{0}^{\Psi_k} i_k\, d\psi_k \qquad (2\text{-}35)$$

For a linear system, this expression may be conveniently expressed in terms of the self- and mutual inductances of the circuits. To find this relation, it is first recalled that the flux linking the kth circuit is a linear function of the currents in all the circuits, namely,

$$\psi_k = \sum_{s=1}^{n} M_{ks} I_s \qquad (2\text{-}36)$$

where M_{ks} is the mutual inductance between conductor k and conductor s and $M_{kk} = L_k$ is the self-inductance of circuit k. This expression may be written

$$\psi_k = L_k I_k + \sum_{\substack{s=1 \\ s \neq k}}^{n} M_{ks} I_s \qquad (2\text{-}37)$$

where, as noted, the summation denoted by Σ' does not include the term for which $s = k$, as this is written explicitly. It follows from Eq. (2-37) that

$$\delta\psi_k = L_k\, \delta I_k + \sum_{s=1}^{n}{}' M_{ks}\, \delta I_s$$

Thus, for the general system, Eq. (2-35) becomes

$$\delta W = \sum_{k=1}^{n} I_k \left(L_k\, \delta I_k + \sum_{s=1}^{n}{}' M_{ks}\, \delta I_s \right) \qquad (2\text{-}38)$$

To make plausible the manner in which this expression may be reduced, consider the specific case of two current circuits. Equation (2-38) becomes

$$\delta W = L_1 I_1 \, \delta I_1 + M_{12} I_1 \, \delta I_2 + L_2 I_2 \, \delta I_2 + M_{21} I_2 \, \delta I_1$$

Since $M_{12} = M_{21}$, this expression may be written in the form

$$\delta W = \delta(\tfrac{1}{2} L_1 I_1^2) + \delta(\tfrac{1}{2} L_2 I_2^2) + \delta(M_{12} I_1 I_2)$$

This shows that we may write for the total magnetic energy stored in the system of two rigid currents

$$W_m = \tfrac{1}{2} L_1 I_1^2 + \tfrac{1}{2} L_2 I_2^2 + M_{12} I_1 I_2 \qquad (2\text{-}39)$$

In the more general case of n rigid currents, the form for the stored magnetic energy appropriate to this case, which is merely an extension of Eq. (2-39), will be

$$W_m = \tfrac{1}{2} \sum_{k=1}^{n} L_k I_k^2 + \tfrac{1}{2} \sum_{k=1}^{n} \sum_{s=1}^{n}{}' M_{ks} I_k I_s$$

The factor $\tfrac{1}{2}$ that appears in the second term arises to compensate for the fact that $M_{ks} = M_{sk}$ will appear twice in the double summation. This may be written

$$W_m = \tfrac{1}{2} \sum_{k=1}^{n} \left(L_k I_k^2 + \sum_{s=1}^{n}{}' M_{ks} I_k I_s \right)$$

or

$$W_m = \tfrac{1}{2} \sum_{k=1}^{n} I_k \left(L_k I_k + \sum_{s=1}^{n}{}' M_{ks} I_s \right) \qquad (2\text{-}40)$$

By Eq. (2-37) this becomes, finally,

$$W_m = \tfrac{1}{2} \sum_{k=1}^{n} I_k \psi_k \qquad (2\text{-}41)$$

But this is just the result specified by Eq. (2-35). Hence, finally, for a linear system

$$W_m = \sum_{k=1}^{n} \int_{0}^{\Psi_k} i_k \, d\psi_k = \tfrac{1}{2} \sum_{k=1}^{n} I_k \psi_k \qquad (2\text{-}42)$$

This expression specifies the total energy supplied during the whole process of building up the currents in the system. It is, therefore, the total amount of energy that is stored in the magnetic field of the system of currents. Note that in the development it is implicitly assumed that the system is magnetically isolated from its surroundings, since externally produced magnetic fields would produce fluxes even when all the currents of the system are zero.

Equation (2-42) may be written in a form that explicitly shows its relation to the magnetic field. Refer to Fig. 2-3, which shows the region of the field due to one current. The total magnetic flux linking the current is seen to be

$$\psi = \sum_{\Delta A} B \, \Delta A \tag{2-43}$$

Also by Ampère's line integral around any path

$$I = \sum_{\Delta l} H \, \Delta l \tag{2-44}$$

Thus the energy stored in the field due to each current is

$$W_{mi} = \tfrac{1}{2} I \psi = \tfrac{1}{2} \sum_{\Delta A} \sum_{\Delta l} BH \, \Delta A \, \Delta l = \tfrac{1}{2} \sum_{\Delta \tau} BH \tag{2-45}$$

In the limit, as $\Delta A \to 0$ and $\Delta l \to 0$, the magnetic energy per unit volume is

$$\frac{\Delta W_{mi}}{\Delta \tau} = \tfrac{1}{2} BH$$

For a linear medium, $B = \mu H$, and so

$$\frac{\Delta W_{mi}}{\Delta \tau} = \frac{B^2}{2\mu} = \tfrac{1}{2} \mu H^2 \tag{2-46}$$

This expression shows that the total energy in the magnetic field of any system of electric currents may be regarded as distributed throughout the entire field with a density at any point equal to

$$w_m = \frac{\Delta W_m}{\Delta \tau} = \sum_i \frac{\Delta W_{mi}}{\Delta \tau} = \tfrac{1}{2} \mu H^2$$

$$\text{joules/unit volume} \tag{2-47}$$

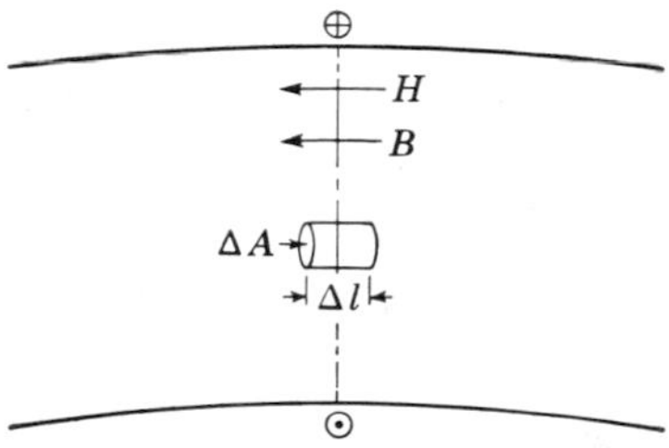

Fig. 2-3. The region of magnetic field due to currents.

Here too, as noted in connection with Eq. (2-7) for the cognate electric-field problem, this statement involves the assumption that magnetic energy is, in its nature, something that can be spatially distributed. Clearly, of course, this expression can suggest such a conclusion, but it in no way demands it.

2-5. Forces in Terms of Energy Changes. The energy expressions discussed in the foregoing section may be used to find expressions for the forces between the currents and certain geometrical parameters of the circuit. If we write

W_{mech} = energy associated with mechanical part of system
W_m = energy stored in magnetic field
W_{elec} = energy associated with electric-circuit part of system

then the system energy balance requires that we write

$$d(W_{\text{mech}}) + d(W_m) = d(W_{\text{elec}}) \tag{2-48}$$

where $d(W_{\text{mech}})$ = energy of system that is converted into mechanical energy

$\qquad\qquad$ = $f_k v_k' \, \Delta t$, where f_k is force exerted by electrical system on mechanical system, and where v_k' is the velocity (not to be confused with voltage v)

$\quad d(W_m)$ = change in magnetic energy stored

$\quad d(W_{\text{elec}})$ = net electrical energy input after copper losses have been taken into account

$\qquad\qquad$ = $\displaystyle\sum_k V_{ki} I_k \, \Delta t - \sum_k I_k^2 R_k \, \Delta t$

In terms of power, Eq. (2-48) may be written

$$f_k v_k' + \frac{dW_m}{dt} + \sum_k I_k^2 R_k - \sum_k V_{ki} I_k = 0 \tag{2-49}$$

Note that there is no energy storage in electric fields for the systems under consideration. Also, the equation has been written so that the electrical and mechanical energy terms (the first and last terms) have positive values for motor action.

Consider the special constant-current process in which the external voltage sources are so controlled that the currents within the system remain constant during any virtual displacements. Neglecting losses, we may write

$$f_k v_k' + \frac{1}{2} \sum_k I_k \frac{d\psi_k}{dt} - \sum_k I_k \frac{d\psi_k}{dt} = 0 \tag{2-50}$$

This expression shows the very interesting fact that, in order to maintain a constant current in the circuits as the geometry changes, the batteries must do exactly twice the amount of work that is done by the external sources, in addition to supplying the heat losses. Physically, this means that in this process, when the field does work on the kth conductor, the battery must supply not only this work but, at the same time, a like additional amount of energy to the stored energy. This is the 50-50 rule for magnetic problems and is the dual of the same rule that was found to exist in electric-field situations.

The converse of the foregoing relates to the case when work is done on the circuits by changing their form against the action of electro-magnetic forces or by pulling them apart. In this case, the energy returned to the sources (essentially by charging the batteries) is twice the amount of the mechanical work that is done, the second half being restored to the sources by a reduction in the stored magnetic energy.

Note that the 50-50 rule is not valid when iron exists in the neighborhood of the currents which may be subject to saturation.

It is now observed that Eq. (2-50) may be written as

$$f_k v_k' = \tfrac{1}{2} \sum_k I_k \frac{d\psi_k}{dt}$$

This is, by Eq. (2-42),

$$f_k v_k' = \frac{\partial W_m}{\partial t} = \frac{\partial W_m}{\partial x_k} v_k' \bigg|_{\substack{I=\text{const} \\ x_i=\text{const},\, i\neq k}}$$

Hence, finally,

$$f_k = \frac{\partial W_m}{\partial x_k} \bigg|_{I=\text{const}} \tag{2-51}$$

Observe now from Eq. (2-49) that the induced-emf terms can be ignored in the force calculations, if the flux linkages are held constant.   Under these circumstances, it follows directly, as above, that

$$f_k = -\frac{\partial W_m}{\partial x_k} \bigg|_{\psi=\text{const}} \tag{2-52}$$

Example 2-5.1.   Show the validity of the force expressions for the singly excited electromechanical system illustrated.
   Solution.   We write in Eq. (2-49)

$$v = L \frac{di}{dt} = \frac{d\psi}{dt}$$

This yields the expression

$$f \frac{dx}{dt} + \frac{dW_m}{dt} = vi$$

But since $W_m = \tfrac{1}{2} L i^2 = \tfrac{1}{2}\psi i$

then clearly $\dfrac{dW_m}{dt} = \dfrac{1}{2}\left(\psi \dfrac{di}{dt} + i \dfrac{d\psi}{dt}\right)$

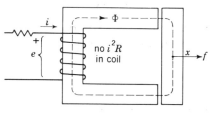

Fig. 2-5.1-1

no i^2R
in coil

Combine with the above to find

$$f \frac{dx}{dt} + \frac{1}{2}\left(\psi \frac{di}{dt} + i \frac{d\psi}{dt}\right) = i \frac{d\psi}{dt}$$

(*a*) For the condition of constant current, this expression reduces to

$$f \frac{dx}{dt} + \tfrac{1}{2} I \frac{d\psi}{dt} = I \frac{d\psi}{dt}$$

from which it follows that

$$f \frac{dx}{dt} = \tfrac{1}{2} I \frac{d\psi}{dt} \bigg|_{I=\text{const}}$$

or

$$f = \tfrac{1}{2} I \frac{d\psi}{dx} \bigg|_{I} = \frac{\partial W_m}{\partial x} \bigg|_{I}$$

(*b*) For the case of ψ constant, then

$$f \frac{dx}{dt} + \tfrac{1}{2}\psi \frac{di}{dt} = 0$$

or

$$f = -\tfrac{1}{2}\psi \frac{di}{dx} \bigg|_{\psi} = -\frac{\partial W_m}{\partial x} \bigg|_{\psi}$$

2-6. Forces and Torques between Circuits in Terms of Changes of Mutual Inductance. An application of Eq. (2-51) which is of considerable practical importance involves two circuits which have self-inductances L_1 and L_2, respectively, and the mutual inductance M. Such a device is known as a doubly excited magnetic-field transducer and might be of the forms illustrated in Fig. 2-4. If the currents in the circuits are I_1 and I_2, then the energy stored in the magnetic field is that specified by Eq. (2-39). Refer to Fig. 2-4a, and suppose that circuit 1 is given a virtual displacement r. If f_1 is the magnetic force on this circuit

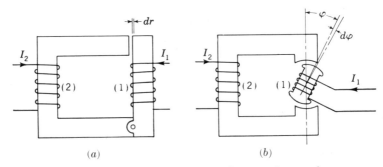

(a) (b)

Fig. 2-4. Two types of doubly excited magnetic transducers.

in the direction of r, the work done by the circuit against the force in displacing the circuit is, by Eq. (2-51),

$$f_{1r} = \tfrac{1}{2}I_1{}^2 \frac{\partial L_1}{\partial r} + \tfrac{1}{2}I_2{}^2 \frac{\partial L_2}{\partial r} + I_1 I_2 \frac{\partial M}{\partial r} \qquad (2\text{-}53)$$

This expression gives the component of the total magnetic force in any direction r on circuit 1 due to circuit 2 in terms of the currents and the space rate of change of inductances in that direction.

An entirely similar procedure may be employed in Fig. 2-4b to find an expression for the component of torque on circuit 1 due to circuit 2 tending to give the circuit an angular displacement ϕ. The result is

$$T_{1\phi} = \tfrac{1}{2}I_1{}^2 \frac{\partial L_1}{\partial \varphi} + \tfrac{1}{2}I_2{}^2 \frac{\partial L_2}{\partial \varphi} + I_1 I_2 \frac{\partial M}{\partial \varphi} \qquad (2\text{-}54)$$

In many cases the self-inductances are constant with displacement, so that the foregoing results are dependent only on the changes in the mutual inductances. The resulting expressions become

$$f_{1r} = I_1 I_2 \frac{\partial M}{\partial r}$$

$$T_{1\phi} = I_1 I_2 \frac{\partial M}{\partial \varphi} \qquad (2\text{-}55)$$

From the fact that the flux linkages in the circuits are

$$\psi_1 = L_1 I_1 + M I_2 \tag{2-56}$$
$$\psi_2 = L_2 I_2 + M I_1$$

then Eqs. (2-55) may be expressed in the form

$$f_{1r} = I_1 \frac{\partial \psi_1}{\partial r}$$
$$T_{1\phi} = I_1 \frac{\partial \psi_1}{\partial \varphi} \tag{2-57}$$

These latter expressions may be given broad interpretation. They show that a force or a torque is produced in a circuit of constant self-inductance regardless of whether the flux linkages are produced by currents in two circuits or by a group of other circuits or magnets. This more general situation will receive further consideration in Sec. 2-9 when magnetic mediums exist in the field.

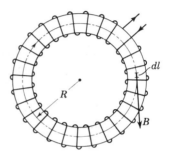

FIG. 2-5. A schematic view of a toroid with N closely spaced turns.

2-7. Energy Storage in a Region Containing Iron. In the derivation of Eq. (2-41) for the magnetic energy in a system of rigid currents, it was assumed that the system was magnetically isolated. That is, it was assumed that the fluxes were linear functions of the currents, which is not necessarily true when iron is present. It is desired to examine the situation when iron exists in the field. For convenience, we shall use the simple case of an ideal toroidal coil wound on an iron core, as illustrated in Fig. 2-5. The iron cross section is taken to be small.

Suppose initially that the iron core is demagnetized and that it is to be magnetized by passing a current through the solenoid winding. For a core material that is isotropic and homogeneous, the magnetizing force **H** at any point inside the iron is parallel to the axis. When the current in the coil is I, then, for a core of small cross section, the magnetizing force is almost uniform. It is obtained by applying the Ampère line integral

$$\oint \mathbf{H} \cdot dl = NI \tag{2-58}$$

from which it follows that

$$H = \frac{NI}{2\pi R} \tag{2-59}$$

Correspondingly, the magnetic-field vector is almost uniform in the core and is directed normal to the loops of the winding. The total flux linkage is

$$\psi = NAB \tag{2-60}$$

Therefore, the total energy that is transferred from the electric circuit to the magnetic field, which is entirely within the iron, is, from Eq. (2-35),

$$W_m = \int_0^\psi I \, d\psi \quad \text{joules} \tag{2-61}$$

This becomes, by combining this with the foregoing expressions,

$$W_m = (2\pi R)(A) \int_0^B H \, dB \tag{2-62}$$

But the volume of the iron torus is just

$$\text{Volume} = (2\pi R)A$$

Therefore, the energy transferred is

$$W_m = \int_0^B H \, dB \times \text{volume of iron} \quad \text{joules} \tag{2-63}$$

for the case when the iron starts from a completely demagnetized state.

It is natural to assume, in the light of the foregoing, that the energy stored in any small volume $\Delta\tau$ of iron is

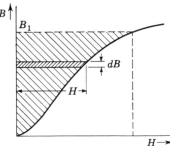

$$\Delta W_m = \Delta\tau \int_0^B H \, dB \quad \text{joules} \tag{2-64}$$

It is observed that, even though this expression has been deduced for an iron ring, it is true in general. Its significance is made evident by an examination of Fig. 2-6. This figure shows that, if the iron starts in the demagnetized state and the flux density is carried to the point B_1, then the shaded area represents the value of the integral contained in Eq.

Fig. 2-6. The energy density stored in the magnetic field.

(2-64), which is the energy input to the magnetic field per unit volume.

If it is assumed that the relation $B = \mu H$ is valid over the entire range of variation of B, although it is known that μ may vary considerably for ferromagnetic substances which are subjected to wide variations in H, then Eq. (2-59) may be written as

$$\Delta W_m = \Delta\tau \int_0^B \frac{B}{\mu} \, dB \quad \text{joules} \tag{2-65}$$

which attains the alternative form

$$\frac{\Delta W_m}{\Delta\tau} = \frac{B^2}{2\mu} = \frac{\mu H^2}{2} = \frac{HB}{2} \quad \text{joules/unit volume} \tag{2-66}$$

Observe that this is precisely the form given by Eq. (2-47) for the energy storage per unit volume of the magnetic field for a system of electric currents. This means, of course, that an expression of the form given in Eq. (2-66) is valid for any composite medium when due account is taken of the different characteristics of the various mediums. The situation here is precisely like that which exists for a composite dielectric medium, with the appropriate expression for the energy storage in the electric field being that given by Eq. (2-6).

2-8. Attraction between Magnetized Iron Surfaces. It is possible to obtain an expression for the force that exists on a piece of magnetic material which is inserted into a magnetic field. More precisely, we are interested in the force between parallel iron surfaces which are separated by a small air gap. Examples of the distributions here contemplated can be found in the electromagnetic relay, in d-c instruments of the D'Arsonval type, and in the magnetic circuit of a rotating machine.

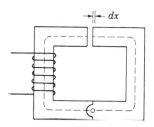

FIG. 2-7. A typical singly excited magnetic transducer.

Consider the singly excited magnetic circuit illustrated in Fig. 2-7. When the magnetic flux and mmf are directly proportional to each other, the energy stored in the field is

$$W_m = \tfrac{1}{2}I\psi = \tfrac{1}{2}F\Phi \qquad (2\text{-}67)$$

where F denotes the mmf. The stored energy can also be expressed in terms of the reluctance of the magnetic path, which is defined as

$$\mathfrak{R} \equiv \frac{F}{\Phi} \qquad (2\text{-}68)$$

or the permeance, which is defined as

$$\mathcal{P} \equiv \frac{1}{\mathfrak{R}} = \frac{\Phi}{F} \qquad (2\text{-}69)$$

With nonlinearity and hysteresis neglected, the reluctance and permeance are constant, and the stored energy is

$$W_m = \tfrac{1}{2}I\Psi = \tfrac{1}{2}F\Phi = \tfrac{1}{2}F^2\mathcal{P} = \tfrac{1}{2}\Phi^2\mathfrak{R} \qquad \text{joules} \qquad (2\text{-}70)$$

To find the force of attraction between the iron members separated by the air gap, we employ the results of Sec. 2-5 (see Example 2-5.1 in particular). Both $\mathfrak{R}$ and Φ are variables, and consequently for differential changes we write

$$dW_m = \tfrac{1}{2}\phi^2 \, d\mathfrak{R} + \mathfrak{R}\phi \, d\phi \qquad (2\text{-}71)$$

from which it follows that

$$f = -\left.\frac{\partial W_m}{\partial x}\right|_\Psi = -\left.\tfrac{1}{2}\Phi^2 \frac{d\mathcal{R}}{dx}\right|_\Psi = \left.\tfrac{1}{2}\Phi^2 \frac{d\mathcal{P}}{dx}\right|_\Psi \qquad \text{newtons} \quad (2\text{-}72)$$

Observe from this expression that a change in reluctance involves an interchange of energy between the field and the mechanical system.

Other useful forms of the force equation can be derived. Both F and $\mathcal{P}$ are variables, and for differential changes we may write

$$dW_m = \tfrac{1}{2}F^2 \, d\mathcal{P} + \mathcal{P}F \, dF \qquad\qquad (2\text{-}73)$$

It follows from this, since $F = NI$, that

$$f = \left.\frac{\partial W_m}{\partial x}\right|_I = \left.\tfrac{1}{2}F^2 \frac{d\mathcal{P}}{dx}\right|_I = -\left.\tfrac{1}{2}F^2 \frac{d\mathcal{R}}{dx}\right|_I \qquad \text{newtons} \quad (2\text{-}74)$$

This expression also shows that a change in permeance or reluctance involves an interchange of energy between the field and the mechanical system. Other equivalent expressions which readily follow are written

$$f = -\left.\tfrac{1}{2}\Phi \frac{dF}{dx}\right|_\Psi \qquad\qquad \text{newtons} \qquad\qquad (2\text{-}75)$$

and
$$f = \left.\tfrac{1}{2}F \frac{d\phi}{dx}\right|_I \qquad\qquad \text{newtons} \qquad\qquad (2\text{-}76)$$

Since $L = N^2/\mathcal{R} = N^2\mathcal{P}$, Eq. (2-74) may be written in terms of current and inductance

$$f = \left.\tfrac{1}{2}I^2 \frac{dL}{dx}\right|_I \qquad\qquad \text{newtons} \qquad\qquad (2\text{-}77)$$

For the device illustrated in Fig. 2-7, the total reluctance of the magnetic path is made up of the reluctance of the iron path and that of the air gap and is given by

$$\mathcal{R} = \mathcal{R}_{\text{iron}} + \frac{x}{\mu_0 A}$$

For a positive incremental change in air-gap length

$$\frac{d\mathcal{R}}{dx} = \frac{1}{\mu_0 A}$$

and Eq. (2-72) becomes

$$f = -\tfrac{1}{2}\Phi^2 \frac{1}{\mu_0 A} = -\frac{1}{2}\frac{B^2 A}{\mu_0} \qquad \text{newtons} \qquad (2\text{-}78)$$

which shows that the force is in such a direction as to decrease the air-gap length.

If there is an actual physical motion resulting from the force, then, in general, the force will change. To find the work done against the field in increasing the air-gap length from x_1 to x_2, for the case when the current in the coil is constant (or constant mmf), then the change in energy may be written directly as

$$\Delta W_m = \frac{1}{2}\frac{F^2}{\mathcal{R}_1} - \frac{1}{2}\frac{F^2}{\mathcal{R}_2} = \tfrac{1}{2}F^2\left(\frac{1}{\mathcal{R}_1} - \frac{1}{\mathcal{R}_2}\right) \qquad \text{joules} \qquad (2\text{-}79)$$

where $\mathcal{R}_1$ is the reluctance corresponding to the air-gap length x_1 and $\mathcal{R}_2$ is the corresponding reluctance for the air gap x_2.

2-9. Forces and Torques on Circuits with Associated Iron.[1]   It is desired now to extend the considerations of Sec. 2-5 to the more general case of a current-carrying circuit which is situated in a field which may contain iron.   Suppose that the circuit is given a virtual displacement δr.   If f_r is the mechanical force on this circuit in the direction of δr, there will be a change in flux linkages in the virtual displacement by an amount $\delta\psi$.   Also, a change will occur in the energy stored in the field. The energy supplied in the virtual displacement is partly stored and partly converted into external work.   By the principle of conservation of energy, we may write

$$I\,\delta\psi = f_r\,\delta r + \delta W \qquad\qquad (2\text{-}80)$$

In the limit as δr becomes vanishingly small, this expression becomes

$$f_r = I\frac{\partial\psi}{\partial r} - \frac{\partial W}{\partial r} \qquad\qquad (2\text{-}81)$$

An entirely similar procedure may be employed to find an expression for the component of torque in giving the circuit a virtual angular displacement $\delta\varphi$.   The result is

$$T_\varphi = I\frac{\partial\psi}{\partial\varphi} - \frac{\partial W}{\partial\varphi} \qquad\qquad (2\text{-}82)$$

Equation (2-81) may be generalized by combining this expression with Eq. (2-35); then

$$f_r = \sum_{k=1}^{n} I_k\frac{\partial\psi_k}{\partial r} - \sum_{k=1}^{n}\frac{d}{dr}\int_0^\Psi i_k\,d\psi_k \qquad (2\text{-}83)$$

The value of the force deduced from this expression is independent of the manner of effecting the virtual displacement, i.e., whether this is done at constant flux linkages or at constant current.   The expression may be written in simpler form, depending on the exact method of effecting the virtual displacement.   The two alternatives will be examined separately.

Constant Linkages.   Suppose that the virtual displacement is made at constant flux linkages.   In this case, the first term on the right of Eq.

[1] R. E. Doherty and R. H. Park, Mechanical Force between Electric Circuits, *Trans. AIEE,* **45**: 240 (1926).

(2-83) vanishes.   Observe that the limits in the integrals of the remaining term are not functions of r and that partial differentiation under the integral sign is permitted.   Thus, Eq. (2-83) becomes, in the present case,

$$f_r = - \sum_{k=1}^{n} \int_0^{\Psi} \frac{\partial i_k}{\partial r} \, d\psi_k \tag{2-84}$$

which may be written, by Eq. (2-42), in the form

$$f_r = - \frac{\partial W_m}{\partial r} \bigg|_{\Psi} \tag{2-85}$$

This shows that the force is the rate of decrease in stored magnetic energy with displacement at constant flux linkages and is identical with Eq. (2-52) for the linear case.

Constant Current.   In the present case it is found convenient to express Eq. (2-83) in slightly different form.   This is accomplished by carrying out a partial integration on the right-hand member of the expression.   Thus by writing

$$\sum \frac{d}{dr} \int_0^{\Psi} i_k \, d\psi_k = \sum \frac{d}{dr} \left(I_k \Psi_k - \int_0^{I_k} \psi_k \, di_k \right) \tag{2-86}$$

Eq. (2-83) becomes

$$f_r = \sum_{k=1}^{n} I_k \frac{\partial \psi_k}{\partial r} - \sum_{k=1}^{n} \frac{d}{dr} \left(I_k \Psi_k - \int_0^{I_k} \psi_k \, di_k \right) \tag{2-87}$$

But, at constant current independent of r, the first term on the right cancels the second term, with the remainder

$$f_r = \sum_{k=1}^{n} \int_0^{I_k} \frac{\partial \psi_k}{\partial r} \, di_k \tag{2-88}$$

It is convenient now to introduce the magnetic coenergy.   This is most conveniently done by reference to Fig. 2-8, which shows a typical graphical plot of ψ versus i for a single circuit.   Note that saturation is placed in evidence, but hysteresis is neglected.   In this graph, the crosshatched area denotes the magnetic energy, according to Eq. (2-35). The area under the curve is the magnetic coenergy.   This figure is the exact magnetic counterpart of Fig. 2-2 for the electric case.   In terms of the magnetic coenergy W'_m, the force equation above becomes

$$f_r = \frac{\partial W'_m}{\partial r} \bigg|_{I = \text{const}} \tag{2-89}$$

Note therefore that the force is the rate of increase of coenergy with displacement at constant current. This equation should be compared with Eq. (2-51). Clearly, when the medium is linear, the results given by Eqs. (2-85) and (2-89) are identical.

A particularly important application of these results is that in which some of the iron moves with the circuit. This is the case of a coil that is attached to an iron core and is precisely the situation of an armature coil in a rotating machine. Equations (2-81) and (2-82) are still valid,

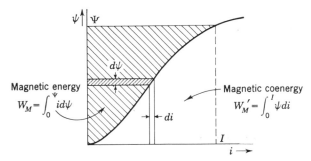

Magnetic energy
$$W_M = \int_0^\Psi i\, d\psi$$

Magnetic coenergy
$$W_M' = \int_0^I \psi\, di$$

Fig. 2-8. To define the magnetic coenergy.

but they now express the force and torque on the entire coil and core assembly, without concern for the distribution of the force and torque between the coil and the iron. This is a very important result, since it allows one to proceed in force and torque calculations by considering only the currents (as in an ideal machine with the conductors on the surface of the armature) without concern for the iron and the shape of the slots or their location in the slot in which the conductors may be embedded.

Actually it is possible to deduce some ideas of the force distribution from the foregoing equations. Mechanical systems ordinarily move in a manner to reduce the stored energy in the field. Consequently, the system tends to move in a direction to increase the flux linkage with the coil. In air-core coils, as by Eqs. (2-57), the $I(\partial\psi/\partial r)$ term prevails, whereas, in fields containing iron but no coils, the $\partial W/\partial r$ term prevails. Iron-clad coils involve both effects, and the general problem of forces on such coils becomes rather difficult.

Example 2-9.1. A simple form of a so-called reluctance motor is illustrated in the accompanying diagram.

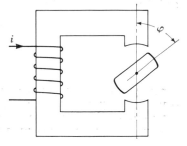

Fig. 2-9.1-1

(a) Express the inductance as measurable at the electrical terminals in analytic form, assuming that the iron is of such high permeability that only the air gap is significant in the magnetic equation.

(b) Write expressions for the energy and the coenergy.

(c) Write the expression for the torque developed.

(d) If an a-c excitation current is present, find expressions for the instantaneous and the average torque.

Solution. (a) Owing to the symmetry of the magnetic structure, the inductance can be expressed approximately by

$$L = L_0 + L_2 \cos 2\varphi$$

(b) Because the system is linear, the energy and coenergy are equal and are given by

$$W_m = W'_m = \tfrac{1}{2}i^2(L_0 + L_2 \cos 2\varphi)$$

(c) The torque developed, assuming constant current, is

$$T = -i^2 L_2 \sin 2\varphi$$

(d) If the a-c current is of the form

$$i = I_m \cos \omega t$$

then the expression for the torque becomes

$$T = -\frac{L_2 I_m{}^2}{2} (\cos^2 \omega t \sin 2\varphi)$$

which may be expanded to the form

$$T = \frac{L_2 I_m{}^2}{2} [- \sin 2\varphi - \tfrac{1}{2} \sin (2\omega t + 2\varphi) + \tfrac{1}{2} \sin (2\omega t - 2\varphi)]$$

Generally speaking, this torque expression averages zero. There are two special cases when the average torque is not zero. These occur when the iron slug rotates at a speed $\omega = \dot{\varphi}$ or $\omega = -\dot{\varphi}$. Under these circumstances we might write

$$\omega t - \varphi = \delta$$

and the average torque becomes

$$\bar{T} = \frac{L_2 I_m{}^2}{4} \sin 2\delta$$

PROBLEMS

2-1. An electrostatic voltmeter is shown schematically in the figure. When a d-c voltage is applied to the plates of the capacitor, the resulting attraction causes the pointer to move up the scale against the restraining action of the spring. If the capacitance varies linearly with deflection according to the relation

$$C = C_0 + C_1\varphi \qquad \text{farads}$$

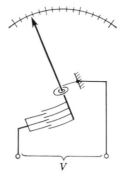

FIG. P2-1

develop an expression for the angular deflection of the pointer as a function of the applied d-c voltage V.   Denote the spring constant as K.

2-2. Suppose that the slab in Example 2-3.1 is only t thick, where $t < d$.   Deduce an expression for the force acting to pull the slab into the region between the plates.

2-3. Deduce an expression for the force tending to pull the plates together, in the capacitor assembly of Prob. 2-2.

2-4. The illustration is that of the so-called Faraday disk generator.   The thin brass disk is situated with its plane normal to a uniform magnetic field of flux density

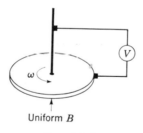

Uniform B

FIG. P2-4

$B = 1$ weber/m². Find the emf between the brushes when the disk rotates at 1,000 rpm.

2-5. Suppose that the two coils of Fig. 2-4 have the values

$$L_1 = 0.63 + 0.39 \cos \varphi$$
$$L_2 = 0.94 + 0.51 \cos \varphi$$
$$M = 0.72 + 0.72 \cos \varphi$$

(a) For constant currents $I_1 = 10$ amp and $I_2 = 7.5$ amp, compute the mechanical work done in increasing φ from 0 to 90°.

(b) Does the torque developed in (a) tend to increase or decrease?

(c) During the motion, how much energy is supplied by source 1?   By source 2?

2-6. Consider the reactor illustrated.   The idealized BH curve of the magnetic material of this reactor is also given.

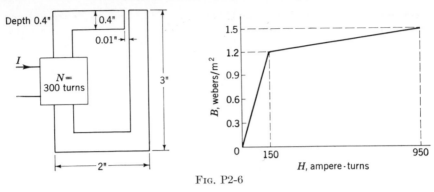

Fig. P2-6

(*a*) Find the energy stored in the magnetic field when the flux density is 1.5 webers/m². Neglect air-gap fringing and leakage.

(*b*) What is the inductance of the reactor?

2-7. A conductor carrying a current *I* is placed in the air-gap field of an electromagnet, as illustrated in the accompanying figure. Deduce an expression for the

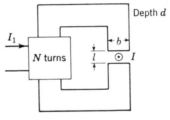

Fig. P2-7

force on the conductor. Assume that the permeability of the iron is infinite, that there is no fringing of the magnetic flux in the air gap, and that the return path of *I* is remote from the field.

2-8. A magnetic circuit has the dimensions indicated in the figure. The magnetizing coil has 150 turns and carries a current of 1 amp. A slab of iron which is just

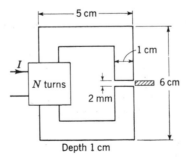

Fig. P2-8

large enough to fill the air gap is available. If the permeability of the iron is assumed to be constant, with $\mu_r = 4,000$, how much work is done in pulling the slab into the air gap?

2-9. An electromagnet is illustrated in the figure. This device is designed to support a weight of 25 lb (which includes the weight of the keeper K). The cross section of the magnetic portions of the circuit is 6 cm². It is required to find the number of

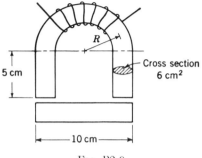

5 cm

Cross section
6 cm²

R

10 cm

FIG. P2-9

turns in the magnetizing coil to support this weight when the exciting current is 2 amp. The permeability of the material varies with B, as given in the following tabulation:

B, webers/m²........	0.36	0.44	0.48	0.60	0.72
μ_r.................	3,300	3,000	2,900	2,600	2,300

2-10. (*a*) Suppose that the current in winding 2 of Fig. 2-4 is maintained at $i_2 = I_m \cos \omega t$. Determine expressions for the transformer and the motional emf in winding 1 when the assembly 1 rotates at a uniform angular velocity ω_r.

(*b*) Suppose that coil 1 is short-circuited. Show that the torque is related to the motional emf. Neglect the resistance of the winding.

2-11. The cylindrical device illustrated has inductances $L_1 = 0.85$ henry, $L_2 = 0.58$ henry, and the mutual inductance between them is $M = 0.65 \cos \varphi$.

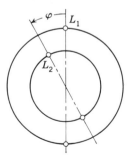

φ L_1

L_2

FIG. P2-11

(*a*) Find an expression for the instantaneous torque on the rotor when $\varphi = 60°$.

(*b*) If $i_1 = 2 \sin \omega t$ and the rotor winding is short-circuited, compute the average torque on the rotor when $\varphi = 60°$.

3

Energy-transfer Devices

This chapter contains a study of the two-winding transformer, a device which consists of two circuits which are fixed with respect to each other and with respect to the magnetic material making up the magnetic structure. Two alternative methods of analysis will be given, one of which leads to a passive network, the second of which leads to equivalent sources (electromotances). The passive-network formulation is of particular importance because it is in a form that permits the ready writing of the integrodifferential equations from which a transient as well as a steady-state analysis may be made. The equivalent-source formulation is the starting point for the so-called "power" analysis of such devices.

Both these analyses, even though they do consider certain aspects of the magnetic fields which are basic to their operation, generally overlook the Maxwellian idea that the conductors forming the electric circuit really serve only to guide the energy which resides, for the most part, in the fields which pervade the mediums surrounding the conductors. It is shown, in fact, that the energy from a generator to a load through a transformer is propagated in the form of an electromagnetic wave from the primary winding to the secondary winding principally through the intervening medium and not through the magnetic structure.

Attention is here called to the fact that the operation of the transformer can be described in electromagnetic-field terms,[1] although this approach is not here adopted. Such an approach leads to an equivalent circuit which reduces, as a special case, to the circuits deduced in our development.

3-1. Winding Directions. Typical physical setups for the two-winding transformer to be studied are shown in Fig. 3-1. These arrangements

---

[1] The features of such a general approach will be found in the discussion in Sec. 9-3 for the doubly excited rotating machine, although the geometry of the rotating machine is somewhat different from that of the static transformer. See also W. H. B. Cooper, Approach to the Operation of Inductors and Transformers in Terms of the Field Impedance, *Proc. IEE*, (2)**95**: 509 (1949).

differ among themselves only in the relation of the windings to the magnetic circuit. The case shown at (a) is the easiest to treat in the introductory sense. The remaining cases are really identical, except for the winding direction or system geometry.

The operation of the transformer is explained in terms of the production of a flux by a current, the induction of a potential in a conductor in the region of a time-changing flux, and the transfer of energy through the electromagnetic fields that are so produced. These effects are specified, respectively, by the laws of Ampère, Faraday, and Poynting. The situation is generally complicated by the fact that currents exist in both windings and potentials are induced in both windings. There is a consequent

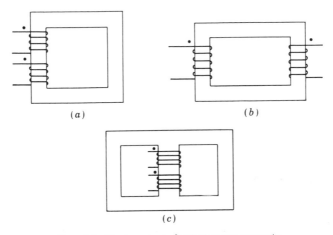

(a)   (b)

(c)

FIG. 3-1. Various transformer arrangements.

flow of power into or out of each winding. It is these factors which will receive detailed consideration in this chapter.

It is customary to designate one winding as the primary and one as the secondary. When this is done, the secondary winding is that to which the load is connected, whence the power flows from the primary to the secondary. A transformer may be incorporated in a network of such complexity that the power flow may change from time to time. In such a case, it is rather pointless to attempt to distinguish one or the other winding as the primary or the secondary. It is convenient, in such a case, to designate the windings by number.

Often in circuit applications interconnections may exist among the various windings of a magnetically coupled system. Under these circumstances it is essential that the relation between the potential polarities and the current directions be known. This information is obtained from the direction of the windings of the various coils relative to the core. This

requires either that the winding directions be clearly indicated, as in
Fig. 3-1, or else that some marking scheme be adopted which provides
substantially the same information.   The dots on the diagram provide
this marking scheme and so are essential to any subsequent discussion.

Consider the two-winding transformers illustrated in Fig. 3-2.   For
convenience, each winding is assumed to have zero resistance.   Suppose
that a varying current exists in winding 1, with winding 2 being open-
circuited.   Under this condition the winding makes up an inductance.

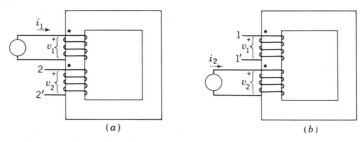

FIG. 3-2. To establish the significance of the winding direction.

For the reference conditions indicated on the diagram, the following
relation applies,

$$v_1 = L_1 \frac{di_1}{dt} \tag{3-1}$$

where L_1 is the self-inductance of winding 1.   This potential is really due
to the induction arising from the varying flux created in the core by
current i_1.

It is observed that winding 2, starting from the terminal marked $+$,
bears the same relation to the core as does winding 1, also starting from
the $+$ terminal.   Therefore, when v_1 is positive, v_2 must also be positive.
This fact is expressed by the relationship

$$v_2 = M_{21} \frac{di_1}{dt} \tag{3-2}$$

In this expression the constant M_{21} should be considered as a proportionality constant.   It is the mutual inductance from winding 1 to winding 2.   If the reference $+$ sign had been placed at the lower terminal on
either winding 1 or winding 2, a negative sign would have appeared in
Eq. (3-2).

An entirely similar situation would exist if the exciting current were to
be applied to winding 2, as in Fig. 3-2*b*.   In terms of the reference markings shown, the voltage across winding 2 is

$$v_2 = L_2 \frac{di_2}{dt} \tag{3-3}$$

Therefore, the voltage v_1 is positive when v_2 is positive, and is given by

$$v_1 = M_{12} \frac{di_2}{dt} \tag{3-4}$$

M_{12} is the mutual inductance from winding 2 to winding 1. But as is known, M is a geometrical factor only, and $M_{12} = M_{21}$, and may be designated by the single symbol M,†

$$M_{12} = M_{21} = M \tag{3-5}$$

Clearly, in the foregoing, the signs to be associated with the equation pairs, Eqs. (3-1) and (3-2), and Eqs. (3-3) and (3-4), follow directly from the winding details and the reference signs.   When it is not convenient to show actual winding directions, the essential information is carried by terminal markings. Thus a dot is placed at one terminal of each pair such that when progressing along the winding from the dotted terminal each winding encircles the core in the same sense.

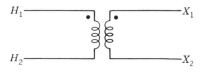

FIG. 3-3. Magnetic-coupling marking scheme.

It may appear redundant to add a dot to Fig. 3-2 when the $+$ signs seem to suffice. It is preferable to use both markings because the dots really carry with it information concerning the physical characteristics of the winding, whereas the $+$ sign is a convenience of notation for use in the analysis of the circuit. The dots can be placed on the terminals by the manufacturer of the transformer; the $+$ sign, by the analyst. There is no requirement that the dots and the $+$ signs coincide.

Marking schemes other than dots are used commercially. In power-transformer practice a numbering system is used in place of dots. The scheme used is illustrated in Fig. 3-3. The letter H is used on each terminal of the high-potential winding, and the letter X is used on each terminal of a low-potential winding. Subscripts are also used, with corresponding subscripts denoting the same winding sense. That is, any two terminals that have the same subscripts may be dotted, as shown. In the case of instrument transformers, two practices prevail. One practice uses a $\pm$ sign, and the other uses a 0 in place of the dot.

3-2. The Transformer as Part of a Network. The foregoing section contains the necessary interrelationships between the currents and voltage in the two windings of the transformer. With this informa-

---

† In the case of a rotating machine, we shall be faced with a situation in which the magnetic coupling is continuously changing. In this case M must be given an algebraic interpretation, with the reference condition for M depending on the current reference directions, with the reference positive condition for M being the condition for which the current reference directions produce magnetically aiding fluxes.

tion, it is possible to analyze a network when a transformer is included within it.   Consider now Fig. 3-4, which is to be discussed in some detail. The Kirchhoff voltage, or loop, equation is applied to each loop of the network.   For the network shown, the controlling differential equation is the following:

$$Z_a i_1 + L_1 \frac{di_1}{dt} + M \frac{di_2}{dt} = v$$

$$M \frac{di_1}{dt} + Z_b i_2 + L_2 \frac{di_2}{dt} = 0$$

(3-6)

These equations become, for the case of a general exponential excitation of the form $v = V e^{st}$,†

$$(Z_a + sL_1)I_1 + sM I_2 = V$$
$$sM I_1 + (Z_b + sL_2)I_2 = 0$$

(3-7)

Attention is called to the fact that, if the dot on one winding were moved to the opposite end of the winding, the sign associated with the mutual-inductance term would be reversed.

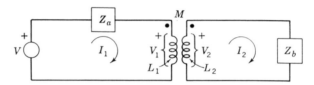

FIG. 3-4. A simple network involving magnetic coupling.

The character of the coupling between two loops may be somewhat more complicated than the simple magnetic coupling of Fig. 3-4.   A common situation is that shown in Fig. 3-5.   In this network both mutual impedance and magnetic coupling exist between the two loops.   The complete network equations would be of the same form as those in Eqs. (3-7), except that now the mutual-coupling terms will be of the form $Z_c + sM$ when the dots have the positions indicated.

A somewhat more complicated case is that illustrated in Fig. 3-6, which shows a pair of magnetically coupled coils on the periphery of one loop in a common branch.   Observe that in this diagram L_1 and L_2 are magnetically coupled, while they both are on the periphery of loop 1.   Coil 2 is in the common branch of the network.   The mutually coupled portion of the network is specified by the equations

$$sL_1 I_1 - sM(I_2 - I_1) = V_1$$
$$sM I_1 + sL_2(I_1 - I_2) = V_2$$

(3-8)

† It is necessary to distinguish between complex quantities and vector quantities, both of which are written with boldface type.   No confusion should result.

Note also from the circuit diagram that

$$\mathbf{V} = \mathbf{V}_1 + \mathbf{V}_2 \tag{3-9}$$

Thus we may write

$$\begin{aligned}
\mathbf{s}(L_1 + L_2 + 2M)\mathbf{I}_1 - \mathbf{s}(L_2 + M)\mathbf{I}_2 &= \mathbf{V} \\
-\mathbf{s}(L_2 + M)\mathbf{I}_1 + (\mathbf{s}L_2 + \mathbf{Z})\mathbf{I}_2 &= 0
\end{aligned} \tag{3-10}$$

which is of the general form

$$\begin{aligned}
\varrho_{11}\mathbf{I}_1 + \varrho_{12}\mathbf{I}_2 &= \mathbf{V} \\
\varrho_{21}\mathbf{I}_1 + \varrho_{22}\mathbf{I}_2 &= 0
\end{aligned} \tag{3-11}$$

where

$$\varrho_{11} = \mathbf{s}(L_1 + L_2 + 2M) \qquad \varrho_{12} = \varrho_{21} = -\mathbf{s}(L_2 + M) \qquad \varrho_{22} = \mathbf{s}L_2 + \mathbf{Z}$$

These equations satisfy the condition of reciprocity, in common with those of the ordinary passive networks without magnetic coupling.

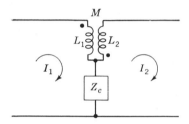

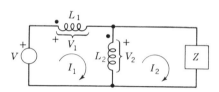

Fig. 3-5. Generalized network with magnetic coupling.

Fig. 3-6. A special case of magnetic coupling.

The expression for ϱ_{11} shows that, when two magnetically coupled coils are in series on a single loop for the dot positions shown, the resultant equivalent inductance is the sum of the individual coil inductances increased by twice the mutual inductance. If the dot position on one coil were moved to the other end of the winding, the resulting inductance would be the sum of the individual coil inductances decreased by twice the mutual inductance. The relationship is the following: If the loop currents enter or leave both dots, the sign of the $2M$ term is positive; otherwise the sign is negative.

3-3. Reference Direction for Flux. It is desired to study the mechanism of the magnetic coupling in terms of the magnetic fluxes that are produced by currents in the several windings of the transformer. Since the fluxes vary with time when the potentials are time-varying, neglecting the effects of eddy currents and hysteresis which can cause differences in the form of the time variations between the two, it is necessary to assign reference directions to the fluxes.

It is recalled that the reference positive polarity and the reference current direction were assigned arbitrarily, the relationship between these quantities being given by Ohm's law, when referred to any element of the circuit. Correspondingly, the reference direction for current and the reference direction for flux are arbitrary. The relationship between the current and the flux is given in terms of the dotted terminals. Refer to Fig. 3-7, which illustrates this matter. Suppose that the current is into the dotted terminal of the winding shown. From the rules established in the study of electricity and magnetism, this will produce a flux in the direction determined by the right-hand-screw rule. This rule states that the direction of the flux is in the direction of advance of a right-handed screw which rotates in the direction that the current encircles the core. The reference direction for flux is ordi-

narily so chosen that the current into any dot will produce flux in the reference direction. This means that the dots are so located that the magnetomotances (mmfs) of all coils are aiding when currents are entering each dotted terminal.

3-4. Flux Relations in a Two-winding Transformer. In the general case of a transformer, there is a current in each winding, and each of these currents contributes to the flux in the core. Furthermore, since no material, including air, is a perfect magnetic insulator, not all the flux remains within the core. Under some conditions a very appreciable portion of the flux "leaks" out of the core.

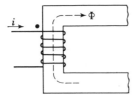

Fig. 3-7. The reference direction for flux.

It is convenient for our further work to distinguish the several components of flux and to classify them according to the currents which produce them and the positions in the circuit at which they are found. The situation is illustrated in Fig. 3-8. The following components exist for the two-winding case:

ϕ_1 = total flux linking coil 1 due to all currents

ϕ_2 = total flux linking coil 2 due to all currents

ϕ_{11} = portion of ϕ_1 which is due to i_1

ϕ_{22} = portion of ϕ_2 which is due to i_2

ϕ_{12} = part of ϕ_1 which is due to i_2

ϕ_{21} = part of ϕ_2 which is due to i_1

ϕ_{s1} = flux due to i_1 which links coil 1 but not coil 2 (this is called the leakage flux of winding 1)

ϕ_{s2} = flux due to i_2 which links winding 2 but not coil 1 (this is the leakage flux of winding 2)

ϕ_M = flux common to both coils due to all currents (this is the mutual flux)

Note that, as drawn in Fig. 3-8, each line represents the appropriate flux component.

The transformer may be analyzed from several viewpoints, and these depend on the groupings of the flux components. When analyzed from the "circuits" point of view, the relations of interest are the following:

$$\phi_1 = \phi_{11} + \phi_{12} \qquad \phi_2 = \phi_{22} + \phi_{21} \qquad (3\text{-}12)$$

Correspondingly, when analyzed from the "power" point of view, the relations of interest are the following:

$$\phi_1 = \phi_{s1} + \phi_M \qquad \phi_2 = \phi_{s2} + \phi_M \qquad (3\text{-}13)$$

with
$$\phi_M = \phi_{12} + \phi_{21}$$

Other useful relations among the flux components are

$$\phi_{s1} = \phi_{11} - \phi_{21} \qquad \phi_{s2} = \phi_{22} - \phi_{12} \qquad (3\text{-}14)$$

The validity of these relations is evident from an examination of Fig. 3-8.

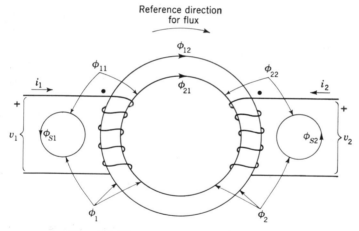

Fig. 3-8. The components of magnetic flux.

In the interests of later needs, it is convenient to define two constants which give a measure of the so-called "tightness" of coupling between two coils. These are

$$K_1 = \frac{\phi_{21}}{\phi_{11}} \qquad K_2 = \frac{\phi_{12}}{\phi_{22}} \qquad (3\text{-}15)$$

Note from the meaning of the components of flux that K_1 and K_2 have meaning even when there is current in both windings. Actually, as defined, K_1 is independent of i_2, and correspondingly K_2 is independent of i_1. If the saturation of the iron core is neglected, each K is a constant.

Note also that each K, which specifies the fraction of flux linking a flux-producing coil with a second coil, is restricted in value to the range from 0 to 1.

3-5. Induced Potentials (Electromotances). This section is in some measure an extension of Sec. 3-1, although it is now supposed that all coils which are mutually coupled may carry currents simultaneously. For convenience, however, it will be assumed, temporarily, that all coils have negligible resistance. The discussion continues from considerations of the Faraday law of electromagnetic induction, which is simply summarized in the equations

$$v_1 = N_1 \frac{d\phi_1}{dt} \qquad v_2 = N_2 \frac{d\phi_2}{dt} \tag{3-16}$$

where the flux is in webers and where the N's denote the number of turns in the respective windings.

These equations are fundamental and apply regardless of the sources of the flux. Attention is specifically directed to the fact that, if the forms for the fluxes given in Eqs. (3-12) are used, the resulting expressions attain one form. The expressions for the fluxes given in Eqs. (3-13) lead to equations which are different in form from those obtained when Eqs. (3-12) are used. Superficially the forms and interpretations are different for these two cases. Basically, of course, the two viewpoints are the same. It is important that both viewpoints be presented in order to display the differences.

Self- and Mutual-inductance Viewpoint. Suppose that Eqs. (3-12) are combined with Eq. (3-16). The result is

$$\begin{aligned}
v_1 &= N_1 \frac{d\phi_{11}}{dt} + N_1 \frac{d\phi_{12}}{dt} \\
v_2 &= N_2 \frac{d\phi_{22}}{dt} + N_2 \frac{d\phi_{21}}{dt}
\end{aligned} \tag{3-17}$$

It is possible to interpret these expressions in terms of previous results. Observe that these expressions take on the following forms when either i_2 or i_1 has a constant value, which is here taken to be zero:

When $i_2 = 0$
$$v_1 = N_1 \frac{d\phi_{11}}{dt}$$

$$v_2 = N_2 \frac{d\phi_{21}}{dt}$$

$$\tag{3-18}$$

When $i_1 = 0$
$$v_1 = N_1 \frac{d\phi_{12}}{dt}$$

$$v_2 = N_2 \frac{d\phi_{22}}{dt}$$

But these conditions are precisely those which applied in the discussion in Sec. 3-1. We may write these equations in terms of L_1, L_2, M as follows:

$$N_1 \frac{d\phi_{11}}{dt} = L_1 \frac{di_1}{dt}$$

$$N_1 \frac{d\phi_{12}}{dt} = M \frac{di_2}{dt}$$

$$N_2 \frac{d\phi_{22}}{dt} = L_2 \frac{di_2}{dt}$$

$$N_2 \frac{d\phi_{21}}{dt} = M \frac{di_1}{dt}$$

(3-19)

These lead to the conclusion that for the most general case, as given in Eqs. (3-17), the equations may be expressed in the equivalent forms

$$v_1 = L_1 \frac{di_1}{dt} + M \frac{di_2}{dt}$$

$$v_2 = M \frac{di_1}{dt} + L_2 \frac{di_2}{dt}$$

(3-20)

Observe that the flux-time derivatives have been replaced by current-time derivatives. This is very useful, because circuits analyzed on the general network bases are usually expressed in terms of currents and potentials.

Equations (3-19) yield expressions for the L's and M in terms of the fluxes and currents. Clearly, it is seen that

$$L_1 = N_1 \frac{d\phi_{11}}{di_1} = N_1 \frac{\phi_{11}}{i_1}$$

$$L_2 = N_2 \frac{d\phi_{22}}{di_2} = N_2 \frac{\phi_{22}}{i_2}$$

$$M = N_1 \frac{d\phi_{12}}{di_2} = N_1 \frac{\phi_{12}}{i_2}$$

$$M = N_2 \frac{d\phi_{21}}{di_1} = N_2 \frac{\phi_{21}}{i_1}$$

(3-21)

Attention is called to the fact that the forms on the right are true when the flux is a linear function of current. This condition is not always fulfilled, and care in the use of these expressions must be exercised.

Suppose that the two forms for M in Eqs. (3-21) are multiplied together. This gives

$$M^2 = \left(N_1 \frac{\phi_{12}}{i_2} \right) \left(N_2 \frac{\phi_{21}}{i_1} \right)$$

This is now rearranged, with the factors ϕ_{11}/ϕ_{11} and ϕ_{22}/ϕ_{22} being included.   The result is

$$M^2 = \left(\frac{\phi_{21}}{\phi_{11}} N_1 \frac{\phi_{11}}{i_1} \right) \left(\frac{\phi_{12}}{\phi_{22}} N_2 \frac{\phi_{22}}{i_2} \right)$$

This result is combined with Eqs. (3-15) and (3-21) to give

$$M^2 = (K_1 L_1)(K_2 L_2) = K_1 K_2 L_1 L_2 \tag{3-22}$$

It is customary to define a new constant

$$k^2 = K_1 K_2 \tag{3-23}$$

which is termed the "coefficient of coupling." Equation (3-22) thus assumes the form

$$M = k \sqrt{L_1 L_2} \tag{3-24}$$

which is the known useful relation between the mutual inductance and the self-inductance of each winding and the coefficient of coupling.

Mutual and Leakage-flux Viewpoint. The development will parallel that in the preceding discussion, with Eqs. (3-17) again being the starting point. Now, however, the fluxes are treated in terms of the components specified in Eqs. (3-13). There now result

$$v_1 = N_1 \frac{d\phi_{s1}}{dt} + N_1 \frac{d\phi_M}{dt}$$
$$v_2 = N_2 \frac{d\phi_{s2}}{dt} + N_2 \frac{d\phi_M}{dt} \tag{3-25}$$

It is convenient to replace the time derivatives of ϕ_{s1} and ϕ_{s2} by the derivatives of i_1 and i_2, respectively, by defining suitable inductances. Since these inductances are to associate the leakage flux of a winding with the current which produces it, they are termed the coil "leakage inductances." Thus, corresponding to Eqs. (3-21), we write

$$S_1 = N_1 \frac{d\phi_{s1}}{di_1} = N_1 \frac{\phi_{s1}}{i_1}$$
$$S_2 = N_2 \frac{d\phi_{s2}}{di_2} = N_2 \frac{\phi_{s2}}{i_2} \tag{3-26}$$

These expressions specify that the leakage fluxes ϕ_{s1} and ϕ_{s2} are, respectively, proportional to i_1 and i_2, with S_1 and S_2 being the proportionality constants. By the very nature of their meaning S_1 and S_2 are less dependent on the saturation of the magnetic-core material than are L_1 and L_2, because much of the leakage paths are in air.

Convenient forms for the S's result when Eqs. (3-26) are combined with Eqs. (3-14). This gives

$$S_1 = N_1 \frac{\phi_{11}}{i_1}\left(1 - \frac{\phi_{21}}{\phi_{11}}\right)$$

$$S_2 = N_2 \frac{\phi_{22}}{i_2}\left(1 - \frac{\phi_{12}}{\phi_{22}}\right) \tag{3-27}$$

which become, by Eqs. (3-15),

$$S_1 = (1 - K_1)L_1 \qquad S_2 = (1 - K_2)L_2 \tag{3-28}$$

It is noted that the development in this section has replaced the effects of ϕ_{11}, ϕ_{22}, ϕ_{12}, ϕ_{21}, ϕ_{s1}, ϕ_{s2}, respectively, by the inductances L_1, L_2, M, S_1, S_2. This permits derivatives of current to replace derivatives of flux in the formulas for potentials. However, the flux ϕ_M has not been so treated, since it is due to two currents instead of one. While it would be possible to replace this by equivalent inductances, it is convenient to handle this somewhat differently, as will now be shown.

3-6. Analysis under Sinusoidal Excitation. It is now desired to examine the transformer as part of a network, as in Sec. 3-2. The analysis on the self- and mutual-inductance viewpoint

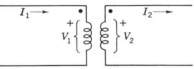

FIG. 3-9. The usual reference conditions for sinusoidal analysis.

is substantially that in Sec. 3-2, although some information not previously presented will be examined. The analysis on the mutual- and leakage-flux viewpoint will introduce some new ideas. In both cases it will be assumed that the elements are linear and that the coil resistances are negligible.

It is desirable in the following to choose the reference conditions shown in Fig. 3-9. This in no way affects the analysis, although negative signs may appear now in a few places, where, in discussing Fig. 3-4, positive signs might have occurred. The purpose in making this change is to present the results in a form which more obviously shows the transformer in the path of power flow from a source of energy to a load. It will also be assumed in the analysis that sinusoidal excitation exists, and the results will be given in terms of the appropriate phasor (sinor) quantities.

Self- and Mutual-inductance Viewpoint. In the analysis now, corresponding to Eqs. (3-20) one readily finds

$$v_1 = L_1 \frac{di_1}{dt} - M \frac{di_2}{dt}$$

$$v_2 = M \frac{di_1}{dt} - L_2 \frac{di_2}{dt} \tag{3-29}$$

For sinusoidal excitation these lead to the phasor expressions

$$\mathbf{V}_1 = j\omega L_1 \mathbf{I}_1 - j\omega M \mathbf{I}_2$$
$$\mathbf{V}_2 = j\omega M \mathbf{I}_1 - j\omega L_2 \mathbf{I}_2 \tag{3-30}$$

A phasor diagram may be drawn, and it will be supposed that Fig. 3-10 corresponds to specified parameters.

Mutual- and Leakage-flux Viewpoint. In the analysis of Fig. 3-9 on the mutual- and leakage-flux viewpoint, the equations would correspond

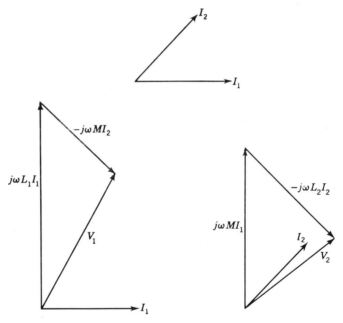

FIG. 3-10. The phasor (sinor) diagrams of a magnetically coupled network from the self- and mutual-inductance viewpoint.

to Eqs. (3-25). Now, because of the reversal of the reference current direction for i_2, the flux components ϕ_{12} and ϕ_{s2} will reverse, for the specified reference direction for flux. However, ϕ_M is still the algebraic sum of $\phi_{21} + \phi_{12}$; so the controlling equations are

$$v_1 = S_1 \frac{di_1}{dt} + N_1 \frac{d\phi_M}{dt}$$
$$v_2 = -S_2 \frac{di_2}{dt} + N_2 \frac{d\phi_M}{dt} \tag{3-31}$$

Since the currents produce the fluxes, then sinusoidal current implies sinusoidal flux and the appropriate phasor expressions become

$$\mathbf{V}_1 = j\omega S_1 \mathbf{I}_1 + j\omega N_1 \boldsymbol{\phi}_M$$
$$\mathbf{V}_2 = -j\omega S_2 \mathbf{I}_2 + j\omega N_2 \boldsymbol{\phi}_M \tag{3-32}$$

The components of these expressions are to be discussed before drawing the phasor diagram. The terms ωS_1 and ωS_2 are called "leakage react-ances." Recall that $\mathbf{V}_1$ and $\mathbf{V}_2$ are each due to a varying linking flux

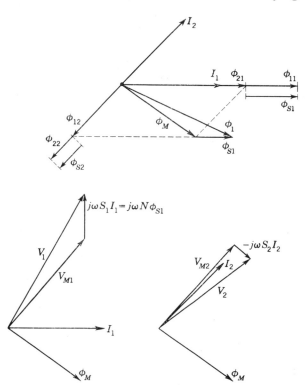

FIG. 3-11. The sinor diagrams on the mutual- and leakage-flux viewpoint.

and are induced potentials. Since, however, the flux appears explicitly only in terms involving $\boldsymbol{\phi}_M$, it is common practice in using these expres-sions to designate the terms

$$\mathbf{V}_{M1} = j\omega N_1 \boldsymbol{\phi}_M \qquad \mathbf{V}_{M2} = j\omega N_2 \boldsymbol{\phi}_M \tag{3-33}$$

as "induced" potentials. They have the important property that

$$\frac{\mathbf{V}_{M1}}{\mathbf{V}_{M2}} = \frac{N_1}{N_2} \tag{3-34}$$

The phasor diagrams appropriate to Eqs. (3-32) are given in Fig. 3-11.

The flux diagram in this figure is a consequence of Eqs. (3-21), which become, for the sinusoidal excitation and the specified reference direction for current I_2,

$$\phi_{11} = \frac{L_1}{N_1} I_1$$

$$\phi_{21} = \frac{M}{N_2} I_1$$

$$\phi_{22} = -\frac{L_2}{N_2} I_2 \tag{3-35}$$

$$\phi_{12} = -\frac{M}{N_1} I_2$$

$$\phi_M = \phi_{12} + \phi_{12}$$

The negative signs in the third and fourth equations arise because of the arbitrary choice of reference direction for flux and that for current.

The two sets of figures, Figs. 3-10 and 3-11, which apply to the same transformer show graphically the differences in the two analytical viewpoints. V_1 and V_2 as found by both methods are identical, although the details of construction are quite different. That is, in so far as the terminal conditions are concerned, both methods yield the same results. In essence, therefore, this indicates that for the simple devices considered involving a magnetic coupling between coils, if the analysis is on the mutual- and leakage-flux basis, there must be an equivalent analysis on the self- and mutual-inductance basis. One is often very interested in deducing such network equivalent diagrams of magnetic-field devices.

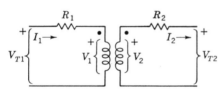

Fig. 3-12. Magnetically coupled coils with resistances not negligible.

3-7. Effect of Resistance. It is desired now to examine the modifications that must be made in the foregoing analyses when the effect of resistance of the windings is taken into account. This is most easily done by considering the resistance of the winding to be external to the coil. Thus, instead of the circuit of Fig. 3-9, the circuit of Fig. 3-12 is now under survey. In this circuit the potentials V_1 and V_2 are no longer accessible to measurement.

By the Kirchhoff potential law, the potentials V_1 and V_2 are related to the terminal potentials by the equations

$$V_{T1} = V_1 + I_1 R_1$$
$$V_{T2} = V_2 - I_2 R_2 \tag{3-36}$$

Now, through the appropriate expressions for V_1 and V_2, the resulting forms will correspond to the viewpoint chosen. For the self- and mutual-inductance viewpoint, the equations become

$$\mathbf{V}_{T1} = (R_1 + j\omega L_1)\mathbf{I}_1 - j\omega M\mathbf{I}_2$$
$$\mathbf{V}_{T2} = j\omega M\mathbf{I}_1 - (R_2 + j\omega L_2)\mathbf{I}_2 \tag{3-37}$$

For the mutual- and leakage-flux viewpoint, the equations become

$$\mathbf{V}_{T1} = j\omega N_1\phi_M + (R_1 + j\omega S_1)\mathbf{I}_1 = \mathbf{V}_{M1} + (R_1 + j\omega S_1)\mathbf{I}_1$$
$$\mathbf{V}_{T2} = j\omega N_2\phi_M - (R_2 + j\omega S_2)\mathbf{I}_2 = \mathbf{V}_{M2} - (R_2 + j\omega S_2)\mathbf{I}_2 \tag{3-38}$$

The complete phasor diagrams corresponding to each, for the situations illustrated in Figs. 3-10 and 3-11, are combined in Fig. 3-13.

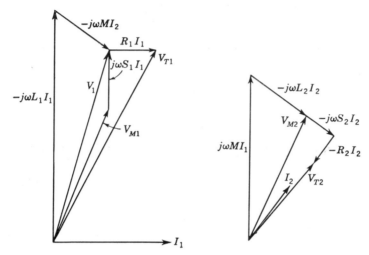

FIG. 3-13. The combined sinor diagrams showing the self- and mutual-inductance and the mutual- and leakage-flux viewpoints.

3-8. The Ideal Transformer.   The ideal transformer is a device that has hypothetical existence only.   The reason for this is that the device assumes the existence of certain limiting conditions, namely

$$\text{Resistance of each winding} \to 0$$
$$\text{Leakage inductance of each winding} \to 0$$
$$\text{Mutual flux} \to 0$$
$$N_1, N_2 \text{ each} \to \infty \tag{3-39}$$
$$\frac{N_1}{N_2} = a \text{ (a constant)}$$

It will be found that the relationships between currents and voltages are much simpler for the ideal transformer than for the physical transformer.   Clearly, the ideal transformer cannot be constructed, but its existence in an analytical sense proves to be very valuable in discussing the performance of the actual transformer in terms of equivalent circuits, as will later be shown. Actually, it is possible to construct transformers which closely approximate the ideal transformer.

Refer to Fig. 3-9, which shows the typical representation of a transformer and which shows broadly the relationship between the potentials and the circuit parameters. The explicit expressions are given by Eqs. (3-30) for the self- and mutual-inductance viewpoint and by Eqs. (3-32) for the mutual- and leakage-flux viewpoint. Now, because of the conditions contained in Eqs. (3-39), $R_1\mathbf{I}_1$, $j\omega S_1\mathbf{I}_1$, and $R_2\mathbf{I}_2$ and $j\omega S_2\mathbf{I}_2$ each become zero. There is thus only a single voltage $\mathbf{V}_1$ or $\mathbf{V}_2$ in each winding. That is,

$$\mathbf{V}_1 = \mathbf{V}_{T1} = \mathbf{V}_{M1}$$
$$\mathbf{V}_2 = \mathbf{V}_{T2} = \mathbf{V}_{M2}$$

Because of this, as shown in Fig. 3-13, if modified according to these requirements, $\mathbf{V}_1$ and $\mathbf{V}_2$ are in phase, and these are related by the turns ratio, in accordance with Eq. (3-34). In the present case, therefore,

$$\frac{\mathbf{V}_1}{\mathbf{V}_2} = \frac{N_1}{N_2} \tag{3-40}$$

in which each potential may be complex, but their ratio is real.

The relationship between the currents is also readily deduced. It is supposed that the mutual flux is made to approach zero by increasing the number of turns on each coil, while the turns ratio is kept constant. As the number of turns increases, the flux needed to provide a given induced potential becomes progressively smaller. In the limit, for fixed $\mathbf{V}_1$ and $\mathbf{V}_2$, as N_1 and N_2 each become infinite, the mutual flux ϕ_M approaches zero. An important consequence of a zero mutual flux is given by the last of Eqs. (3-35), which requires that

$$\phi_{21} = -\phi_{12} \tag{3-41}$$

This shows that ϕ_{12} and ϕ_{21} are identical in magnitude and opposite in phase. Now introduce the second and fourth equations of Eqs. (3-35), which yields

$$\frac{M}{N_2}\mathbf{I}_1 = \frac{M}{N_1}\mathbf{I}_2 \tag{3-42}$$

This last expression may be written in the form

$$\frac{\mathbf{I}_1}{\mathbf{I}_2} = \frac{N_2}{N_1} \tag{3-43}$$

This expression is the counterpart of Eq. (3-40) for the potential ratio. It also shows the very fundamental fact that a balance exists between the mmfs produced by the primary and secondary currents. This means that the mmf due to a current change in one winding is completely compensated by a change in the mmf due to the other winding.

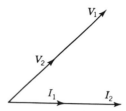

The phasor diagram for the ideal transformer is considerably simpler than that shown in Fig. 3-13, the simple form shown in Fig. 3-14 being now assumed.

3-9. Equivalent Circuit of a Two-winding Transformer. A rearrangement of Fig. 3-13 will permit a relatively simple circuit interpretation. This rearrangement, which is given in Fig. 3-15, has done the following: The potentials R_1I_1 and $j\omega S_1I_1$ have been moved to different positions on the figure; the arrow directions and the signs of $-R_1I_1$ and $-j\omega S_2I_2$ are reversed; the current I_1 is resolved into two components. Suppose now that the potential and current

Fig. 3-14. The sinor diagram for the ideal transformer.

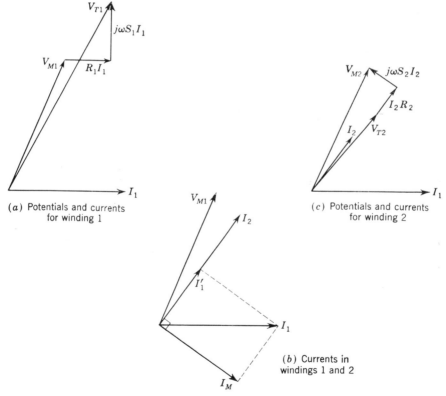

Fig. 3-15. Currents and potentials for a physical transformer.

relationships illustrated in these phasor diagrams are grouped as follows:

   a. Relationships among $\mathbf{V}_{T1}$, $\mathbf{I}_1$, and $\mathbf{V}_{M1}$
   b. Relationships among $\mathbf{V}_{M1}$, $\mathbf{V}_{M2}$, $\mathbf{I}_1$, and $\mathbf{I}_2$
   c. Relationships among $\mathbf{V}_{M2}$, $\mathbf{I}_2$, and $\mathbf{V}_{T2}$

It is possible to represent the entire situation in the block diagram shown in Fig. 3-16. Observe that the groupings among specified relationships above, which correspond to the phasor diagrams of Fig. 3-15, are specified by the blocks in Fig. 3-16. Thus $\mathbf{V}_{M1}$ is common to groups (a) and (b); $\mathbf{V}_{M2}$ is common to groups (b) and (c). Thus, the present

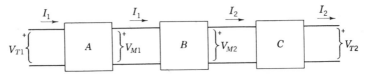

Fig. 3-16. The block network equivalent of a physical transformer.

problem is that of finding the appropriate components to be included in each of the rectangles in Fig. 3-16.

Groups (a) and (c) are simplest to treat. Reference to Fig. 3-15a and c shows that rectangles A and C are to be replaced by RL circuits. Rectangle B requires detailed treatment. The terminal currents are shown in Fig. 3-15, with $\mathbf{I}_1$ resolved into two components $\mathbf{I}_1'$ and $\mathbf{I}_M$. The component $\mathbf{I}_1'$ is chosen along $\mathbf{I}_2$, and the current $\mathbf{I}_M$ is chosen along $\boldsymbol{\phi}_M$, as given in Fig. 3-11. Now, upon comparing Fig. 3-15b with the corresponding figure of Fig. 3-11, it follows that

$$\frac{\mathbf{I}_1'}{\mathbf{I}_1} = - \frac{\phi_{12}}{\phi_{21}} \tag{3-44}$$

By the second and fourth of Eqs. (3-35), this expression becomes

$$\mathbf{I}_1' = - \mathbf{I}_1 \left(- \frac{M}{N_1} \mathbf{I}_2 \right) \frac{N_2}{M \mathbf{I}_1} = \frac{N_2}{N_1} \mathbf{I}_2 \tag{3-45}$$

This is an important result, for it shows that $\mathbf{I}_1'$ and $\mathbf{I}_2$ are related as in an ideal transformer; $\mathbf{I}_1'$ is that component of $\mathbf{I}_1$ whose resulting mmf just cancels the mmf of $\mathbf{I}_2$.

Since $\mathbf{I}_M$ is the difference between $\mathbf{I}_1$ and $\mathbf{I}_1'$, this current appears in a shunt path that must be connected to the left-hand side of box B. To find the nature of this element across the input to box B, compare Fig. 3-11 with Fig. 3-15c. It is seen that

$$\frac{\mathbf{I}_M}{\mathbf{I}_1} = \frac{\phi_M}{\phi_{21}} \tag{3-46}$$

Since, however, $\boldsymbol{\phi}_M = \mathbf{V}_{M1}/j\omega N_1$ and $\boldsymbol{\phi}_{21} = K_1 L_1 \mathbf{I}_1/N_1$, then, by substituting these expressions into Eq. (3-46), there follows

$$\mathbf{I}_M = \frac{\mathbf{V}_{M1}}{j\omega K_1 L_1} \tag{3-47}$$

Thus the circuit branch for $\mathbf{I}_M$ is a shunt-connected inductance of value

$$L_{M1} = K_1 L_1 \tag{3-48}$$

The detailed form of Fig. 3-16 is that illustrated in Fig. 3-17. Attention is called to the fact that $S_1 + L_{M1} = L_1$, and hence $S_1 = (1 - K_1)L_1$, in accordance with the first of Eqs. (3-28).

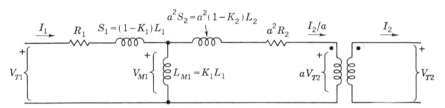

FIG. 3-17. The equivalent network of the physical transformer with the "magnetizing admittance" on the primary side.

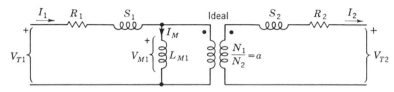

FIG. 3-18. Equivalent network referred to the primary.

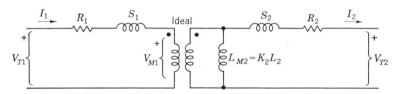

FIG. 3-19. The equivalent network of the physical transformer with the "magnetizing admittance" on the secondary side.

Figure 3-17 may be redrawn by referring the secondary quantities S_2 and R_2 to the primary side of the ideal transformer. This is shown in Fig. 3-18. This is a particularly useful form because it effectively reduces the analysis to that for a 1:1 transformer, since the ideal transformer to the right is simply a scaling device.

A second equivalent network corresponding to Fig. 3-17 results if the phasor current diagram in Fig. 3-15b begins by resolving the secondary current $\mathbf{I}_2$ into two components, instead of the current $\mathbf{I}_1$. The consequent analysis would follow precisely as above, except that now the shunting element would be on the output end of block B. The resulting equivalent network in this case is that shown in Fig. 3-19. Now, an equivalent circuit referred to the secondary follows from this, as shown in Fig. 3-20.

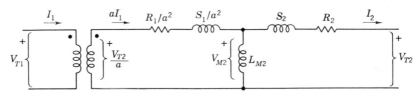

FIG. 3-20. Equivalent circuit referred to the secondary.

3-10. Generalization of the Equivalent Circuit. The equivalent networks discussed above are of considerable interest, since they stem from physical pictures. Actually, however, these represent only a few of many possible equivalent circuits. All these are derived from the basic transformer equations given by Eqs. (3-37). Consider these equations again,

$$(R_1 + j\omega L_1)\mathbf{I}_1 - j\omega M\mathbf{I}_2 = \mathbf{V}_{T1}$$
$$j\omega M\mathbf{I}_1 - (R_2 + j\omega L_2)\mathbf{I}_2 = \mathbf{V}_{T2} \tag{3-49}$$

Suppose that $\mathbf{I}_2$ and $\mathbf{V}_{T2}$ are scaled by the factors $1/b$ and b, respectively, where b is an arbitrary real number. This introduces the quantities

$$\mathbf{V}'_{T2} = b\mathbf{V}_{T2}$$
$$\mathbf{I}'_2 = \frac{1}{b}\mathbf{I}_2 \tag{3-50}$$

and Eqs. (3-49) now assume the form

$$(R_1 + j\omega L_1)\mathbf{I}_1 - j\omega b M\mathbf{I}'_2 = \mathbf{V}_{T1}$$
$$j\omega b M\mathbf{I}_1 - (R_2 + j\omega L_2)b^2\mathbf{I}'_2 = \mathbf{V}'_{T2} \tag{3-51}$$

The circuit corresponding to these equations is that given in Fig. 3-21. Observe that this is precisely of the form of Fig. 3-18, except that now

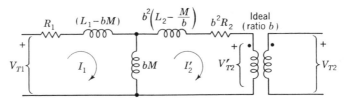

FIG. 3-21. The generalized equivalent circuit.

the factor b is arbitrary and is not necessarily the original turns ratio. Several interesting special cases are considered.

Suppose that $b = 1$. No ideal transformer is now required in the representation, and the branches have the inductances $L_1 - M$ and

$L_2 - M$. In many cases this may lead to a negative inductance in one branch or the other, since M can be greater than L_1 or L_2. For analytic purposes the existence of a nonphysically realizable element does not vitiate the subsequent analysis.

As a second case, suppose that b is chosen to be

$$b = \sqrt{\frac{L_1}{L_2}} \tag{3-52}$$

Now the circuit is that illustrated in Fig. 3-22. This is similar to the circuit in Fig. 3-18, except for the appearance of k throughout, rather

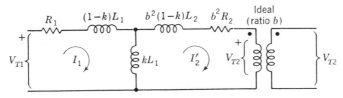

FIG. 3-22. Generalized equivalent circuit, with $b = \sqrt{\bar{L}_1/L_2}$.

than K_1 and K_2. Observe that this circuit is symmetrical in appearance. Actually, Fig. 3-18 follows if b is chosen as $b = \sqrt{K_1 L_1 / K_2 L_2}$.

3-11. Transient Response of Coupled Coils. The transient response of coupled coils will follow directly from a study of the differential equations corresponding to Eqs. (3-37), which specify the equilibrium conditions of the circuit involving the transformer. The resultant response can often be quite complicated and will depend on the excitations that are applied to the two windings.

Let us consider in some detail an analysis of the circuit of Fig. 3-23 under initially relaxed conditions. A source (the general exponential excitation function) described by the form $v = V_0 e^{s_0 t} u_{-1}(t)$, where s_0 is a complex number in general and where $u_{-1}(t)$ denotes the discontinuous unit step function that prescribes that the excitation is suddenly applied at time t, is applied to the network. Since s_0 is complex in general, it includes the d-c excitation with $s_0 = 0$ and the

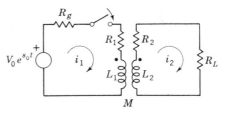

FIG. 3-23. Step-function response of a coupled circuit.

sinusoidal excitation function with $s_0 = j\omega$. The controlling equilibrium equations are the following, with $p \equiv d/dt$:

$$v = (R_g + R_1 + L_1 p)i_1 - M p i_2$$
$$0 = -M p i_1 + (R_L + R_2 + L_2 p)i_2 \tag{3-53}$$

Suppose now that the Laplace transform is applied to these equations. For zero initial conditions the equations become

$$\mathbf{V}(s) = (R_1' + L_1 s)\mathbf{I}_1(s) - M s \mathbf{I}_2(s)$$
$$0 = -M s \mathbf{I}_1(s) + (R_2' + L_2 s)\mathbf{I}_2(s)$$

which are written

$$\mathbf{V}(s) = R_1'(1 + T_1 s)\mathbf{I}_1(s) - M s \mathbf{I}_2(s)$$
$$0 = -M s \mathbf{I}_1(s) + R_2'(1 + T_2 s)\mathbf{I}_2(s) \tag{3-54}$$

where

$$R_1' = R_g + R_1 \qquad T_1 = \frac{L_1}{R_1'}$$

$$R_2' = R_L + R_2 \qquad T_2 = \frac{L_2}{R_2'}$$

Equations (3-54) are now solved for $\mathbf{I}_1(s)$ and $\mathbf{I}_2(s)$. By Cramer's rule there results

$$\mathbf{I}_1(s) = \frac{\Delta_1}{\Delta} \qquad \mathbf{I}_2(s) = \frac{\Delta_2}{\Delta} \tag{3-55}$$

where
$$\Delta_1 = \begin{vmatrix} \mathbf{V}(s) & -Ms \\ 0 & R_2'(1 + T_2 s) \end{vmatrix} \qquad \Delta_2 = \begin{vmatrix} R_1'(1 + T_1 s) & \mathbf{V}(s) \\ -Ms & 0 \end{vmatrix}$$

$$\Delta = \begin{vmatrix} R_1'(1 + T_1 s) & -Ms \\ -Ms & R_2'(1 + T_2 s) \end{vmatrix}$$

The denominator determinant Δ, which specifies the natural modes of the system, i.e., the response which depends only on the network and not on the form of the excitation, as will be seen below, may be written

$$\Delta = R_1' R_2'(1 + T_1 s)(1 + T_2 s)$$
$$= R_1' R_2' \left[\left(T_1 T_2 - \frac{M^2}{R_1' R_2'} \right) s^2 + (T_1 + T_2)s + 1 \right] \tag{3-56}$$

But since

$$\left(T_1 T_2 - \frac{M^2}{R_1' R_2'} \right) = T_1 T_2 \left(1 - \frac{M^2}{L_1 L_2} \right) = T_1 T_2 (1 - k^2)$$

then Δ may be written as

$$\Delta = R_1' R_2'(s - s_1)(s - s_2) \tag{3-57}$$

where
$$s_1, s_2 = -\frac{(T_1 + T_2) \pm \sqrt{(T_1 + T_2)^2 - 4 T_1 T_2 (1 - k^2)}}{2 T_1 T_2 (1 - k^2)}$$

The expressions for the currents are

$$\mathbf{I}_1(s) = \frac{(1 + T_2 s)\mathbf{V}(s)}{R_1'(s + s_1)(s - s_2)} = \frac{T_2(s + 1/T_2)\mathbf{V}(s)}{R_1'(s - s_1)(s - s_2)}$$

and
$$\mathbf{I}_2(s) = \frac{Ms\mathbf{V}(s)}{R_1' R_2'(s - s_1)(s - s_2)} \tag{3-58}$$

These expressions are now combined with the expression $\mathbf{V}(s)$ appropriate to the applied voltage, $V_0 e^{s_0 t}$, which is $V_0/(s - s_0)$. Thus

$$
\begin{aligned}
\mathbf{I}_1(s) &= \frac{T_2 V_0}{R_1'} \frac{(s + 1/T_2)}{(s - s_1)(s - s_2)(s - s_0)} \\
\mathbf{I}_2(s) &= \frac{M V_0}{R_1' R_2'} \frac{s}{(s - s_1)(s - s_2)(s - s_0)}
\end{aligned}
\tag{3-59}
$$

The solution continues by expanding the expressions for $\mathbf{I}_1(s)$ and $\mathbf{I}_2(s)$ into partial-fraction form. This yields the expressions

$$
\mathbf{I}_1(s) = \frac{T_2 V_0}{R_1'} \left(\frac{\mathbf{A}_1}{s - s_1} + \frac{\mathbf{A}_2}{s - s_2} + \frac{\mathbf{A}_3}{s - s_0} \right)
$$

and
$$
\mathbf{I}_2(s) = \frac{M V_0}{R_1 R_2} \left(\frac{\mathbf{B}_1}{s - s_1} + \frac{\mathbf{B}_2}{s - s_2} + \frac{\mathbf{B}_3}{s - s_0} \right)
\tag{3-60}
$$

where, in general,

$$
\mathbf{A}_k = \lim_{s \to s_k} \left[(s - s_k) \frac{R_1'}{V_0 T_2} \mathbf{I}_1(s) \right]
$$

and
$$
\mathbf{B}_k = \lim_{s \to s_k} \left[(s - s_k) \frac{R_1' R_2'}{M V_0} \mathbf{I}_2(s) \right]
\tag{3-61}
$$

The complete solution, which is obtained by taking the inverse Laplace transform of $\mathbf{I}_1(s)$ and $\mathbf{I}_2(s)$, will then be of the form

$$
\begin{aligned}
i_1(t) &= \mathbf{A}_1 e^{s_1 t} + \mathbf{A}_2 e^{s_2 t} + \mathbf{A}_3 e^{s_0 t} \\
i_2(t) &= \mathbf{B}_1 e^{s_1 t} + \mathbf{B}_2 e^{s_2 t} + \mathbf{B}_3 e^{s_0 t}
\end{aligned}
\tag{3-62}
$$

Observe that the complete response functions are made up of functions involving s_1 and s_2, which were determined entirely by the network parameters, and a term which is the response due to the impressed forcing function.

As a special case, we first examine the step-function response. This is given by Eqs. (3-62) with $s_0 = 0$. The result is

$$
\begin{aligned}
i_1(t) &= \mathbf{A}_1 e^{s_1 t} + \mathbf{A}_2 e^{s_2 t} + \mathbf{A}_3 \\
i_2(t) &= \mathbf{B}_1 e^{s_1 t} + \mathbf{B}_2 e^{s_2 t}
\end{aligned}
\tag{3-63}
$$

B_3 has been assumed zero, since it is known that there can be no steady d-c current term without a direct-coupled source in the loop. This factor would automatically become zero in the evaluation for $s_0 = 0$.

As a second special case, suppose that the excitation function is the sinusoid, of the form $V_0 \cos \omega t = \text{Re} \, (V_0 e^{j\omega t})$. The response is then of the form

$$
\begin{aligned}
i_1(t) &= \frac{V_0 T_2}{R_1'} \, \text{Re} \, (\mathbf{A}_1 e^{s_1 t} + \mathbf{A}_2 e^{s_2 t} + \mathbf{A}_3 e^{j\omega t}) \\
i_2(t) &= \frac{V_0 M}{R_1' R_2'} \, \text{Re} \, (\mathbf{B}_1 e^{s_1 t} + \mathbf{B}_2 e^{s_2 t} + \mathbf{B}_3 e^{j\omega t})
\end{aligned}
\tag{3-64}
$$

Finally a point of some interest is the system transfer functions. These are defined, in general, as the ratio of the Laplace transform of the response to the Laplace transform of the excitation. These are given by Eqs. (3-58) and are written as

$$\mathbf{T}_1(\mathbf{s}) = \frac{\mathbf{I}_1(\mathbf{s})}{\mathbf{V}(\mathbf{s})} = \frac{T_2}{R_1'} \frac{(\mathbf{s} + 1/T_2)}{(\mathbf{s} - \mathbf{s}_1)(\mathbf{s} - \mathbf{s}_2)}$$

$$\mathbf{T}_2(\mathbf{s}) = \frac{\mathbf{I}_2(\mathbf{s})}{\mathbf{V}(\mathbf{s})} = \frac{M}{R_1' R_2'} \frac{\mathbf{s}}{(\mathbf{s} - \mathbf{s}_1)(\mathbf{s} - \mathbf{s}_2)}$$

$$(3\text{-}65)$$

A plot of the functions $\mathbf{T}_1(j\omega)$ and $\mathbf{T}_2(j\omega)$, which can readily be determined experimentally by applying an a-c source to coil 1, varying the frequency, and measuring the corresponding currents, permits the ready

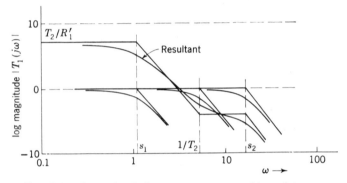

Fig. 3-24. Open-circuit frequency response of transformer.

determination of the time constants defined through $\mathbf{s}_1$ and $\mathbf{s}_2$. Specifically, refer to Fig. 3-24, which gives a plot on log-log scales of $|\mathbf{T}(j\omega)|$ and ω. There corresponds to each term in the expression for $\mathbf{T}(\mathbf{s})$ a simple curve which shows a "break point" at frequencies specified by the roots. The resultant system response is the appropriately chosen sum (or difference) of the terms which make up $|\mathbf{T}(j\omega)|$, as illustrated in the figure. From the experimentally determined break points, the corresponding roots can be found.

3-12. Power Transformers. The usual starting point for discussing power transformers is Fig. 3-18, which shows the equivalent network of the physical transformer with the magnetizing admittance on the primary side. In power transformers an effort is made to reduce the leakage inductance to a minimum, and usually the shunt inductance is at least one hundred times the leakage inductance. Because of this, it is possible to replace Fig. 3-18 by an approximately equivalent circuit from which subsequent performance calculations are made.

To deduce the approximate equivalent circuit, it will be supposed that open- and short-circuit tests will be made on the transformer. If the output terminals are open-circuited, then, because the shunt inductance is much larger than the leakage inductance, the input impedance is almost entirely that due to the shunt inductance. Also, if the output terminals are short-circuited, then, since the current through the shunt element is small compared with that in the series elements, the effective impedance is that due approximately to the series elements only.

An approximation that is also made is to suppose that the current through the shunt inductance is small compared with that in the series elements, especially under load conditions. Then it is possible to move the position of the shunt element from its normal position to a position across the input terminals   Under these circumstances, the approximate equivalent circuit has the form given in Fig. 3-25.   It will be observed

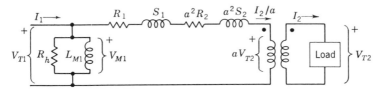

FIG. 3-25. The approximate equivalent circuit of the power transformer.

that a resistor has been added to the circuit across the input terminals. The resistance of this element is so chosen that the power loss in it is equal to the heating losses due to hysteresis and eddy currents in the iron core of the transformer. Observe that this resistor must be in the position specified since the hysteresis and eddy-current losses are both known to depend on the flux density, and so upon the total flux in the iron core. But since V_{M1} varies directly with the flux in the core, then the power loss in R_h will depend on the flux in the manner required. The results that are obtained by using this equivalent circuit prove to be quite adequate for most engineering purposes.

In the absence of data to the contrary, several additional assumptions are usually made. It is assumed that the magnetic coupling of the primary and secondary turns with the magnetic circuit is the same. It is also assumed that the diameter of the wire used for the windings is chosen to provide the same allowable current density in the conductors of each winding. In consequence of these assumptions, approximately half the input impedance, say, relative to the primary terminals, is due to the primary-winding parameters, the second half being that due to the effect of the secondary winding as reflected into the primary circuit; that is, it is assumed that

$$R_1 = a^2 R_2$$
$$S_1 = a^2 S_2$$

(3-66)

The first of these relations specifies that under full-load conditions the heating losses in each winding are approximately equal to each other.

Example 3-12.1. Open-circuit and short-circuit tests on a 5-kva 2,200/110-volt 60-cps transformer yield the following data measured on the high-potential side:

Open circuit: 2,000 volts, 0.2 amp, $P = 200$ watts
Short circuit: 100 volts, 2.0 amp, $P = 141.4$ watts

Find the input potential and power when the transformer delivers 6 kva at 100 volts and a leading power factor of 0.707.

Solution. From the given data, the following pertinent quantities may be calculated:

$$Z_{\text{open}} = \frac{2,000}{0.2} = 10,000 \text{ ohms}$$

$$P_{\text{iron}} = 200 \text{ watts}$$

$$Z_{sc} = {}^{100\!/_2} = 50 \text{ ohms}$$

$$P_{\text{cu}} = 141.4 \text{ watts}$$

$$I_{\text{sec}} = 2 \times 20 = 40 \text{ amp}$$

$$\text{Power factor} = \frac{141.4}{100 \times 2.0} = 0.707$$

The equivalent circuit in the present case has the form illustrated. For the specified

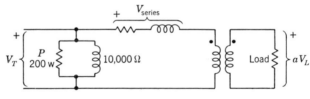

Fig. 3-12.1-1

6-kva output,

$$I = \frac{6,000}{100} = 60 \text{ amp in secondary}$$

$$P_{\text{cu}} = 141.4 \left(\frac{60}{40}\right)^2 = 318 \text{ watts (this accounts for the fact that the original}$$
measurements were for 40 amp secondary current)

$P_{\text{iron}} = 200$ watts (since the input potential is nearly 2,000 volts, even though the transformer has a primary rating of 2,200 volts)

$V_{\text{series}} = 100(\!{}^3\!/_2) = 150$ volts (the potential difference across the series elements for 3 amp primary instead of the initially measured results at 2.0 amp)

Now   Input power $= 6,000 \times 0.707 + 20.0 + 318 = 4,760$ watts

Input potential (refer to Fig. 3-12.1-2) $= \mathbf{V}_L + \mathbf{V}_S$

$$\mathbf{V}_T = (1,414 - j1,414) + (106 + j106) = 1,520 - j1,308 = 2,000 \text{ volts}$$

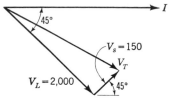

$$\text{FIG. 3-12.1-2}$$

Example 3-12.2. The per-unit values of a 1,100/220-volt 90-kva transformer are $R_1 = 0.015$, $R_2 = 0.018$, $X_1 = X_2 = 0.056$, $G = 0.007$, $B = 0.085$. Find the actual values of these parameters and the equivalent values when referred to the primary.

Solution. By definition

$$\text{pu value} = \frac{\text{actual value (in any unit)}}{\text{base value (in same unit)}}$$

Thus we must find the base values for the desired parameters.

Rated primary current: $\qquad I_{1r} = \dfrac{90,000}{1,100} = 81.8 \text{ amp}$

Rated secondary current: $\qquad I_{2r} = \dfrac{90,000}{220} = 5 \times 81.8 = 409 \text{ amp}$

Rated primary impedance: $\qquad Z_{1r} = \dfrac{1,100}{81.8} = 13.45 \text{ ohms}$

Rated secondary impedance: $\qquad Z_{2r} = \dfrac{220}{409} = \dfrac{13.45}{5^2} = 0.538 \text{ ohm}$

Rated primary admittance: $\qquad Y_{1r} = \dfrac{1}{Z_{1r}} = \dfrac{1}{13.45} = 0.0745 \text{ mho}$

Rated secondary admittance: $\quad Y_{2r} = \dfrac{1}{Z_{2r}} = \dfrac{1}{0.538} = 1.862 \text{ mho}$

The actual values are

$$R_1 = 0.015 \times 13.45 = 0.202 \text{ ohm}$$
$$X_1 = 0.056 \times 13.45 = 0.754 \text{ ohm}$$
$$R_2 = 0.018 \times 0.538 = 0.0097 \text{ ohm}$$
$$X_2 = 0.056 \times 0.538 = 0.0301 \text{ ohm}$$
$$G = 0.007 \times 0.0745 = 0.0521 \times 10^{-3} \text{ mho}$$
$$B = 0.085 \times 0.0745 = 6.32 \times 10^{-3} \text{ mho}$$

Referred to its primary, the secondary resistance and leakage reactance are

$$R_2' = n^2 R_2 = 5^2 \times 0.0097 = 0.242 \text{ ohm}$$
$$= 0.018 \times Z_{1r} = 0.018 \times 13.45$$
$$X_2' = n^2 X_2 = 5^2 \times 0.0301 = 0.753 \text{ ohm}$$
$$= 0.056 Z_{1r} = 0.056 \times 13.45$$

3-13. Audio Transformers. There is a very important class of iron-core transformers that is designed for use in audio-amplifier applications. The equivalent circuit to be used is the approximate equivalent circuit illustrated in Fig. 3-25. These transformers are ordinarily so small physically and contain so little iron that the losses specified by R_h are negligible and R_h may be neglected. For a high-power modulation transformer this approximation cannot be made, of course. These transformers must operate over a range of frequencies; and it is desirable that the output-input ratio remain independent over as wide a frequency range as possible.

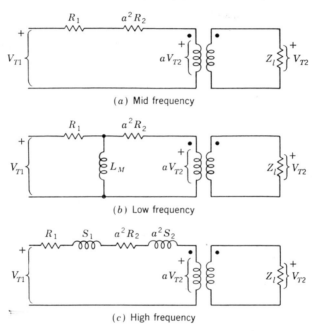

(a) Mid frequency

(b) Low frequency

(c) High frequency

FIG. 3-26. The approximate equivalent circuits at mid-frequency, low-frequency, and high-frequency ranges of a transformer.

We shall neglect the distributed capacitances between turns and the interwinding capacitance, in the interests of simplicity. There are three frequency ranges of interest: intermediate, low, and high. These will be considered in turn.

In the intermediate-frequency range, the series impedances are considered negligible, and the shunt impedance is considered so high that it does not influence the results. The resultant equivalent circuit is that shown in Fig. 3-26a. In the low-frequency range, the series-impedance elements are negligible, but the shunt inductance represents a substantial loading on the output. Now the approximate equivalent circuit is that shown in Fig. 3-26b. At the high-frequency end of the range the series-impedance elements produce a significant effect, but the shunt element may be neglected. The equivalent circuit appropriate to this case is shown in Fig. 3-26c.

An analysis of the circuits appropriate to each frequency range is readily effected. It is supposed that a source of potential $\mathbf{V}_g$ and of internal resistance R_g is connected to the input terminals of the transformer, which feeds a load of resistance R_l. The results for each approximate circuit follow.

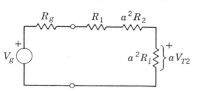

FIG. 3-27. The mid-frequency equivalent circuit, referred to the primary.

Mid-frequency Range. Refer to Fig. 3-27, which applies to this case. All calculations are referred to the primary. It follows directly that

$$aV_{T2} = \frac{V_g}{R_{11} + a^2R_{22}} a^2R_l$$

where
$$R_{11} = R_g + R_1$$
$$R_{22} = R_2 + R_l$$

Hence it follows that

$$\frac{aV_{T2}}{V_g} = \frac{a^2R_l}{R_{11} + a^2R_{22}} = \frac{a^2R_l}{R_s} \tag{3-67}$$

where
$$R_s = R_{11} + a^2R_{22}$$

Observe that this expression is a constant, independent of frequency.

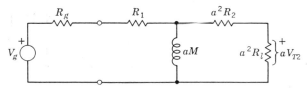

FIG. 3-28. The low-frequency equivalent circuit, referred to the primary.

Low-frequency Range. In this case the circuit becomes that shown in Fig. 3-28. It follows that

$$\frac{aV_{T2}}{V_g} = \frac{\dfrac{a^2R_{22}(j\omega aM)}{a^2R_{22} + j\omega aM} a^2R_l}{R_{11} + \dfrac{a^2R_{22}(j\omega aM)}{a^2R_{22} + j\omega aM} a^2R_{22}}$$

$$= \frac{a^2R_l}{R_{11} + a^2R_{22}} \frac{1}{1 - j\dfrac{a^2R_{11}R_{22}}{R_{11} + a^2R_{22}}\dfrac{1}{\omega aM}}$$

Now write
$$R_s = R_{11} + a^2R_{22}$$
$$R_p = \frac{a^2R_{11}R_{22}}{R_{11} + a^2R_{22}} = \frac{a^2R_{11}R_{22}}{R_s}$$

Then the above equation attains the form

$$\frac{a\mathbf{V}_{T2}}{\mathbf{V}_g} = \frac{a^2 R_l}{R_s} \frac{1}{1 - j(R_p/\omega aM)}$$

It is convenient to consider the relative response ratio, which gives the frequency response relative to that at the mid-frequency. This expression is the following:

$$\frac{\mathbf{V}_{T2}\Big)_{lf}}{\mathbf{V}_{T2}\Big)_{mf}} \frac{1}{1 - j(R_p/\omega aM)} = \frac{1}{1 - j(\omega_l/\omega)} \qquad (3\text{-}68)$$

where

$$\omega_l = \frac{R_p}{aM}$$

The amplitude and phase characteristic of transformers specified by this equation are contained in the universal response characteristic of transformers given in Fig. 3-29.

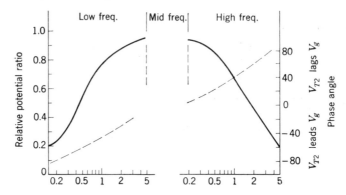

FIG. 3-29. Universal amplitude and phase characteristics of transformers.

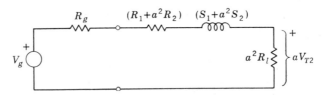

FIG. 3-30. The high-frequency equivalent circuit, referred to the primary.

High-frequency Range. The equivalent circuit in this case is given in Fig. 3-30. An analysis of this circuit gives

$$\frac{a\mathbf{V}_{T2}}{\mathbf{V}_g} = \frac{a^2 R_l}{R_g + (R_1 + a^2 R_2) + a^2 R_l + j\omega(S_1 + a^2 S_2)}$$

$$= \frac{a^2 R_l}{R_s + j\omega S_s}$$

where
$$R_s = (R_g + R_1) + a^2(R_2 + R_l)$$
$$S_s = S_1 + a^2 S_2$$

By rearranging the expression,

$$\frac{a\mathbf{V}_{T2}}{\mathbf{V}_g} = \frac{a^2 R_l}{R_s} \frac{1}{1 + j\omega S_s/R_s}$$

which has the form

$$\frac{a\mathbf{V}_{T2}}{\mathbf{V}_g} = \frac{a^2 R_l}{R_s} \frac{1}{1 + j\omega/\omega_h}$$

where
$$\omega_h = \frac{R_s}{S_s}$$

The relative response ratio, which defines the universal high-frequency characteristic, is

$$\frac{\mathbf{V}_{T2}\Big)_{\text{hf}}}{\mathbf{V}_{T2}\Big)_{\text{mf}}} = \frac{1}{1 + j\omega/\omega_h} \qquad (3\text{-}69)$$

The amplitude and phase characteristics of transformers specified by this equation are also contained in Fig. 3-29.

A composite sketch showing the typical performance of the audio transformer is given in Fig. 3-31. The frequencies f_l and f_h, which are

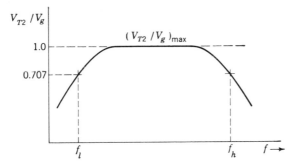

FIG. 3-31. The frequency-response characteristics of an iron-core transformer.

those frequencies at which the output-input ratio is 0.707, are known, respectively, as the low-frequency and high-frequency cutoff values. These correspond to those values of ω equal, respectively, to ω_l and ω_h, in which case the denominators of Eqs. (3-67) and (3-68) become $1 - j1$ and $1 + j1$, or an amplitude of $\sqrt{2}$.

It is noted that for practical audio transformers, owing to the effects of distributed winding and interwinding capacitances, a resonant peak often appears in the curve at the higher frequencies. Good-quality audio transformers are usually constructed in such a way as to reduce this resonant peak and, also, to have it occur for frequencies outside the normally desired range of operation, usually 10,000 cps or somewhat higher.

3-14. Energy-flow Considerations. It is desired to study the flow of energy between the two conductor configurations of the transformer, which are here assumed for convenience to be wound separately on opposite legs of the transformer core. It will be found that the energy flow occurs from the primary conductor configuration into the region

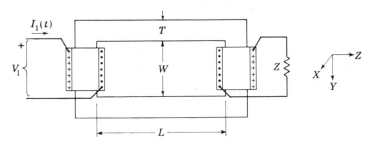

Fig. 3-32. The simple two-winding transformer.

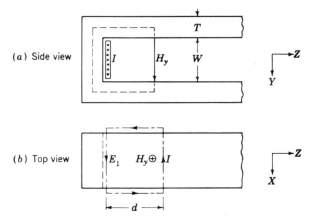

Fig. 3-33. The side and top view of the unit slice of ideal transformer.

of space between the windings, and then from the field in the region of space to the second conductor configuration.

Consider the transformer configuration that is illustrated in Fig. 3-32. It will be assumed that the secondary winding is open and that the fields exist only within the window region of the transformer. This assumption may be considered to be the equivalent of choosing initially a structure of infinite depth and then selecting a slice of unit depth from this infinite structure. The side and top projection views of the slice chosen are illustrated in Fig. 3-33.

The current in the winding produces a field H_y in the interplanar space, which can be evaluated by an application of the Ampère line integral

$$\oint \mathbf{H} \cdot d\mathbf{l} = NI$$

The path is chosen around the iron and through the interplanar space, as shown in Fig. 3-33a. The permeability of the iron is chosen large, so that approximately there results

$$H_y W = N_1 I_1 \qquad \text{peak} \tag{3-70}$$

Likewise, an application of Faraday's law around the path shown in Fig. 3-33b containing the current-carrying conductor yields

$$\int \mathbf{E} \cdot d\mathbf{l} = -j\mu\omega \int \mathbf{H} \cdot \mathbf{n} \, dA$$

from which

$$E_1 = j\mu\omega H_y d \tag{3-71}$$

From this we may write for the winding of N_1 turns

$$V_1 = N_1 E_1 = j\mu\omega N_1 H_y d$$

Now by combining this expression with Eq. (3-70) there results

$$\left. \begin{aligned} V_1 &= j\omega \left(\mu N_1{}^2 \frac{d}{W} \right) I_1 = j\omega S I_1 \\ S &= \mu N_1{}^2 \frac{d}{W} \end{aligned} \right\} \tag{3-72}$$

where

S is the leakage inductance of the winding.

Because of the presence of the $\mathbf{E}$ and $\mathbf{H}$ fields, there is a Poynting radiation from the winding surface to the interplanar space. This is

$$S_{z1} = \tfrac{1}{2} \operatorname{Re} (E_1 H_y^*) = \tfrac{1}{2} j\mu\omega |H_y|^2 d \tag{3-73}$$

The total power through the winding surface is then

$$P_{z1} = \int S_{z1} \, dx \, dy = S_z W$$

or

$$P_{z1} = \tfrac{1}{2} j\mu\omega |H_y|^2 W d \tag{3-74}$$

which is

$$P_{z1} = \frac{\omega}{2} \mu |H_y|^2 \text{ (volume)} \qquad \text{reactive power} \tag{3-75}$$

which may also be written in the form

$$P_{z1} = \tfrac{1}{2} V_1 I_1 \tag{3-76}$$

This expression shows the exchange of energy from the winding to the storage volume.

It is now desired to examine the situation that prevails at the secondary winding when it is closed to the load. The geometry appropriate to this problem is that given in Fig. 3-34. For the limiting case of infinite permeability, it is required that

$$N_1 I_1 = N_2 I_2$$

Moreover, the emf that is induced in the second winding must equal

$$V_2 = I_2 Z = \frac{N_1 I_1 Z}{N_2}$$

But this emf must be associated with an electric field E_2 which acts along the winding. Therefore

$$N_2 E_2 = V_2 \tag{3-77}$$

But, in the manner of the development leading to Eq. (3-74), the power that flows from the field space into winding 2 is given by

$$P_{z2} = \tfrac{1}{2} \operatorname{Re} (R_2 H_y^*) W \tag{3-78}$$

which is

$$P_{z2} = \frac{1}{2} \frac{V_2}{N_2} \frac{N_1 I_1}{W} W$$

or

$$P_{z2} = \tfrac{1}{2} V_2 I_2 = \frac{1}{2} \frac{V_2^2}{Z} = \tfrac{1}{2} V_1 I_1 \tag{3-79}$$

Observe therefore that the power from the space into the secondary winding is precisely equal to that which passed through the primary

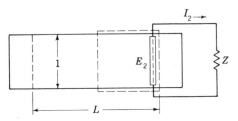

Fig. 3-34. The top view of the transformer.

winding into the space. This shows the interesting fact in the transformer with iron of infinite permeability that the power transfer from the source to the load occurs through the air space and not through the iron of the transformer core. For a finite permeability, some of the power flow occurs into and through the iron.

PROBLEMS

3-1. Set up the loop equations for the accompanying circuit, and give an expression for I_2 in determinantal form. It is not required to expand the determinants.

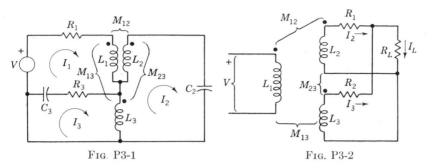

FIG. P3-1   FIG. P3-2

3-2. The situation illustrated is that in which two windings of a transformer are operated in parallel. Obtain determinantal solutions for the currents I_2, I_3, and I_L.

3-3. The air-core transformer of the accompanying diagram has the following parameters:

$$N_1 = 1,500 \text{ turns} \qquad N_2 = 3,000 \text{ turns}$$
$$L_1 = 0.3 \text{ henry} \qquad L_2 = 1.2 \text{ henrys}$$
$$R_1 = 50 \text{ ohms} \qquad R_2 = 180 \text{ ohms}$$
$$K_1 = K_2 = 0.75 \qquad \omega = 1,000 \text{ radians/sec}$$

(a) Plot a sinor diagram showing the various flux components defined in the text. Use a common reference direction in the core for all the flux components. Choose this direction so that ϕ_{11} is in phase with i_1.

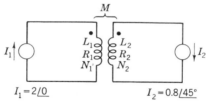

$$I_1 = 2\underline{/0} \qquad\qquad I_2 = 0.8\underline{/45°}$$

FIG. P3-3

(b) Draw the necessary sinor diagrams to determine the potentials $\mathbf{V}_{T1}$ and $\mathbf{V}_{T2}$ in accordance with the leakage- and mutual-flux viewpoint. Flux sinors may be taken from the diagrams obtained in part a.

(c) Draw the necessary sinor diagrams to determine the potentials $\mathbf{V}_{T1}$ and $\mathbf{V}_{T2}$ in accordance with the self- and mutual-inductance viewpoint.

3-4. Consider a transformer having the following characteristics:

$$N_1 = 2,000 \text{ turns} \qquad N_2 = 6,000 \text{ turns}$$
$$L_1 = 2 \text{ henrys} \qquad L_2 = 4 \text{ henrys}$$
$$R_1 = 100 \text{ ohms} \qquad R_2 = 300 \text{ ohms}$$
$$k = \text{coefficient of coupling} = 0.4$$

(a) Find the coefficients K_1 and K_2 defined in the text.

(b) Construct an equivalent circuit similar to Fig. 3-17, evaluating all parameters.

(c) Construct an equivalent circuit similar to Fig. 3-18, evaluating all parameters.

(d) Construct an equivalent circuit similar to Fig. 3-21, taking $b = \sqrt{L_1/L_2}$ and evaluating all parameters.

(e) Construct an equivalent circuit similar to Fig. 3-21, taking $b = \sqrt{K_1 L_1/K_2 L_2}$ and evaluating all parameters. Compare with part c.

3-5. The air-core transformer of the accompanying diagram has the following parameters:

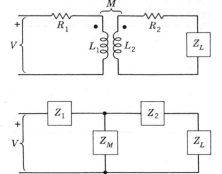

$L_1 = 0.094$ henry $L_2 = 0.0108$ henry
$R_1 = 3.3$ ohms $R_2 = 0.775$ ohm
$M = 0.0256$ henry
$f = 60$ cps

This is to be replaced by an equivalent T circuit. Calculate Z_1, Z_2, and Z_M in the T equivalent.

Fig. P3-5

3-6. A three-winding "ideal" transformer is shown in Fig. P3-6a. The conditions defined in the text for the ideal transformer apply: the coupling coefficients are all unity, and each coil has infinite inductance, while all turns ratios remain finite.

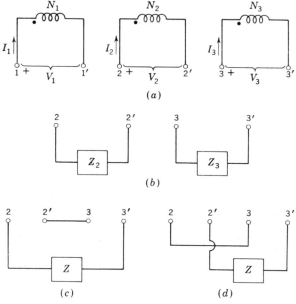

Fig. P3-6

(a) Write an equation giving the relationship among the three currents indicated.

(b) Give mathematical relationships among the three potentials indicated.

(c) Let impedances Z_2 and Z_3 be connected respectively to coils 2 and 3, as shown in Fig. P3-6b. Obtain an expression for the impedance seen when looking into coil 1.

(d) Derive a formula for the impedance seen when looking into coil 1 when coils 2 and 3 are connected as shown in Fig. P3-6c. Repeat this for the case shown in Fig. P3-6d.

3-7. The telephone "hybrid" coil shown in Fig. P3-7 is a six-winding transformer which approximates the ideal. Each coil has a 1:1 turns ratio to each other coil. When suitable impedances are connected to the windings, the device has the property of accepting energy at one pair of terminals and transmitting it to two other pairs, but not to the fourth pair. This is true no matter what pair is chosen as the input, as the following procedure will verify:

(a) A potential source V is applied to terminals 1, and a resistor of value R is attached to each of the remaining terminals. Find the current in each resistor. Which of the resistors could be changed with no effect on the result?

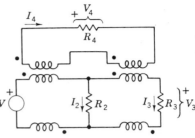

Fig. P3-7

(b) Repeat part a, with the potential source at terminals 2.

(c) Repeat part a, with the potential source at terminals 3.

(d) Repeat part a, with the potential source at terminals 4.

3-8. A transformer that is supplying power to a given load is specified by the following quantities:

$$N_1 = 3,000 \text{ turns} \qquad N_2 = 1,000 \text{ turns}$$
$$L_1 = 1.0 \text{ henry} \qquad L_2 = 0.15 \text{ henry}$$
$$I_1 = 1.0/\underline{0} \text{ amp} \qquad I_2 = 2.0/\underline{45^\circ}$$
$$\omega = 1,000 \text{ radians/sec} \qquad M = 0.3 \text{ henry}$$

(a) Deduce the following: $\mathbf{V}_1$, $\mathbf{V}_2$; input power P_1, Q_1; output power P_2, Q_2; leakage inductances S_1, S_2.

(b) Draw an equivalent circuit referred to the primary.

3-9. The resistances and leakage reactances of a 10-kva 60-cps 2,400/240-volt transformer are as follows:

$$R_1 = 4.2 \text{ ohms} \qquad R_2 = 0.042 \text{ ohm} \qquad X_1 = 5.5 \text{ ohms} \qquad X_2 = 0.055 \text{ ohm}$$

The subscript 1 refers to the 2,400-volt winding, and subscript 2 refers to the 240-volt winding.

(a) Find the equivalent impedance referred to the high-voltage side and referred to the low-voltage side.

(b) Consider the transformer to deliver its rated kva at 0.80 power factor lagging to a load on the low-potential side with 240 volts across the load. Find the potential at the primary terminals.

(c) Consider the core loss to be 70 watts. Find the efficiency under the conditions of (b).

(d) Repeat (b) for power factor of 0.80 leading, and calculate the efficiency.

(e) Suppose that the load in (b) should accidentally become short-circuited. Find the steady-state current in the high-potential lines, assuming the potential impressed on the transformer to remain the same as in (b).

(f) The exciting current of the transformer is 2.9 per cent of full-load current. If the transformer is given an open-circuit test at rated potential and a short-circuit test at rated current, what will be the reading of the wattmeter, voltmeter, and ammeter in each case? Give the results when the instruments are on the high-potential side; on the low-potential side.

3-10. Open-circuit and short-circuit tests on a 5-kva 2,200/110-volt 60-cps transformer yield the following data measured on the high-potential side:

Open circuit: 2,300 volts, 0.1 amp, 0.4 pf

Short circuit: 72 volts, rated current, 100 watts

The transformer is delivering 4.4 kw at 110 volts to a load having a 0.9 lagging power factor. Determine: (a) Input power. (b) Input power factor. (c) Efficiency. (d) Input potential; draw the sinor diagram. (e) Secondary terminal potential without load, if the primary potential remains as in (d).

3-11. A 50-kva 2,300/230-volt transformer has an equivalent resistance of 1.2 per cent (percentage of effective impedance under full-load conditions) and a reactance of 5 per cent. It is connected in parallel with a 100-kva 2,200/220-volt transformer having an equivalent resistance of 1.1 per cent and a reactance of 8 per cent. They supply 130 kva at 225 volts and 0.7 lagging power factor.

(a) What kva is each transformer carrying?

(b) What is the primary potential?

3-12. Show how to connect a 5-kva 2,300/230-volt transformer to give a 10 per cent boost on a 2,300-volt power line. What load can be safely supplied by this booster transformer? HINT: Determine rated coil currents, and do not exceed these values.

3-13. A constant-current transformer is shown schematically in Fig. P3-13. It consists of two coils mounted on an iron core. One of the coils is fixed with respect to the iron core; the second is movable with respect to the first. The weight of the movable coil is partially counterbalanced by the weight W. The force between the two coils will vary with the separation x between the two coils. Assume that $M(x)$ decreases as the coils are moved apart according to the relation

$$M \doteq M_0(1 - ax)$$

where a is a constant.

(a) Show that the force between the coils is practically independent of x.

(b) Find an expression for the currents for a specified W.

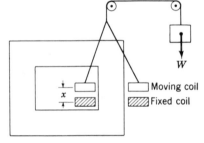

Fig. P3-13

3-14. An audio-frequency output transformer has a primary-to-secondary turns ratio of 31.6. Its primary inductance measured with the secondary open is 19.6 henrys and measured with the secondary short-circuited is 0.207 henry. The winding resistances are negligible. This transformer is used to connect an 8-ohm resistance load to a source which may be represented by a variable-frequency internal emf in series with an internal impedance of 5,000 ohms resistance. Compute the following that relate to the frequency characteristics of the circuit:

(a) The upper half-power frequency.

(b) The lower half-power frequency.

(c) The geometric mean of these frequencies.

(d) The ratio of load potential to source potential at the frequency under part c.

(e) Sketch the frequency characteristic.

3-15. An audio-frequency output transformer has a turns ratio of 17.32. It is to be used to match a source having an internal resistance of 3,000 ohms to a resistance load of 10 ohms. The upper and lower half-power frequencies are to be 50 and 10,000 cps. Neglect core loss and winding resistance. Specify:

(a) The primary self-inductance

(b) The equivalent leakage inductance referred to the primary

4

Duals and Analogs

The general aspects of duals and analogs which will be discussed in this chapter are of interest in themselves. More than this, however, is the fact that the study shows how the highly refined techniques of electrical-circuit theory may be employed in the solution of nonelectrical problems. In so far as our broader interests are concerned, this study provides the background for an introduction and understanding of a general and very powerful method for the analysis of dynamic systems which will be introduced in the following chapter.

4-1. Introduction. Systems that constitute two different physical representations of the same set of integrodifferential equations are said to be analogous systems. Observe, therefore, that the only requirement is that the physical systems be described by the same integrodifferential equation or set of integrodifferential equations in order that they be analogs. Clearly, the formal solution of the differential equations representing one physical system automatically provides a formal solution to the differential equations of any analogous problem. Since the electrical engineer is familiar with the analytical techniques of transient (Laplace transforms) and steady-state (complex numbers, for sinusoidal excitation) a-c circuit theory and has had considerable experience in the solution of electrical-network problems, the ability to draw an electrical circuit which is the analog of a mechanical, a thermal, or an acoustical system permits previous technical experience to be brought to bear in finding a solution of the physically analogous problem.

It will be found possible, in fact, to draw two electrical networks which are the analog of, say, a given mechanical system. This arises from the existence of the principle of duality in electrical-circuit theory. According to duality, it is usually possible (although in general the network must be mappable on a sphere, i.e., the network must be flat) to find an electrical network the equilibrium equations of which, when deduced from a loop analysis by an application of the Kirchhoff potential law, have the same mathematical form as the equilibrium equations of another electrical network which are deduced from a node analysis by an application of the Kirchhoff current law. According to the discussion above, the two dual electrical systems are also analogs. However, the term analog is usually reserved for comparing different physical systems, with the term dual being reserved for the electrical networks which have the mathematically similar equilibrium equations.

4-2. Duality vs. Equivalence. The idea of duality in network analysis is founded on the interchange of independent and dependent variables in the equations which express the behavior of the circuit elements. In the following tabulation (Table 4-1) the dually related equations between

TABLE 4-1

$$v_R = R\,i_R \qquad\qquad i_G = G\,v_G$$

$$v_L = L\,\frac{di_L}{dt} \qquad\qquad i_C = C\,\frac{dv_C}{dt}$$

$$v_C = \frac{1}{C}\int i_C\,dt \qquad\qquad i_L = \frac{1}{L}\int v_L\,dt$$

potential difference and current are given for the three basic network parameters: resistance, inductance, and capacitance. Each pair of equations on a horizontal line in Table 4-1 are dually related. Among the other dual relationships which exist in electrical networks, the important ones are contained in Table 4-2. The only exception to the

TABLE 4-2. DUAL RELATIONSHIPS

Loop concept	Node concept
Loop interior	Junction other than the datum junction
Circuit exterior	Datum junction
Potential source in an external branch	Current source with one terminal connected to the datum junction
Loop current	Junction potential to the datum junction
Potential source in a common branch	Current source shunting a common branch
Branch impedance	Branch admittance

general applicability of these results is the nonflat network when analyzed on a loop basis, because nonflat networks have branches which are common to more than two loops. The dual, which would require branches common to more than two junctions, is nonexistent.

A word of caution here is needed to emphasize again the meaning of the word duality. It is important to note that duality does *not* imply equivalence. It means only that the mathematical representations of the circuits are similar, but no aspect of equivalence should be associated with dually related circuits. Equivalent circuits are quite possible, and often aid materially in the solution of a given problem. Equivalent circuits are of two types: (1) those which produce identical effects at specified terminals, and (2) networks which have identical controlling equations as those of the specified network. The circuits may be equivalent with respect to two terminals only; with respect to several pairs of terminals; or with respect to any number of terminals.

A common example of an equivalent circuit with respect to one pair of terminals is that obtained from an application of the Thévenin-Helmholtz theorem. In the application of this theorem, a complicated network is replaced at a single frequency by a simple potential source and a series impedance. The equivalence in this case is restricted to one pair of terminals at a single specified frequency. The usual objective in using an equivalent circuit is to replace a complicated portion of a network by a simple one for purposes of calculation, comprehension, or construction. The equivalent circuit may be impossible of physical realization because of the size of the physical components needed. However, the inability to construct the circuit physically in no way invalidates its use for purposes of calculation or understanding. Reduction to an equivalent circuit often avoids lengthy general methods of solution that yield more information than may be necessary for certain required results.

Equivalent networks of the type classed in (2) above are often useful in analysis, since they permit a change in the form of the circuit, with otherwise identical performance at all frequencies. An example of such an equivalent network is one in which a given network with transformer coupling is replaced by an equivalent network in which the transformer is replaced by a T equivalent. Moreover, as discussed in Chap. 3, a variety of equivalent representations exist for the transformer.

It is possible, of course, to make the admittance of each branch of one network numerically equal to the impedance of the corresponding branch of the dual network. A branch admittance measurement in the first network will give the same numerical result as the corresponding branch impedance measurement in the dual network. Dual networks which result in numerically reciprocal values at corresponding terminals are called "reciprocal," or "inverse," networks. Note again, however, that no aspect of equivalence is implied.

4-3. Dual Circuits. For certain applications, and a number of these will be examined below, it is convenient to be able to construct a circuit which is the dual of another circuit. As already noted, a dual exists and can be found for any circuit as long as it can be made flat and does not include transformers in such a way that they cannot be replaced by equivalent circuits.

A simple graphical procedure may be used to draw the dual of the specified network. The rules of the "dot" method follow. Some discussion of particular features of the techniques are given below in connection with the specific example considered. The procedure is:

1. Place a numbered dot in each independent loop of the given network, and also enclose the network by a continuous line. Each internal dot becomes a nondatum junction, and the outside line becomes the datum junction.

2. On a separate diagram place the appropriate number of dots as required in (1). The nodes are numbered to correspond to the loops in which they appear.

3. In the original circuit, draw lines between pairs of dots, making sure that each line passes through one circuit element only and that each circuit element has only one line passing through it. Sources are included within the meaning of the term "circuit element."

4. Replace each element crossed by a line, as specified in (3), by its dual between the corresponding dots in the second, or dual, diagram. That is, the appropriate nodes are to be connected by a branch which is the dual of the branch which is common to its dually related loops. This procedure is carried out for each pair of nodes, including the datum junction.

The necessary information for the drawing of dual branches is found in the two tables of dual relationships (Tables 4-1 and 4-2). For example, the series connection of R, L, C is the dual of the parallel combination of G, C, L. Also, the current-source equivalent (a current source in parallel with an admittance Y) is the dual of the potential-source equivalent (a potential source in series with an impedance Z). Moreover, Y and Z are dually related.

In setting up the dual circuit, it is necessary to choose reference conditions in accordance with a consistent set of rules. Two considerations are involved, (1) the reference direction of the current sources, and (2) the reference polarity at the junctions. The rules depend on the algebraic interpretations given to each set of equations, i.e., whether potential rises are written on the left or right and whether entering currents are on the left or right of the controlling equilibrium equations of the network.

Suppose that a positive term on the right of a set of network equations, say, in a loop analysis, represents a potential rise in a clockwise direction and that a positive term of the dual equations represents a current toward a nondatum junction. Rule 1 follows: If a potential source in a loop is a rise in the clockwise direction, its dual is a current source directed toward the dually related node. Similarly, for a typical term on the left side of the network equations, Rule 2 follows: If a current has a clockwise direction in a loop, its dual is a positive potential at the dually related node.

An example of the procedure dictated by the above set of rules is given in the two networks of Fig. 4-1.

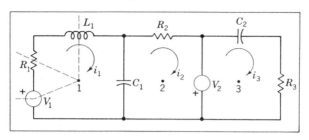

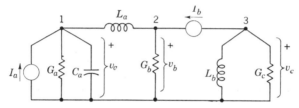

Fig. 4-1. Dually related networks.

4-4. Electromechanical Analogs—Direct System.[1] It is now desired to examine the general problem of electromechanical analogs. This is conveniently done in terms of several specific examples.

Consider the parallel mechanical circuit illustrated in Fig. 4-2, consisting of a mass that is hanging from a spring-supported mount, which is subject to a viscous damping force and an applied external force. The controlling differential equation that governs the motion of the system is obtained by drawing a free-body diagram of the system in accordance with D'Alembert's principle and summing the forces acting on the system, which is now considered to be in equilibrium. The system illustrated is described by the force equation

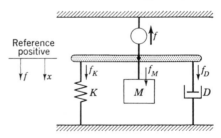

Fig. 4-2. A parallel mechanical circuit.

$$f = f_M + f_D + f_k \qquad (4\text{-}1)$$

which may be written in the form

$$f = M \frac{dv}{dt} + Dv + k \int v \, dt \qquad (4\text{-}2)$$

[1] There is no general agreement on electromechanical-analog terminology.

where x is measured from the zero-force equilibrium position. In this latter equation:

k = linear spring constant, force/unit length

M = mass

D = viscous- (velocity-) damping constant, force/unit velocity

v = velocity

f = applied force

The steady-state expression for the velocity for an assumed applied sinusoidal excitation force is readily effected by writing

$$f = \text{Im} \left(\sqrt{2}\, F e^{j(\omega t + \alpha)} \right) \tag{4-3}$$

where Im indicates that the imaginary part of the expression is to be chosen. The solution for the velocity is then given by

$$v = \text{Im} \left(\sqrt{2}\, \frac{F}{W} e^{j(\omega t + \alpha - \phi)} \right) \tag{4-4}$$

where
$$\mathbf{W} = W e^{j\phi} = D + j \left(\omega M - \frac{K}{\omega} \right) \tag{4-5}$$

The factor $\mathbf{W}$, which is the ratio between the phasors (sinors) representing the force and the velocity, is seen to be analogous to the electrical impedance or admittance. The term "mechanical impedance" is usually applied to $\mathbf{W}$.

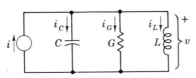

It is observed that Eq. (4-2) is mathematically identical with the controlling equilibrium equation of the simple parallel circuit of Fig. 4-3, which is

FIG. 4-3. A simple parallel electrical network.

$$i = C \frac{dv}{dt} + Gv + \frac{1}{L} \int v \, dt \tag{4-6}$$

The steady-state solution of this expression under sinusoidal excitation is obtained from network-theory considerations, by writing

$$i = \text{Im} \left(\sqrt{2}\, I_m e^{j(\omega t + \alpha)} \right) \tag{4-7}$$

Then it follows that

$$\left. \begin{aligned} v &= \text{Im} \left(\sqrt{2}\, \frac{I_m}{Y} e^{j(\omega t + \alpha - \phi)} \right) \\ \mathbf{Y} &= Y e^{j\phi} = G + j \left(\omega C - \frac{1}{\omega L} \right) \end{aligned} \right\} \tag{4-8}$$

where

Attention is directed to the fact that the differential equations and the solutions of the two networks have precisely the same form, and it is therefore convenient to choose these networks as analogs. The resulting analogous quantities are those specified in Table 4-3. Note that in this development the analogy between D'Alembert's principle and the Kirchhoff current law has been used. This analogy, since it draws a parallel between the fact that the sum of the forces at the centroid of the system $\Sigma f = 0$ and the fact that the sum of the currents at the junction

TABLE 4-3. DIRECT ANALOGS

Mechanical quantity.....	M	D	k	v'	f	W
Electrical analog.........	C	G	$1/L$	v	i	Y

$\Sigma i = 0$, may be called the (M_f,E_i) or (M_v,E_v) system and is here called the direct analog. This analog yields an electrical circuit for nodal analysis.

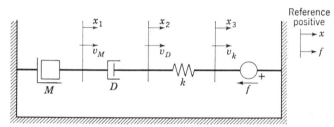

FIG. 4-4. A series mechanical circuit.

Consider now the series mechanical circuit that is illustrated in Fig. 4-4. From the fact that

$$x_3 = (x_3 - x_2) + (x_2 - x_1) + x_1$$

the equilibrium of this system may be specified by

$$v = v_k + v_D + v_M \tag{4-9}$$

This expression may be written in the form

$$v = \frac{1}{k}\frac{df}{dt} + \frac{f}{D} + \frac{1}{M}\int f\,dt \tag{4-10}$$

Suppose that the simple series RLC circuit is now examined, as given in Fig. 4-5. The controlling differential equation is

$$v = L\frac{di}{dt} + Ri + \frac{1}{C}\int i\,dt \tag{4-11}$$

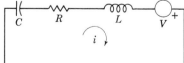

A comparison of Eqs. (4-10) and (4-11) indicates the analogous form of the

FIG. 4-5. A simple series electrical circuit.

equations, and by reference to Table 4-3 it will be seen that these series mechanical and electrical systems are the direct analogs of each other.

Attention is called to the fact that, just as the parallel and series electrical circuits of Figs. 4-3 and 4-5 are electrical duals, then the parallel and series mechanical circuits of Figs. 4-2 and 4-4 are mechanical duals. Moreover, in the forms chosen, the geometrical configurations of the mechanical and the analogous electrical circuit also correspond.

4-5. Electromechanical Analogs—Inverse System. Owing to the dual nature of the parallel and series electrical and mechanical circuits, it is perfectly possible and reasonable to relate, for example, the parallel mechanical circuit and the series electrical circuit, and also the series mechanical circuit and the parallel electrical circuit. In this case, the analogous equations become, for the two appropriate pairs,

Mechanical circuit: $\quad f = M\dfrac{dv}{dt} + Dv + k\displaystyle\int v\,dt$

$$(4\text{-}12)$$

Electrical circuit: $\quad v = L\dfrac{di}{dt} + Ri + \dfrac{1}{C}\displaystyle\int i\,dt$

and

Mechanical circuit: $\quad v = \dfrac{1}{k}\dfrac{df}{dt} + \dfrac{f}{D} + \dfrac{1}{M}\displaystyle\int f\,dt$

$$(4\text{-}13)$$

Electrical circuit: $\quad i = C\dfrac{dv}{dt} + Gv + \dfrac{1}{L}\displaystyle\int v\,dt$

The resulting analogous quantities for the inverse system are those contained in Table 4-4. This system of analogs may be called the (M_f, E_v) or (M_v, E_i) system.

TABLE 4-4. INVERSE ANALOG

Mechanical quantity...........	M	D	k	v	f	W	x
Electrical analog...............	L	R	$1/C$	i	v	z	q

What is here being termed the inverse system of analogs is sometimes called the "classical" analogy. This name stems from the early concepts of electric-circuit elements, when the comparisons were ordinarily made between the masslike inertia effect of inductance, the springlike and storage properties of a capacitor, etc.

The whole relationship discussed above may be summarized in graphical form, as in Fig. 4-6.

4-6. Other Analog Systems. In addition to the fundamental four-system set which is portrayed graphically in Fig. 4-6, other analog systems are also possible. This should bring into focus the fact that analog systems are neither exclusive nor unique.   Moreover, only limited types of problems are in a form for which an analog is possible.

Frequently in mechanical problems of the type illustrated in Fig. 4-2 the linear displacement x, rather than the velocity v, is desired.   Often, in this case, the controlling force equation is written in the form

$$f = M \frac{d^2x}{dt^2} + D \frac{dx}{dt} + kx \tag{4-14}$$

This is, of course, simply Eq. (4-2) with the substitution $v = dx/dt$. The direct analog does not exist, but the indirect analog might exist,

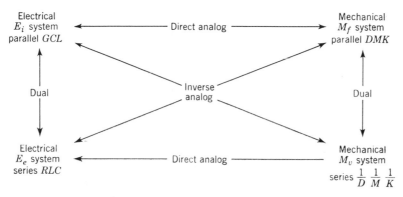

FIG. 4-6. The analog relationships among the two types of mechanical and two types of electrical systems.

since, from Eqs. (4-12), by writing $i = dq/dt$, the resulting form for the electrical circuit becomes

$$v = L \frac{d^2q}{dt^2} + R \frac{dq}{dt} + \frac{q}{C} \tag{4-15}$$

Ordinarily, however, the evaluation of the charge q in electrical-circuit theory is not usually accomplished directly.   A somewhat more useful analogy can be found by differentiating the second of Eqs. (4-12), which leads to

$$\frac{dv}{dt} = L \frac{d^2i}{dt^2} + R \frac{di}{dt} + \frac{i}{C} \tag{4-16}$$

which has the same form as Eq. (4-14).   The resulting analogous quantities in the (M_x, E_i) system are as shown in Table 4-5.

TABLE 4-5. THE (M_x, E_i) ANALOG SYSTEM

Mechanical quantity......	M	D	k	x	f	$\int f \, dt$
Electrical analog.........	L	R	$1/C$	i	dv/dt	v

Suppose that it is required to find the steady-state solution of Eq. (4-14) when the force f is sinusoidal and of the form

$$f = \text{Im} \left(\sqrt{2}\, Fe^{j(\omega t + \alpha)} \right)$$

The analogous electric circuit is to be solved for an applied potential

$$v = \text{Im} \left(\frac{\sqrt{2}\, F}{j} e^{j(\omega t + \alpha)} \right)$$

The solution leads directly to the following expression for x:

$$x = \text{Im} \left(\frac{\sqrt{2}\, F}{jW} e^{j(\omega t + \alpha - \phi)} \right) = \text{Im} \left(\frac{\sqrt{2}\, F}{W} e^{j(\omega t + \alpha - \phi - \pi/2)} \right) \qquad (4\text{-}17)$$

This is just the mechanical equivalent of $V/Q = jV/I$.

As a second example of the use of an analog system to solve a mechanical problem, consider a mechanical system in rotational motion, as illustrated in Fig. 4-7. This mechanical system is analogous to the simple

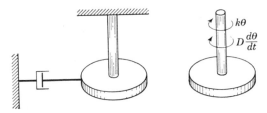

FIG. 4-7. A simple rotational system, and its free-body diagram.

mechanical system of Fig. 4-2 in translational motion. The controlling differential equation is

$$T = J \frac{d\omega}{dt} + D\omega + k \int \omega \, dt \qquad (4\text{-}18)$$

or correspondingly $\qquad T = J \frac{d^2\theta}{dt^2} + D \frac{d\theta}{dt} + k\theta \qquad (4\text{-}19)$

In this case, the analog systems of Tables 4-3 through 4-5 may be used, with the appropriate change in symbols.

For convenience in relating electrical with mechanical quantities, Tables 4-6 and 4-7 are included.

4-7. Systems with More than One Degree of Freedom. The foregoing ideas of analogs may be extended to mechanical systems having more than one degree of freedom. As is readily surmised, the analogs of such systems would be multinode or multiloop electrical circuits.

As a specific example of a coupled mechanical system, refer to Fig. 4-8, which shows two coupled spring-mounted masses. Also included in this figure are the free-body diagrams for each mass. Attention is called to

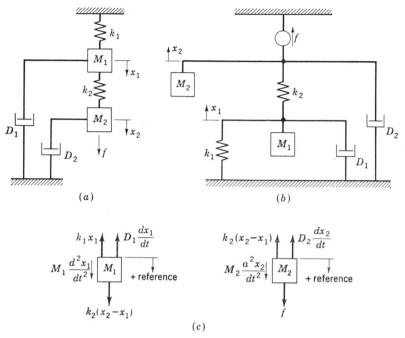

Fig. 4-8. A mechanical system with two degrees of freedom.

Fig. 4-8b, which shows that the mechanical system in Fig. 4-8a is actually a coupled parallel system, even though it might appear at first that it is a series mechanical system. The following set of equations result from the system of forces acting on each mass:

$$M_1 \frac{dv_1'}{dt} + D_1 v_1' + k_1 \int v_1' \, dt - k_2 \int (v_2' - v_1') \, dt = 0$$

$$M_2 \frac{dv_2'}{dt} + D_2 v_2' + k_2 \int (v_2' - v_1') \, dt = f$$

(4-20)

The corresponding equations for the direct analog will be, from Table 4-3,

$$C_1 \frac{dv_1}{dt} + G_1 v_1 + \frac{1}{L_1} \int v_1 \, dt - \frac{1}{L_2} \int (v_2 - v_1) \, dt = 0$$

$$C_2 \frac{dv_2}{dt} + G_2 v_2 + \frac{1}{L_2} \int (v_2 - v_1) \, dt = i$$

(4-21)

Likewise, the corresponding equations for the inverse analog will be, from Table 4-4,

$$L_1 \frac{di_1}{dt} + R_1 i_1 + \frac{1}{C_1} \int i_1 \, dt - \frac{1}{C_2} \int (i_2 - i_1) \, dt = 0$$

$$L_2 \frac{di_2}{dt} + R_2 i_2 + \frac{1}{C_2} \int (i_2 - i_1) \, dt = v$$

(4-22)

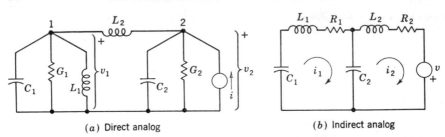

(a) Direct analog   (b) Indirect analog

Fig. 4-9. The two electrical-analog networks of the mechanical system of Fig. 4-8

The appropriate electrical networks which are the analogs of the mechanical system of Fig. 4-8 are illustrated in Fig. 4-9. Observe that these electrical networks are duals of each other, as they must be.

Example 4-7.1. A pulley of moment J about its axis of rotation is restrained by a spring of constant k_1, as shown. From the other side of the pulley a spring of constant k_2 and mass M are suspended.

(a) Find the equations of motion of the system.

(b) Draw the electrical analogs of the system.

Solution. For no slippage, the free-body diagrams and the appropriate equations are

$$M\ddot{x} = k_2(x_1 - x)$$
$$M\ddot{x} + k_2 x = k_2 x_1 = k_2 r\theta \qquad (4\text{-}23)$$

or

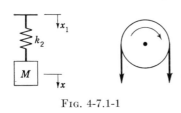

Fig. 4-7.1-1

Here the dot notation for time differentiation is employed, with $\dot{x} = dx/dt$, $\ddot{x} = d^2x/dt^2$, etc. The second equation is

$$J\ddot{\theta} = r[-k_2(x_1 - x) - k_1 x_1]$$
$$J\ddot{\theta} + (k_1 + k_2)r x_1 = k_2 r x$$
$$J\ddot{\theta} + (k_1 + k_2)r^2\theta = k_2 r x \qquad (4\text{-}24)$$

or

or

To find the electrical analogs, the mechanical equations are first rewritten in the form

$$M\frac{dv'}{dt} + k_2 \int v' \, dt - k_2 r \int \omega \, dt = 0$$
$$\frac{J}{r}\frac{d\omega}{dt} + (k_1 + k_2)r \int \omega \, dt - k_2 \int v' \, dt = 0 \qquad (4\text{-}25)$$

By a change of notation, these equations may be written in the following electrical form:

$$L_1\frac{di_1}{dt} + \frac{1}{C_1}\int i_1 \, dt - \frac{1}{C_2}\int i_2 \, dt = 0$$
$$L_2\frac{di_2}{dt} + \frac{1}{C_3}\int i_2 \, dt - \frac{1}{C_2}\int i_1 \, dt = 0$$

These expressions are now rewritten as follows:

$$L_1\frac{di_1}{dt} + \left(\frac{1}{C_1} - \frac{1}{C_2}\right) \int i_1\, dt + \frac{1}{C_2}\int (i_1 - i_2)\, dt = 0$$

$$L_2\frac{di_2}{dt} + \left(\frac{1}{C_3} - \frac{1}{C_2}\right) \int i_2\, dt + \frac{1}{C_2}\int (i_2 - i_1)\, dt = 0$$

(4-26)

These equations may be given the electrical-circuit representation of Fig. 4-7.1-2a.

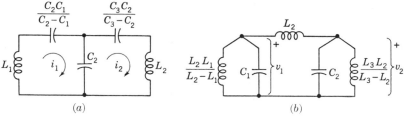

(a)   (b)

FIG. 4-7.1-2

The equations can also be written in the following form:

$$C_1\frac{dv_1}{dt} + \left(\frac{1}{L_1} - \frac{1}{L_2}\right) \int v_1\, dt + \frac{1}{L_2}\int (v_1 - v_2)\, dt = 0$$

$$C_2\frac{dv_2}{dt} + \left(\frac{1}{L_3} - \frac{1}{L_2}\right) \int v_2\, dt + \frac{1}{L_2}\int (v_2 - v_1)\, dt = 0$$

(4-27)

The appropriate electrical circuit for these equations is illustrated in Fig. 4-7.1-2b.

4-8. Procedure in Drawing Analogs. In the foregoing discussions, the procedure for finding the electrical analog of a given mechanical system proceeded from the differential equations of the mechanical system. The mechanical parameters appearing in the equations are then changed to their electrical analogs. Subsequently an electric circuit is sought from which the resulting equations may be obtained by an application of one of the Kirchhoff laws.

A second procedure is possible in certain examples in which the mechanical quantities are first changed into their electrical analogs and these are then interconnected in an appropriate manner. The controlling equations for the system are then written from the electrical circuit. This procedure leads naturally to the direct system of analogs.

Consider the case of the parallel mechanical system (see Figs. 4-2 and 4-9) for which one writes $\Sigma f = 0$ for each inertial group, with the direct analog being that for which the corresponding $\Sigma i = 0$ for each node. Since forces are measured with respect to ground, the mass M is represented by a capacitor between a nondatum and the datum node. All elements connected to M and which contribute forces are replaced by their electrical analogs connected to the nondatum node. Whether the electrical elements are connected to the datum node is determined by whether the mechanical elements which contribute the force are a force between the mass and ground or between the mass and some other element. Clearly, therefore, in such cases the electrical analog can be drawn by inspection of the mechanical system.

Attention is called to the fact that this second procedure, while it is most convenient in those cases for which it applies, has applicability only to a few types of mechanical system. It does not lend itself generally to application to systems with rigid physical couplings among the elements. However, since the classes of problems to which the procedure is applicable are important, the method is of considerable value.

4-9. Energy and Analogs. It is often possible to draw the electrical analog of a given mechanical system from an examination of the expressions for the energies of the system. This technique requires finding an electrical network for which the elements of the system have energy functions of a form appropriate to the system for which an analog is

TABLE 4-6

	Resistor	Capacitor	Inductor
Electrical	$i_G = G(v_1 - v_2)$ $i_G = G v_G$	$i_C = C\dfrac{d}{dt}(v_1 - v_2)$ $i_C = C\,dv_C/dt$	$i_L = \dfrac{1}{L}\displaystyle\int (v_1 - v_2)\,dt$ $i_L = \dfrac{1}{L}\displaystyle\int v_L\,dt$
	Viscous damper	Inertia	Spring
Mechanical (translational)	$f_D = D(v_1 - v_2)$	$f_M = M\,dv/dt$	$f_k = k\displaystyle\int (v_1 - v_2)\,dt$
	Torsional damper	Inertia	Shaft stiffness
Mechanical (rotational)	$T_D = D(\omega_1 - \omega_2)$	$T_J = J\,d\omega/dt$	$T_S = k\displaystyle\int (\omega_1 - \omega_2)\,dt$

TABLE 4-7

	Resistor	Capacitor	Inductor
Electrical	$v_R = R(i_1 - i_2)$	$v_C = \dfrac{1}{C}\int (i_1 - i_2)\,dt$	$v_L = L\,\dfrac{di_L}{dt}$
	Viscous damper	Spring	Inertia
Mechanical (translational)	$f_D = D(v_1 - v_2)$	$f_k = k\int (v_1 - v_2)\,dt$	$f_M = M\,\dfrac{dv}{dt}$
	Torsion damper	Shaft stiffness	Inertia
Mechanical (rotational)	$T_D = D(\omega_1 - \omega_2)$	$T_S = k\int (\omega_1 - \omega_2)\,dt$	$T_J = J\,\dfrac{d\omega}{dt}$

sought. The procedure is made evident by reference to Tables 4-6 and 4-7, which illustrate the electrical and the mechanical analogs, and Table 4-8, which expresses the form of the energy and power functions in electrical elements.

TABLE 4-8. ELECTRICAL ENERGY AND POWER DISSIPATION FUNCTIONS

	Inductor	Capacitor	Resistor	Mutual inductance
Direct analog	$\dfrac{1}{2L}\left(\int v\,dt\right)^2 = \dfrac{1}{2L}\psi^2$	$\tfrac{1}{2}Cv^2 = \tfrac{1}{2}C\dot{\psi}^2$	$Gv^2 = G\dot{\psi}^2$	
Inverse analog	$\tfrac{1}{2}Li^2$	$\dfrac{1}{2C}\left(\int i\,dt\right)^2 = \dfrac{1}{2}\dfrac{q^2}{C}$	Ri^2	Mi_1i_2

The appropriate forms for the energy and power dissipation functions in a mechanical system are the following:

$$\mathfrak{T} = \tfrac{1}{2}Mv'^2 \qquad \text{kinetic-energy function}$$
$$\mathrm{U} = \tfrac{1}{2}kx^2 \qquad \text{potential-energy function}$$
$$\mathfrak{F} = \tfrac{1}{2}Dv'^2 \qquad \text{Rayleigh dissipation function}$$

The Rayleigh dissipation function is not often introduced into electrical-engineering analysis, but it is seen to be simply one-half the total power dissipation. This function will arise in our further work.

Several mechanical systems will be examined, to illustrate the procedure involved in finding the electrical analog from considerations of the energy functions.

Example 4-9.1. Refer to the mechanical system of Fig. 4-2, and deduce the electrical analog from energy considerations.

Solution. The total energy and power dissipation in the mechanical circuit of Fig. 4-2 is, by an application of the law of conservation of energy,

$$\begin{aligned}\text{Applied energy} &= \text{kinetic} + \text{potential} + \text{dissipation}\\ &= \tfrac{1}{2}Mv'^2 + \tfrac{1}{2}kx^2 + \tfrac{1}{2}Dv'^2\end{aligned}$$

A direct application of Table 4-8 leads to the circuit of Fig. 4-3 and its dual, Fig. 4-5.

Example 4-9.2. Consider the double pendulum of Fig. 4-9.2-1 for the restricted case of small oscillations and no viscous damping. It is required to find an electrical analog of this mechanical system from considerations of the energy of the system.

Solution. It is required to find expressions for the energy terms. These are, relative to the fixed reference frame,

FIG. 4-9.2-1

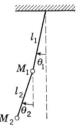

Kinetic energy:

$$\mathfrak{T} = \tfrac{1}{2}M_1(l_1\dot\theta_1)^2 + \tfrac{1}{2}M_2(l_1\dot\theta_1 + l_2\dot\theta_2)^2 \tag{4-28}$$

Potential energy:

$$U = M_1gl_1(1 - \cos\theta_1) + M_2g[l_2(1 - \cos\theta_2) + l_1(1 - \cos\theta_1)] \tag{4-29}$$

The expression for $\mathfrak{T}$ is expanded and rearranged as follows,

$$\begin{aligned}\mathfrak{T} &= \tfrac{1}{2}M_1l_1^2\dot\theta_1 + \tfrac{1}{2}M_2l_1^2\dot\theta_1^2 + \tfrac{1}{2}M_2l_2^2\dot\theta_2^2 + M_2l_1l_2\dot\theta_1\dot\theta_2\\ \text{or}\quad \mathfrak{T} &= \tfrac{1}{2}(M_1 + M_2)l_1^2\dot\theta_1^2 + M_2(l_1\dot\theta_1)(l_2\dot\theta_2) + \tfrac{1}{2}M_2l_2^2\dot\theta_2^2\end{aligned} \tag{4-30}$$

The expression for the potential energy is rewritten, by expanding the cosine terms into series form, with only the first two terms in the expansion being retained. This leads to

$$U = \frac{M_1gl_1\theta_1^2}{2} + M_2g\left(\frac{l_2\theta_2^2}{2} + \frac{l_1\theta_1^2}{2}\right)$$

or

$$U = \tfrac{1}{2}(M_1 + M_2)gl_1\theta_1^2 + \tfrac{1}{2}M_2gl_2\theta_2^2 \tag{4-31}$$

Now compare the resulting expressions for $\mathfrak{T}$ and U with the following expression for an electrical system, according to Table 4-8:

$$\begin{aligned}\mathfrak{T} &= \tfrac{1}{2}(L_1i_1^2 + 2Mi_1i_2 + L_2i_2^2)\\ U &= \frac{1}{2}\left(\frac{q_1^2}{C_1} + \frac{q_2^2}{C_2}\right)\end{aligned} \tag{4-32}$$

Since these electrical forms are identical with those for the mechanical circuit, the electrical network specified by Eqs. (4-32) will thus be an analog for the mechanical system. The circuit is that given in Fig. 4-9.2-2.

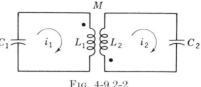

M

FIG. 4-9.2-2

4-10. Energy, Analogs, and Force Equations. Particular reference is made to Example 4-9.2, which considers the energy functions of the double pendulum and the subsequent deduction of an electrical analog from considerations of the energy functions alone. One subsequent step which follows directly from the electrical analog is the equilibrium network equations which will be obtained by a direct application of the Kirchhoff potential law to the two-loop magnetically coupled network. This process is quite general, and in those cases where an electrical network can be found from energy considerations, the appropriate set of equilibrium equations (the force equations) can be directly deduced from a study of the electrical network.

PROBLEMS

4-1. For the networks shown, it is required to:
(a) Write the equilibrium equations.
(b) Draw the dual circuit.
(c) Write the equilibrium equations of the dual network.

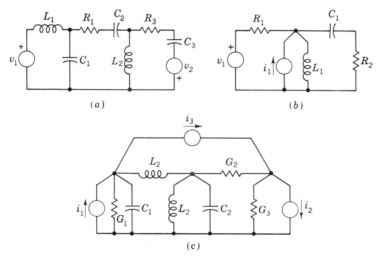

(a)   (b)

(c)

FIG. P4-1

4-2. The following are a series of mechanical problems. It is required to deduce the equations of motion of these systems and then to draw both the direct and the inverse analogs of these systems, clearly identifying all terms.

(a) One of the problems encountered in the manufacture of forged turbine blades or buckets is the transmission of the impact energy of the hammer to the anvil base (see Fig. P4-2a). This energy is in the form of vibrations and interfering elastic waves which must be damped to avoid impairing the operation of the hammer. The basic elements of a hammer installation are shown. The impact forces of the hammer result in an initial velocity v_0 of the combined mass of the hammer and anvil. The mass is supported on an elastic medium of spring constant k lb/ft and viscous-damping constant D lb-sec/ft. (The ultimate requirement here would be to establish the properties of the damping medium to yield the minimum peak transmitted force to the immediate vicinity of the machine.)

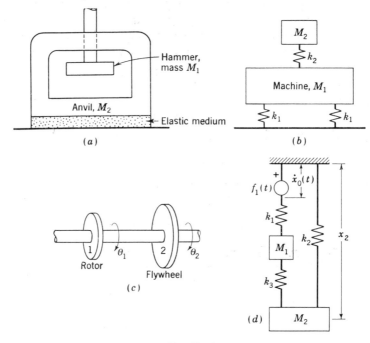

FIG. P4-2

(b) A system consists of a massive machine mounted on an elastic foundation and a small mass attached elastically to the machine, as indicated in the accompanying figure. Owing to inherent unbalance of its rotating parts the machine is subjected to a vertical component of force which varies sinusoidally in time at constant frequency. All motions are constrained to the vertical. (The question here is whether or not there are any conditions under which the presence of the small mass reduces the force transmitted through the elastic foundation of the machine.)

(c) A flywheel is coupled to a motor shaft in order to damp the oscillations produced by the driven machine (see figure). The data specify:

D_1 = damping coefficient due to rotation of rotor
D_2 = damping coefficient due to rotation of flywheel
K = torque constant of shaft
J_1 = moment of inertia of rotor
J_2 = moment of inertia of flywheel

(The problem here might be to determine the maximum angle of twist in the shaft for a specified applied alternating torque.)

(d) The coupled mechanical system illustrated is excited by a source of known velocity. [The problem here might be to find $f_1(t)$ delivered by the source and the velocity $\dot{x}_2(t)$.]

4-3. The equivalents of a number of different mechanical circuits are given. It is required to draw the direct and inverse analog circuits without first writing the

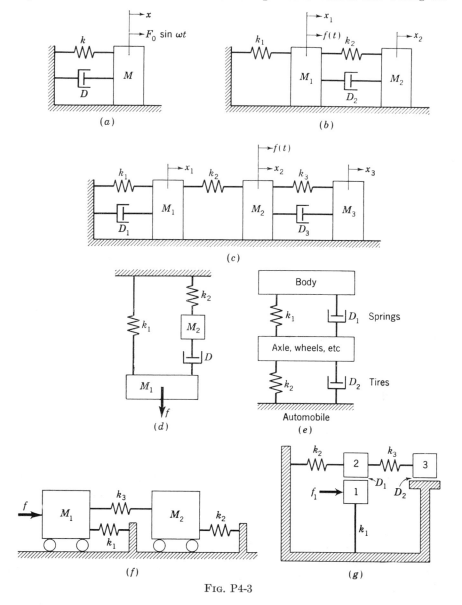

FIG. P4-3

mechanical equations.   The validity of your analogs should be checked by comparing the equilibrium equations from the analog with those from the original system.

4-4. Find the electrical analogs of the mechanical systems shown.

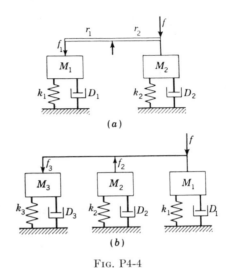

(a)

(b)

Fig. P4-4

4-5. In the operation of rotating machinery, pronounced rotational vibrations are sometimes encountered which in aggravated cases may cause shaft failure.   A rotational vibration damper is sometimes used to reduce this type of vibration.   One such damper is shown, which consists of an extra flywheel, with moment of inertia J_2, which is free to turn on the shaft and is coupled to the fixed flywheel by means of a torsional spring.

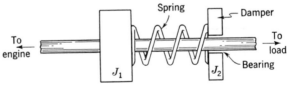

Fig. P4-5

(a) Analyze the operation of the system, assuming that the prime mover creates a rotational torque component with an amplitude of 500 ft-lb at a frequency of 11 cps.   The important numerical data are:

Flywheel-engine load system: $WR^2 = 95$ lb-ft^2

Damper: $WR^2 = 15$ lb-ft^2

Spring constant: $k = 800$ lb-ft/radian

Friction torque damper bearing: $D = 1.2$ lb-ft/radian/sec

(b) Have the oscillations been damped?   What might be done to improve the situation?

4-6. Consider the two mechanical systems illustrated in the accompanying figures.

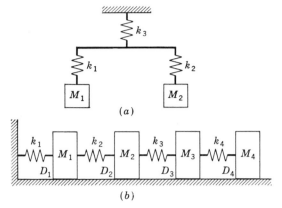

(a)

(b)

Fig. P4-6

(a) Set up equations for the energy functions (kinetic, potential, dissipation) of the systems shown.

(b) From the functions in (a), draw the electrical equivalents of the systems.

(c) Write the appropriate electrical-circuit equations.

5

Lagrange's Equations and Dynamical System Analysis

Some of the broader aspects of the relationships between the energy functions and the electromechanical analogs will be exploited. The systematization of such exploitation proceeds through the use of the Lagrange generalized equations, which are introduced.

5-1. Energy, Analogs, and Force Equations. Particular reference is made to Example 4-9.2, which considers the energy functions of the double pendulum and the subsequent deduction of the electrical analog from considerations of the energy functions alone. With the network established, the voltage equations through an application of the Kirchhoff law follow immediately. In essence, therefore, what has been accomplished is the following sequence of steps: energy functions, to network, to force equations.

A question of considerable importance is whether or not it is possible to proceed directly from the energy-function formulation to the force equations, without the intermediate step of finding the network. More precisely, the question is whether or not the appropriate force equations for a given system can be deduced directly from the energy functions. Fortunately, such a general procedure is possible, and owing to its broad generality the procedure is a most important one in dynamical system analysis.

To introduce the general problem, consider initially a single inductor through which passes a current. From our past work in electric-circuit theory, and as a simple case for illustrative purposes, the following two relations may be written:

$$\mathfrak{I} = \tfrac{1}{2} L i^2 \qquad v_L = L \frac{di}{dt}$$

Now remember that the energy stored in the inductor may be deduced from power and energy considerations,

$$\text{Energy stored} = \int_0^T v_L i \, dt = \int_0^i L i \, di = \tfrac{1}{2} L i^2 \tag{5-1}$$

Clearly from the first and third terms, if the energy is first derived with respect to i and then with respect to the time, the value of v_L results. That is,

$$\frac{d}{dt}\left[\frac{\partial(\text{energy stored})}{\partial i} \right] = L \frac{di}{dt} = v_L$$

In the most general case, it is preferred to write this relation in the form

$$\frac{d}{dt}\left(\frac{\partial \mathfrak{I}}{\partial i} \right) = v_L \tag{5-2}$$

Suppose now that the circuit contains a capacitor. In a manner somewhat similar to the foregoing, and upon noting that the following two relations may be written,

$$U = \frac{q^2}{2C} \qquad v_C = \frac{q}{C}$$

then it is clear that the following relation is valid:

$$\frac{\partial U}{\partial q} = \frac{q}{C} = v_C \tag{5-3}$$

Finally, now consider the case of a circuit that contains both an inductor and a capacitor in series. The following expressions are a logical combination of the above. For the two elements in series

$$\mathfrak{I} = \tfrac{1}{2} L i^2 \qquad U = \frac{q^2}{2C}$$

$$v_L + v_C = L \frac{di}{dt} + \frac{q}{C} = 0$$

It is seen that this result is consistent with the expression in the form

$$\frac{d}{dt}\left(\frac{\partial \mathfrak{I}}{\partial i} \right) + \frac{\partial U}{\partial q} = 0 \tag{5-4}$$

If it is recalled that i and q are related by the form

$$i = \frac{dq}{dt} = \dot{q}$$

where the dot terminology for designating time derivatives is again being used, then Eq. (5-4) now attains the form

$$\frac{d}{dt}\left(\frac{\partial \mathfrak{I}}{\partial \dot{q}} \right) + \frac{\partial U}{\partial q} = 0 \tag{5-5}$$

This expression is a special form of what is known as the Lagrange equations.

Before examining the more general aspects of the Lagrange equations, attention is called to the fact that Kirchhoff equilibrium equations for Example 4-9.2, which follow directly from an inspection of Fig. 4-9.2-2, follow directly from Eqs. (4-32) through the use of the Lagrange equations, since in the form given in Eq. (5-5) the Lagrange equation must be applied for each coordinate, $(q_1, \dot{q}_1)$ and $(q_2, \dot{q}_2)$, separately. Two applications of the Lagrange equations must be made in this case, which then leads to the appropriate two equations.

5-2. Lagrange's Equations. The special form of the Lagrange equation that was discussed above involved the charge q and the current $\dot{q}$ ($= i$) as the variables. If the mechanical analog were used, the variables would be x and $\dot{x}$. On the other hand, the variables which appeared in Eqs. (4-30) and (4-31) were $l\theta$ and $l\dot{\theta}$. Suppose, therefore, that the quantities $q_1, q_2, \ldots, q_m$ be a set of m scalar quantities such that, when their values are known at a specified time, the configuration of the system will be determined completely at that time. As noted, these quantities may denote charges, they may denote displacements, they may denote angles; in fact, they may denote any quantities which define the state of the system. If the system varies in configuration, the values of $q_1, \ldots, q_m$ will vary continuously in a corresponding manner. These scalar quantities are called *generalized coordinates*.

Now refer to Eq. (4-30) for the special example of the double pendulum. Observe that the kinetic energy $\mathfrak{I}$ is a quadratic function of the *generalized velocities* $\dot{q}_1, \dot{q}_2, \ldots, \dot{q}_m$. In the general case, the coefficients in $\mathfrak{I}$ will involve the generalized coordinates, and perhaps the time, if variable constraints exist (Example 5-3.2 is an example of this type). Hence, in its most general form, $\mathfrak{I}$ may be expressed functionally as

$$\mathfrak{I} = \mathfrak{I}(t, q_1, \ldots, q_m, \dot{q}_1, \ldots, \dot{q}_m) \tag{5-6}$$

Note also from Eq. (4-31) that the potential energy is a function of the generalized coordinates. It denotes, in fact, the work done on the system by conservative forces as it passes from one terminal configuration to the standard state, which may be selected arbitrarily. Therefore,

$$U = U(q_1, \ldots, q_m) \tag{5-7}$$

In its general form, Lagrange's equations of motion become, for *each* coordinate,

$$\frac{d}{dt}\left(\frac{\partial \mathfrak{I}}{\partial \dot{q}}\right) - \frac{\partial \mathfrak{I}}{\partial q} + \frac{\partial U}{\partial q} = P \tag{5-8}$$

where P is the generalized component of the impressed *force*[1] tending to increase the coordinate q.

In order to expand still further the concept of system forces, the Rayleigh dissipation function $\mathfrak{F}$ is introduced. This function, as already noted, represents one-half the rate at which energy is dissipated into heat by friction. Typical forms of the function are

$$\mathfrak{F} = \tfrac{1}{2}Dv^2 \qquad \text{for a mechanical system}$$
$$\mathfrak{F} = \tfrac{1}{2}Ri^2 \qquad \text{for an electrical system}$$

and the frictional forces are then given as the derivatives with respect to the velocities; that is, $f_D = Dv$; $v_R = Ri$. The final equations of motion in generalized coordinates then become

$$\frac{d}{dt}\left(\frac{\partial \mathfrak{F}}{\partial \dot{q}}\right) - \frac{\partial \mathfrak{F}}{\partial q} + \frac{\partial U}{\partial q} + \frac{\partial \mathfrak{F}}{\partial \dot{q}} = P \tag{5-9}$$

In this expression $\partial U/\partial q$ denotes the conservative forces, $\partial \mathfrak{F}/\partial \dot{q}$ denotes the dissipative forces, and P specifies all other forces and would be the actual external force components acting on the system in the direction of q. In summary, therefore, the Lagrange equations of Eq. (5-9) specify the equations of motion for each generalized coordinate, and these are deduced from a specification of the energy functions which describe the system.

It is customary to define a new function L, which is called the Lagrangian, which is written as

$$L = \mathfrak{F} - U \tag{5-10}$$

In terms of this function, Eq. (5-9) is written as

$$\frac{d}{dt}\left(\frac{\partial L}{\partial \dot{q}}\right) - \frac{\partial L}{\partial q} + \frac{\partial \mathfrak{F}}{\partial \dot{q}} = P \tag{5-11}$$

In the case of the conservative system, this expression assumes the simple form

$$\frac{d}{dt}\left(\frac{\partial L}{\partial \dot{q}}\right) - \frac{\partial L}{\partial q} = 0 \tag{5-12}$$

Attention is called to the fact that in the discussion above it has been assumed that the functions $\mathfrak{F}$ and U are linear, since the development was in terms of constant electrical parameters R, L, C and constant mechanical parameters M, D, k, etc. We shall later see that the Lagrangian for electromechanical systems must be defined[2] in terms of coenergy $\mathfrak{F}'$ (mechanical energy + electrical coenergy) rather than in terms of

---

[1] The term force is here being used in its broadest sense. For example, if the coordinate is an angle, P will represent the torque tending to change the angle.

[2] O. K. Mawardi, On the Concept of Coenergy, *J. Franklin Inst.*, **264**: 313 (1957).

energy $\mathfrak{I}$ (mechanical energy + electrical energy). When so defined, the Lagrangian formulation is not restricted to linear systems.

5-3. Examples of the Use of Lagrange's Equations. In order to illustrate the application of Lagrange's equations in setting up the equations of motion of dynamical systems, some selected mechanical and electrical problems will be considered. The more general problems involving mixed electrical and mechanical coordinates will be considered in subsequent sections.

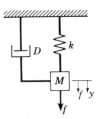

Example 5-3.1. A body is suspended from a spring and is subjected to a forcing function. Use Lagrange's equations to find the equation of motion of the system. The system is illustrated in Fig. 5-3.1-1.

Solution. When the body is in motion, the kinetic energy associated with the motion is

Fig. 5-3.1-1

$$\mathfrak{I} = \tfrac{1}{2}M\dot{y}^2$$

The corresponding potential energy of the spring, when the body is displaced by an amount y from its equilibrium position, is

$$U = \tfrac{1}{2}ky^2$$

where k is the spring constant. Likewise, the dissipation function is

$$\mathfrak{F} = \tfrac{1}{2}D\dot{y}^2$$

Upon applying Lagrange's equation [Eq. (5-9)], it is found that

$$\frac{d}{dt}(M\dot{y}) + ky + D\dot{y} = f$$

or
$$M\ddot{y} + D\dot{y} + ky = f \tag{5-13}$$

which is the expected form of the controlling differential equation of motion of the simple system illustrated.

Example 5-3.2. Consider a simple pendulum the point of suspension of which is subjected to a periodic displacement about its point of equilibrium. It is required to find the equations of motion of this oscillating pendulum. The system is illustrated in Fig. 5-3.2-1.

Solution. It is supposed that the pendulum is constrained to move in a plane, whence the constraint equation is

$$y = 0$$

The point of support must execute a simple harmonic motion along the X axis about the origin 0. If λ denotes the departure of the point of support from 0, then

$$\lambda = \lambda_0 \cos \omega t$$

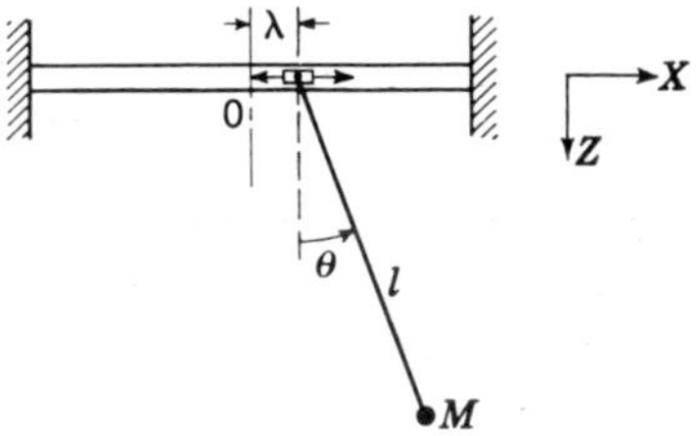

Fig. 5-3.2-1

where λ_0 is the maximum departure and ω is the periodicity of the prescribed motion. This equation represents a variable constraint, since the time t is explicitly involved.

The system will have but one degree of freedom, so that one generalized coordinate together with the time is sufficient for its specification. This coordinate is taken to be the angle θ. Thus the equations expressing the relations between the coordinates (x,y,z) and the generalized coordinate θ and the time are

$$
\begin{aligned}
x &= \lambda_0 \cos \omega t + l \sin \theta \\
y &= 0 \\
z &= l \cos \theta
\end{aligned}
\tag{5-14}
$$

The cartesian components of velocity $(\dot{x},\dot{y},\dot{z})$, in terms of the generalized velocity and the time, are then

$$
\begin{aligned}
\dot{x} &= -\omega\lambda_0 \sin \omega t + l \cos \theta\,\dot{\theta} \\
\dot{y} &= 0 \\
\dot{z} &= -l \sin \theta\,\dot{\theta}
\end{aligned}
\tag{5-15}
$$

The kinetic-energy function of the system is given by the expression

$$
\mathfrak{J} = \tfrac{1}{2}M(\dot{x}^2 + \dot{y}^2 + \dot{z}^2) = \tfrac{1}{2}M(l^2\dot{\theta}^2 + \omega^2\lambda_0^2 \sin^2 \omega t - 2\omega\lambda_0 l \cos \theta \sin \omega t\,\dot{\theta}) \tag{5-16}
$$

The corresponding potential energy of the body, when deflected by the angle θ, is

$$
U = Mgl(1 - \cos \theta) \tag{5-17}
$$

An application of Lagrange's equation yields

$$
\frac{d}{dt}\,[\tfrac{1}{2}M(2l^2\dot{\theta} - 2\omega\lambda_0 l \cos \theta \sin \omega t)] + M\omega\lambda_0 l \sin \theta \sin \omega t\,\dot{\theta} + Mgl \sin \theta = 0
$$

from which it follows that

$$
Ml^2\ddot{\theta} - Ml\lambda_0\omega^2 \cos \theta \cos \omega t + 2M\omega\lambda_0 l \sin \theta \sin \omega t\,\dot{\theta} + Mgl \sin \theta = 0
$$

or finally $\ddot{\theta} + \dfrac{2\omega\lambda_0}{l}\,\dot{\theta} \sin \theta \sin \omega t + \left(\dfrac{g}{l} \sin \theta - \dfrac{\omega^2\lambda_0}{l} \cos \theta \cos \omega t\right) = 0 \tag{5-18}$

This is a complicated differential equation, the solution of which specifies the motion of the mass M.

Example 5-3.3. A two-loop network is excited by a potential source $v(t)$. Find the network equations by an application of Lagrange's equations.

Solution. The energy functions are written directly, as follows:

$$
\begin{aligned}
\mathfrak{J} &= \tfrac{1}{2}L_1 i_1{}^2 + \tfrac{1}{2}L_2 i_2{}^2 \\
&= \tfrac{1}{2}L_1 \dot{q}_1{}^2 + \tfrac{1}{2}L_2 \dot{q}_2{}^2
\end{aligned}
\tag{5-19}
$$

$$
U = \frac{1}{2}\frac{(q_1 - q_2)^2}{C_1} + \frac{1}{2}\frac{q_2{}^2}{C_2}
$$

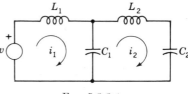

Fig. 5-3.3-1

Since this system has two degrees of freedom, a Lagrange equation must be written for each generalized coordinate.

(a) Upon applying the Lagrange equation to coordinate q_1, it follows that

$$
\frac{d}{dt}\,(L_1 \dot{q}_1) + \frac{q_1 - q_2}{C_1} = v
$$

(b) When the Lagrange equation is applied to coordinate q_2, there follows

$$
\frac{d}{dt}\,(L_2 \dot{q}_2) - \frac{q_1 - q_2}{C_1} + \frac{q_2}{C_2} = 0
$$

When written in the notation that is more customary in electrical-network theory, these equations become

$$L_1 \frac{di_1}{dt} + \frac{1}{C_1} \int (i_1 - i_2) \, dt = v$$

$$L_2 \frac{di_2}{dt} + \frac{1}{C_2} \int i_2 \, dt - \frac{1}{C_1} \int (i_1 - i_2) \, dt = 0$$

(5-20)

which are seen to be correct.

It is observed that the logical loop variables are $\dot{q} \, (= i)$, q for use in the kinetic- and potential-energy functions, respectively.

Example 5-3.4. A two-node network is excited by a current source, as illustrated in the accompanying figure. Find the network equations by an application of Lagrange's equations.

Solution. The energy functions are written directly from an inspection of the network. These are

$$\mathfrak{J} = \tfrac{1}{2} C_1 v_1^2 + \tfrac{1}{2} C_2 v_2^2$$

$$U = \frac{1}{2L_1} \left[\int (v_1 - v_2) \, dt \right]^2 + \frac{1}{2L_2} \left(\int v_2 \, dt \right)^2$$

(5-21)

It is convenient to write these equations in a form that more nearly resembles Eqs. (5-19). This may be done if the flux-linkage variable is introduced, with $\psi = \int v \, dt$. The energy equations may thus be written

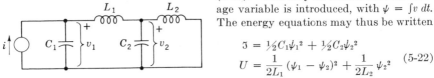

Fig. 5-3.4-1

$$\mathfrak{J} = \tfrac{1}{2} C_1 \dot{\psi}_1^2 + \tfrac{1}{2} C_2 \dot{\psi}_2^2$$

$$U = \frac{1}{2L_1} (\psi_1 - \psi_2)^2 + \frac{1}{2L_2} \psi_2^2$$

(5-22)

We may consider $\dot{\psi}, \psi$ the logical nodal variables for the kinetic- and potential-energy functions, respectively.

Observe that here, as in Example 5-3.3, the system possesses two degrees of freedom and that a Lagrange equation must be written for the two generalized coordinates. In this case, it is noted that the generalized coordinates and generalized velocities are, respectively, $q = \psi = \int v \, dt$; $\dot{q} = \dot{\psi} = v$. The application of Lagrange's equation yields the two relations

$$\frac{d}{dt} (C_1 v_1) + \frac{1}{L_1} \int (v_1 - v_2) \, dt = i$$

$$\frac{d}{dt} (C_2 v_2) + \frac{1}{L_2} \int v_2 \, dt - \frac{1}{L_1} \int (v_1 - v_2) \, dt = 0$$

When written in the more customary network theory notation, these equations are

$$C_1 \frac{dv_1}{dt} + \frac{1}{L_1} \int (v_1 - v_2) \, dt = i$$

$$C_2 \frac{dv_2}{dt} + \frac{1}{L_2} \int v_2 \, dt - \frac{1}{L_1} \int (v_1 - v_2) \, dt = 0$$

(5-23)

Attention is called to the fact that Fig. 5-3.4-1 is the dual of Fig. 5-3.3-1, and correspondingly the sets of equations, Eqs. (5-23) and (5-20), are also duals.

5-4. Lagrange's Equations and Electromechanical Systems. The application of Lagrange's equation to several mechanical systems and to several electric circuits has been carried out in some detail in Sec. 5-3.

It is now desired to study a combined electromechanical system. The Lagrange equation is very well suited to the study of such problems, since the variables which describe the mechanical motion of the system can be chosen as one set of generalized coordinates, while the electrical coordinates are chosen to belong to another set. Moreover, because of the vector nature of both the mechanical and electrical forces, the use of the scalar energy functions often circumvents the inherent difficulties of vector quantities. This is accomplished, of course, at the cost of additional mathematical manipulation, and particularly with the loss of some physical insight into the problem. This latter is not serious, since the resulting force equations can be examined for an understanding of the physical implications.

Example 5-4.1. Consider the electromechanical system illustrated in the accompanying figure. This system consists of a heavy metallic plate P_1 of mass M which is suspended by means of a spring of stiffness k. Plate P_1 is assumed to be parallel to a second plate P_2 which will not move. A constant-potential source V is connected to the two plates. The plate P_1 is given an initial deflection and is then released. Deduce the equations of motion of the plate.

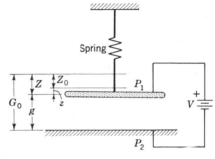

FIG. 5-4.1-1

Solution. In so far as the electrical circuit is concerned, it consists of the d-c polarizing potential source V which supplies charge to plates P_1 and P_2, which together form a capacitor. As plate P_1 oscillates, the capacitance varies instantaneously, causing a current variation in the electrical circuit, the total instantaneous charge on the plates thereby varying. As a first approximation, the fringing is neglected, and the capacitance is given by the expression

$$C = \frac{\epsilon A}{g}$$

where g denotes the spacing between P_1 and P_2. When measured from the level G_0, the normal position of P_1 when there is no polarizing potential, the expression for C may be written in the form

$$C = \frac{\epsilon A}{G_0 - Z} \qquad (5\text{-}24)$$

where Z is the distance from G_0 to plate P_1. ϵ and A are, respectively, the permittivity of free space and the plate area.

Two generalized coordinates are used to describe the system: the mechanical displacement Z from the normal rest position G_0 of the mass M, and the total instantaneous charge Q on either of the two plates of the capacitor. The appropriate energy functions[1] of the system are readily deduced. The kinetic energy is purely mechanical

[1] From the results of Example 5-3.3 the use of $\dot{q}$ and q as the electrical variables establishes the energy functions in a form appropriate to a loop-type analysis (see Prob. 5-10).

and is that due to the motion of the movable plate P_1. It is

$$\mathfrak{I} = \tfrac{1}{2}M\dot{Z}^2 \tag{5-25}$$

The potential energy, which is specified with respect to the rest position G_0, contains two terms, one mechanical and one electrical. It is

$$U = \tfrac{1}{2}kZ^2 + \frac{Q^2}{2C}$$

which may be written, by Eq. (5-23), in the form

$$U = \tfrac{1}{2}kZ^2 + \frac{(G_0 - Z)Q^2}{2\epsilon A} \tag{5-26}$$

The equations of motion are deduced by an application of the Lagrange equation to each of the generalized coordinates.

1. For the Z coordinate,

$$\frac{d}{dt}\left(\frac{\partial \mathfrak{I}}{\partial \dot{Z}}\right) + \frac{\partial U}{\partial Z} = P$$

or

$$\frac{d}{dt}(M\dot{Z}) + kZ - \frac{Q^2}{2\epsilon A} = 0$$

which is

$$M\ddot{Z} + kZ - \frac{Q^2}{2\epsilon A} = 0 \tag{5-27}$$

2. For the Q coordinate, there results

$$\frac{Q(G_0 - Z)}{\epsilon A} = V \tag{5-28}$$

This relationship could have been written down from purely electrostatic considerations.

Refer to Eq. (5-27). The presence of Q^2 in this expression means that the electric force is independent of the polarity of Q. Thus, if Q were to be varied sinusoidally with time, then the force equation would contain a $\sin^2 \omega t$ term, which means, since $\sin^2 \alpha = (1 - \cos 2\alpha)/2$, that the equation of motion contains a double-frequency term. Likewise, the solution of this differential equation could contain such a double-frequency term as well. This could constitute a serious distortion, particularly if this system were a transducer that was to produce a mechanical motion that is linearly dependent on the force.

To avoid such distortion, one would provide a bias level about which the system motion would occur. It will be found that if the signal is small compared with the bias, resulting in what is known as "small-signal," or "incremental," operation, the distortion problem can be avoided. In fact, such a biasing scheme will ensure the linear character of the equilibrium equation about the bias reference level for incremental operation. Not only will this allow an acceptable linear transducer to result, but it also will permit an electrical analog to be found to represent the response of the system relative to the reference level. That the biasing scheme will accomplish the desired results will now be demonstrated.

Suppose that the displacement Z is written as

$$Z = Z_0 + z \tag{5-29}$$

where Z_0 is the normal equilibrium level of the system when in equilibrium, but with the polarizing potential V applied. That Z_0 is different from zero follows from the fact that, with V applied to the capacitor plates, one is charged positively and the other is charged negatively. As a result, there is a force of attraction between the plates which causes the spring to extend beyond the normal zero-bias level G_0. Hence z is the instantaneous displacement of the plate P_1 about the fixed level $G_0 - Z_0$.

Correspondingly, the charge Q is conveniently written as

$$Q = Q_0 + q \qquad (5\text{-}30)$$

where Q_0 is the charge under equilibrium conditions, with V applied, but with no motion of the plates, and q is the instantaneous charge relative to this reference level.

Equations (5-29) and (5-30) are combined with the dynamic equations of the system, given by Eqs. (5-27) and (5-28). The following equations result:

$$M(\ddot{Z}_0 + \ddot{z}) + k(Z_0 + z) - \frac{(Q_0 + q)^2}{2\epsilon A} = 0$$

$$\frac{(Q_0 + q)(G_0 - Z_0 - z)}{\epsilon A} = V \qquad (5\text{-}31)$$

But Z_0 and Q_0 are independent of time. Also, it will be assumed that the motion of plate P_1 is small, so that second-order quantities may be neglected. The expansion of $(Q_0 + q)^2$ thus becomes approximately

$$(Q_0 + q)^2 \doteq Q_0{}^2 + 2qQ_0 \qquad (5\text{-}32)$$

Also the second of (5-30) becomes (it being noted that z is small)

$$\frac{(Q_0 + q)(G_0 - Z_0 - z)}{\epsilon A} = \frac{Q_0(G_0 - Z_0)}{\epsilon A} + \frac{q(G_0 - Z_0)}{\epsilon A} - \frac{Q_0 z}{\epsilon A} = V \qquad (5\text{-}33)$$

On the basis of Eqs. (5-32) and (5-33), Eqs. (5-31) may be written in the rearranged form

$$M\ddot{z} + kz - \frac{Q_0 q}{\epsilon A} = \left[\frac{Q_0{}^2}{2\epsilon A} - kZ_0 \right]$$

$$q\frac{G_0 - Z_0}{\epsilon A} - \frac{Q_0 z}{\epsilon A} = \left[V - \frac{Q_0(G_0 - Z_0)}{\epsilon A} \right] \qquad (5\text{-}34)$$

But the force terms in the brackets on the right vanish, since they express the balance conditions which define Q_0 and Z_0 as required under quiescent conditions, by Eqs. (5-27) and (5-28). Thus

$$Q_0 = \frac{\epsilon A}{G_0 - Z_0} = C_0 V$$

$$Z_0 = \frac{Q_0{}^2}{2k\epsilon A} = \frac{C_0{}^2 V^2}{2k\epsilon A} \qquad (5\text{-}35)$$

where C_0 denotes the "quiescent" capacitance under conditions of applied V but no motion. The resulting incremental equations now have the form

$$M\ddot{z} + kz - \frac{Q_0}{\epsilon A} q = 0$$

$$-\frac{Q_0}{\epsilon A} z + \frac{q}{C_0} = 0 \qquad (5\text{-}36)$$

The solution of this set of equations will specify the motion of the hanging plate about the quiescent level. Attention is called to the fact that these expressions show the reciprocity of the mutual-interaction terms, since they have the same coefficients and both have negative signs.

An equivalent electrical analog of the incremental system may be drawn. This follows by making the following substitutions in notation:

$$M \rightarrow L \qquad z \rightarrow i_1$$
$$k \rightarrow \frac{1}{C} \qquad q \rightarrow \int i_2 \, dt$$
$$\frac{Q_0}{\epsilon A} \rightarrow \frac{1}{C_1}$$

With this change in notation, Eqs. (5-35) become

$$L \frac{di_1}{dt} + \frac{1}{C} \int i_1 \, dt - \frac{1}{C_1} \int i_2 \, dt = 0$$

$$- \frac{1}{C_1} \int i_1 \, dt + \frac{1}{C_0} \int i_2 \, dt = 0 \qquad (5\text{-}37)$$

The electrical network appropriate to these equations is given in Fig. 5-4.1-2.

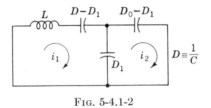

$$D \equiv \frac{1}{C}$$

FIG. 5-4.1-2

PROBLEMS

In each of the following problems it is required to write the energy functions, and from these, by an application of Lagrange's equations, the equilibrium equations are to be found. Carry out any other requirements of the problems.

5-1. The equilibrium equations are required for the following electrical network.

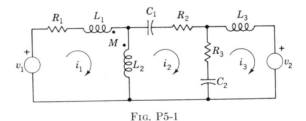

FIG. P5-1

5-2. The equilibrium equations are required for the electrical network shown.

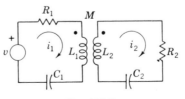

FIG. P5-2

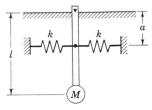

FIG. P5-3

5-3. Find the period of the pendulum, under the assumption of small amplitude oscillations.

5-4. A 6-lb weight is attached to the upper end of a flexible vertical rod. A horizontal force of 0.6 lb will deflect the upper end of the rod 1 in. The rod is 18 in. long. If the support at the lower end of the rod oscillates horizontally with an amplitude of 0.04 in. at a frequency of 54 cps, what is the amplitude of the oscillation of the weight? Neglect the weight of the rod.

5-5. A mass M is suspended from two identical springs, as shown, the angle α being that under static conditions.

    (a) Find the natural up-down frequency.

    (b) Find the natural right-left frequency.

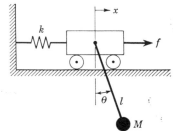

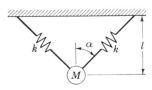

FIG. P5-5

FIG. P5-6

5-6. A simple pendulum which consists of a concentrated mass M and a weightless string of length l is mounted on a massless support which is elastically restrained by means of a spring, having a spring constant k, as shown.

5-7. An engine with an unbalanced rotor is mounted on a "vibration absorber." The equivalent system has the form illustrated. The unbalanced force is shown as that due to a mass M_1 that rotates with an angular velocity ω at a distance r from the axis of rotation. Find the electrical analogs of this mechanical system.

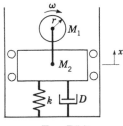

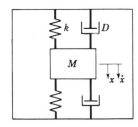

FIG. P5-7

FIG. P5-8

5-8. Delicate apparatus is sometimes packaged for shipping in a container suspended by springs within the packing case, as shown. If the container is constrained to vertical motion, the two springs are identical and the system is dropped vertically from h ft above the ground with no rebound.

    (a) Draw the electrical analogs of this system.

    (b) Find an expression for the displacement of the apparatus.

5-9. A linear accelerometer consists essentially of a spring-supported mass which is attached to a container. The entire assembly is attached to the body whose acceleration is to be measured. If the accelerometer is attached vertically to a body undergoing vertical motion:

(a) Find the differential equation relating the displacement of M with respect to the frame (the output indication will be proportional to this quantity).

(b) Specify the conditions required in order that this unit be an accelerometer.

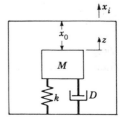

Fig. P5-9

5-10. (a) Find the energy functions for Example 5-4.1 when it is intended that the resulting Lagrange equations be in a form appropriate to a nodal analysis.

(b) Show that the resultant electromechanical force equation obtained from the energy functions in (a) is the same as that given by Eq. (5-27).

5-11. The equilibrium equations are required for the electromechanical system illustrated. Make the following assumptions: the permeability of the iron is infinite; fringing may be neglected; no friction exists between the iron structure and the hanging iron slug. Interpret the electrical equation.

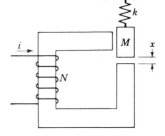

Fig. P5-11

5-12. Find the equations of motion for the electromagnet illustrated. The relationship between the current and the flux in the system is nonlinear and has the form shown. Choose the magnetic coenergy to be the electrical kinetic energy.

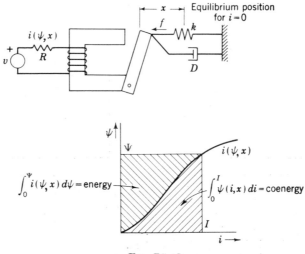

Fig. P5-12

6

Incremental-motion Transducers

The incremental-motion transducers with which we shall here be concerned constitute a class of energy-conversion devices in which a signal from one system transfers power to another system through a predominantly electric coupling field or a magnetic coupling field. This supposes that the signal either at the input port or at the output port will be in electrical form. The second port may be mechanical, acoustical, or otherwise in form.

6-1. Introduction. We shall distinguish between the incremental-motion transducer, which is to receive detailed treatment in this chapter,

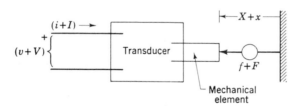

Fig. 6-1. The general features of transducers.

and gross-motion energy converters. The incremental-motion transducer can be represented by the general form illustrated graphically in Fig. 6-1. Illustrated in this diagram are the total variables $v + V$, $i + I$, $f + F$, $x + X$, etc., where the capital letters denote the no-signal quiescent or equilibrium values of the variables, and the small letters denote the incremental variations measured with respect to the quiescent or bias levels. In the case of gross-motion energy converters, the description is given in terms of variables which cannot be separated into two variables.

The incremental variables in the figure have the following meanings:

$v =$ instantaneous incremental potential at electric terminals of transducer (the reference positive potential is that given in the figure)

i = instantaneous incremental current into electric terminals of transducer, with the reference current direction as shown

$(v + V)(i + I)$ = total instantaneous power flow into transducer (the incremental power flow is measured with respect to the reference level VI)

x = instantaneous incremental displacement of mechanical element

$\dot{x}$ = velocity appropriate to the variable x (the positive direction is that corresponding to the motion of the mechanical element when the electrical power input is positive, and when there is no external mechanical restraint)

f = incremental force applied to mechanical element (positive force is in the reference positive direction, which is taken in the direction of positive velocity)

The capital letters specify the appropriate quiescent or reference levels about which the incremental variables are measured.

In the incremental-motion transducers here under survey, the signal information is contained either in the amplitude of the displacement or in the velocity. This means, of course, that a moving element exists as the input or output, this moving element and the associated stationary element defining the air gap in which the electromagnetic-coupling-field energy is stored.

Consider two representative transducers—the microphone and the loudspeaker. The microphone is an acoustic-electrical device; and the loudspeaker, the more common form of which is an electroacoustical device, is assumed to be familiar to the reader. In both devices, energy is transferred through the coupling field. In the case of the microphone, a mechanical motion that is caused by the acoustic wave power contained in the impinging sound is converted into an electrical signal. In the case of the loudspeaker, an electrical signal is converted into mechanical motion of a cone or diaphragm, which in turn is converted into acoustic power. In both cases an electromagnetic-field energy is stored in an air gap, and the energy conversion between the electrical and the mechanical variables occurs in this region of the transducer. The energy transfer is ordinarily small compared with the energy storage. Usually the mechanical displacement from the equilibrium position is small, although in a high-power loudspeaker this may not actually be so.

If the microphone is of the capacitor type, the stored energy of the coupling field is of the electric variety and this device is classed as an electric-field transducer. If the loudspeaker is of the magnetic type (and these are often loosely known as "dynamic" loudspeakers), the stored energy is principally in the magnetic field and the device is classed as a magnetic-field transducer.

The microphone and loudspeaker, and this is true of transducers in general, are information-transmitting devices. This requires that they possess a frequency bandwidth which is sufficient for the signals or information that they process; otherwise distortion results, and some of the information is lost. Moreover, they must be capable of meeting the energy requirements of the load or the sensitivity requirements of the source. Hence careful design is involved in achieving the desired characteristics.

6-2. Types of Transducers. There are four important types of magnetic-field transducers that will receive some attention. These are (1) singly excited, (2) multiply excited, (3) permanent-magnet, and (4) magnetostriction devices. There are two types of electric-field transducers that will be discussed. These are (1) singly excited capacitor-type and (2) piezoelectric devices.

Magnetic-field Transducers. A short description will be given of the four types mentioned above.

SINGLY EXCITED. The basic form of the device is illustrated in Fig. 6-2. As shown, the device includes a single winding and a spring-restrained armature. A reference current in the winding produces a constant magnetic field, and so a magnetic force that balances the spring force. As a result, the armature achieves a reference, or neutral, position. A signal current is superimposed on the reference current which will cause the armature to move in either direction from the quiescent position in accordance with the signal current. The microphone and loudspeaker are representative of this class of transducer, with a variety of other important transducers of this type being available.

MULTIPLY EXCITED. The multiply excited transducer consists, as the name implies, of more than one winding for providing excitation. The transducer of Fig. 6-2 would be converted into a multiply excited device (two windings) by adding a second winding. Often the reference current I_0 is introduced in one winding, which serves to maintain the armature in a quiescent position, and the signal is introduced in the current i in the second winding.

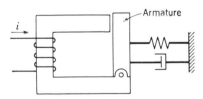

FIG. 6-2. Singly excited magnetic-field transducer.

A sketch of an elementary multiply excited magnetic system is given in Fig. 6-3.

Many of the electromechanical transducers of the magnetic type are of the multiply excited class, with one group of windings mounted on the stationary member and another group of windings on the movable member. The operation depends upon the fact that mechanical forces result when the magnetic-field energy changes owing to the motion of one group of windings with respect to the other group. Devices for denoting translational and rotational motion are often of this general type.

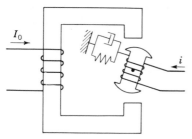

FIG. 6-3. The elements of a multiply excited magnetic transducer.

PERMANENT MAGNET. The situation in these transducers is not too different from that in the multiply excited types, except that now the reference field in the air gap is produced by a permanent magnet rather than by the presence of a reference winding. A second type of device is one in which the signal winding is mounted permanently, but the reluctance of the magnetic circuit is varied by an armature of magnetic material. Typical of these transducers in which the air gap changes are permanent-magnet loudspeakers and permanent magnetic displacement or velocity devices. The varying-reluctance devices include earphones and certain loudspeakers.

MAGNETOSTRICTIVE. This device, which finds its greatest use at sonic and ultrasonic frequencies, depends for its action on the magnetostrictive properties of certain magnetic materials, such as nickel and nickel alloys. Rods of these materials change their physical length when magnetized

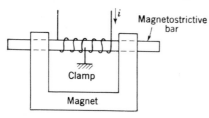

FIG. 6-4. A magnetostrictive magnetic-field transducer.

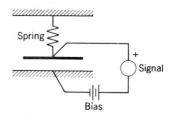

FIG. 6-5. The elements of a capacitor-type electric-field transducer.

along the length of the rod. Thus, in the device illustrated in Fig. 6-4, the signal winding produces a longitudinal magnetic field, and changes in current, and so in the magnetic field, result in the movement of the faces of the rod. The permanent magnet, or a reference winding on an iron core, will produce a magnetic bias in the rod in order to permit motion in accordance with the magnitude and sense of the signal current.

Electric-field Transducers. A variety of electric-field transducers are of considerable importance.

CAPACITOR. The electromechanical system which was examined in some detail as Example 5-4.1 is representative of this type of device, although a signal source must be provided, as illustrated in Fig. 6-5. The principal shortcoming of such a device is that the force possible in a reasonable sized unit is small, unless high potentials are employed. The capacitor microphone is representative of this class of device.

PIEZOELECTRIC. Such devices depend for their action on the property of piezoelectric materials that a change in applied electric field results in a

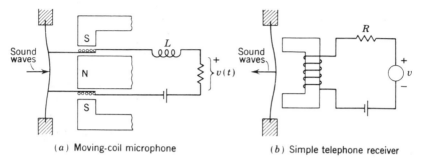

(a) Moving-coil microphone   (b) Simple telephone receiver

FIG. 6-6. Two practical magnetic transducers.

mechanical deformation of the crystal and, conversely, a change in the mechanical deformation of the crystal results in a changed surface charge. Transducers of the piezoelectric type include microphones, phonograph pickups, earphones, accelerometers. Often different crystals are cemented together to improve the mechanical deformation characteristics.

6-3. Magnetic-field Transducer—Singly Excited. It is desired to examine a specific example of a singly excited magnetic-field transducer. Typical of this class of device are the moving-coil microphone and also the telephone receiver. The essential features of these devices are illustrated in Fig. 6-6. Note that, while these two examples differ somewhat in detail, they are substantially equivalent systems.

A diagrammatic representation of the essential elements of the simple telephone receiver is given in Fig. 6-7. The varying signal, represented

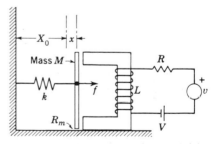

FIG. 6-7. The equivalent representation of a telephone receiver.

by the generator v, results in a changing current in the magnetic excitation winding. As a result, the diaphragm, which is made of magnetic material, is caused to vibrate, thereby translating the mechanical displacements into sound-pressure waves. Two effects must be considered, the electrical and the mechanical.

Owing to the manner of mounting of the diaphragm, a mechanical displacement is equivalent to the motion of the mass M in Fig. 6-7, with an elastic restoring force that is represented by the spring k. The damping of the motion of the diaphragm by the air cushion between it and the rest of the confined structure is represented by the damping constant R_m. The mechanical displacement of the diaphragm is caused by a changing signal current, and this provides the changing force between the electromagnet and the diaphragm.

In so far as the electrical circuit is concerned, it consists of the d-c polarizing potential source V, which supplies a current to the electromagnet winding through a resistor, as illustrated, plus a signal source v. As the diaphragm vibrates owing to the signal source, the resulting inductance of the electromagnet changes instantaneously, owing to the change in the reluctance of the magnetic path. The resulting vibration of the diaphragm is assumed to be a mechanical reproduction of the applied signal v. But most of the reluctance of the magnetic circuit is in the air gap rather than in the iron. The self-inductance of the electromagnet can be assumed to vary as

$$L = L_0 + (X - 0)\frac{\partial L}{\partial X} = L_0 + L_0'X \qquad (6\text{-}1)$$

where X denotes the displacement of the diaphragm from the reference position and $L_0' = \partial L/\partial X$. Note that this expression is simply the first two terms of a Taylor's-series expansion for the inductance relative to the reference position X.

Two generalized coordinates are used to describe the system: the total mechanical displacement X of the mass M, and the total instantaneous current I through the electromagnetic winding. The appropriate energy functions of the system are

$$\mathfrak{I} = \tfrac{1}{2}M\dot{X}^2 + \tfrac{1}{2}LI^2 \qquad (6\text{-}2)$$

which includes the kinetic energy due to the mechanical motion of the diaphragm and the electrical energy stored in the inductor;

$$U = \tfrac{1}{2}kX^2 \qquad (6\text{-}3)$$

which specifies the energy stored in the spring; and

$$\mathfrak{F} = \tfrac{1}{2}(R_m\dot{X}^2 + RI^2) \qquad (6\text{-}4)$$

which takes into account the dissipation, both mechanical and electrical.

A Lagrange equation is now written for each of the generalized coordinates. The resulting expressions are

$$\begin{aligned} M\ddot{X} - \tfrac{1}{2}L_0'I^2 + kX + R_m\dot{X} &= f \\ L\dot{I} + L_0'I\dot{X} + RI &= v + V \end{aligned} \qquad (6\text{-}5)$$

In these expressions:

1. The current I is conveniently written in the form of the steady part I_0 and the varying part i, such that

$$I = I_0 + i$$

2. The displacement X is written as the sum of the quiescent or average displacement X_0 and the variation from it, x, such that

$$X = X_0 + x$$

Equations (6-5) become

$$M\ddot{x} - \tfrac{1}{2}L_0'(I_0 + i)^2 + k(X_0 + x) + R_m\dot{x} = f$$
$$L\dot{i} + L_0'(I_0 + i)\dot{x} + R(I_0 + i) = v + V \qquad (6\text{-}6)$$

since both I_0 and X_0 are independent of the time. It is now assumed that the varying current i is much smaller than the quiescent value I_0. Then the term involving $(I_0 + i)^2$ becomes approximately

$$\tfrac{1}{2}L_0'(I_0 + i)^2 \doteq \tfrac{1}{2}L_0'(I_0^2 + 2I_0 i) \qquad (6\text{-}7)$$

Equations (6-6) are now written in the form

$$M\ddot{x} - L_0'I_0 i + kx + R_m\dot{x} = f + (\tfrac{1}{2}L_0'I_0^2 - kX_0)$$
$$L_{00}\dot{i} + L_0'I_0\dot{x} + Ri = v + (V - RI_0) \qquad (6\text{-}8)$$

where
$$L_{00} = L_0 + L_0'X_0$$

and where higher-order terms are neglected.

The force terms in the parentheses vanish, as these express the balances which define I_0 and X_0. The resulting equations then become

$$M\ddot{x} + R_m\dot{x} + kx - L_0'I_0 i = f$$
$$L_{00}\dot{i} + Ri + L_0'I_0\dot{x} = v \qquad (6\text{-}9)$$

These are the final differential equations which specify the incremental motion of the system under review. Attention is called to the fact that reciprocity of the mutual-interaction terms does not hold in this set of equations, since the signs of the interaction terms are not the same.

It is of considerable interest to find both the direct and the inverse analogs of these equations. First we consider the direct analog. To find this, define the quantities

$$L_0'I_0\dot{x} = v_2$$
$$i = -i_s$$

Then the first of Eqs. (6-9) becomes

$$\frac{M}{L_0'I_0}\frac{dv_2}{dt} + \frac{R_m}{L_0'I_0}v_2 + \frac{k}{L_0'I_0}\int v_2\,dt = f - L_0'I_0 i_s \qquad (6\text{-}10)$$

and the second equation becomes

$$L_{00}\frac{di_s}{dt} + Ri_s - v_2 = v$$

Now define the following quantities

$$C' = \frac{M}{(L'_0 I_0)^2} \qquad G' = \frac{R_m}{(L'_0 I_0)^2} \qquad L' = \frac{(L'_0 I_0)^2}{k} \qquad i_2 = \frac{f}{L'_0 I_0}$$

Equations (6-10) now become

$$C' \frac{dv_2}{dt} + G'v_2 + \frac{1}{L'} \int v_2 \, dt = i_2 - i_s$$

$$L_{00} \frac{di_s}{dt} + Ri_s = v + v_2 \tag{6-11}$$

The electrical network for which these are the equations is given in Fig. 6-8. Observe therefore that the analog circuit for the transducer itself, excluding the external excitation source, is that given in Fig. 6-9.

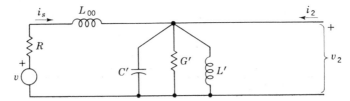

FIG. 6-8. The electrical analog of the telephone receiver.

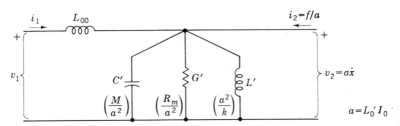

FIG. 6-9. The analog circuit for a singly excited magnetic-circuit transducer, according to the direct analog.

There is some interest in examining the analog circuit for this transducer according to the inverse analog. To find this, again refer to Eqs. (6-9), and define the new variables

$$i_2 = \frac{L'_0 I_0}{R} \dot{x}$$

and multiply the first of Eqs. (6-9) by $R/L'_0 I_0$. Now define the following quantities:

$$L_2 = M \left(\frac{R}{L'_0 I_0}\right)^2 \qquad R_2 = R_m \left(\frac{R}{L'_0 I_0}\right)^2$$

$$C_2 = \frac{1}{k} \left(\frac{L'_0 I_0}{R}\right)^2 \qquad v_2 = \frac{R}{L'_0 I_0} f$$

$$\left.\begin{array}{c} \\ \\ \\ \\ \\ \\ \end{array}\right\} \tag{6-12}$$

The equations may now be written in the form

$$L_2 \frac{di_2}{dt} + R_2 i_2 + \frac{1}{C_2} \int i_2 \, dt - Ri = v_2$$

$$L_{00} \frac{di}{dt} + Ri + Ri_2 = v \tag{6-13}$$

These equations represent a two-loop network, as shown in Fig. 6-10. There is need, however, for the special coupling element which is dictated by the mutual terms. Such a special element is known as a gyrator.[1] The gyrator has achieved practical form as a microwave device, but has not yet attained practical realization as a common network element.

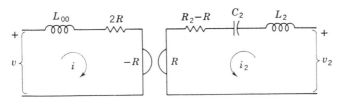

FIG. 6-10. The analog circuit for a singly excited magnetic-circuit transducer, according to the inverse analog.

Observe that the gyrostatic coupling terms appear only in the inverse analog, and not in the direct analog. Since the gyrator as a network element does exist, either analog may theoretically be used. However, owing to the rather special characteristics of this device, it is probably more desirable to adopt Fig. 6-9, the direct analog, as the most suitable for the magnetic-circuit transducer, as it leads to an easier network to analyze or to construct, if analog-computer studies were to be made.

It is desired to examine the energy-flow and energy-conversion process that has taken place in the transducer under study. This is directly accomplished by examining the interaction terms in Eqs. (6-6). Suppose that the mechanical element is allowed to move with a velocity $\dot{x}$, while the current i is maintained constant. Then, losses being neglected, the rate of electrical energy input is, from the second of Eqs. (6-6),

$$\text{Rate of electrical energy input} = v(I_0 + i) = L_0'(I_0 + i)^2 \dot{x}$$

Correspondingly, from the first of Eqs. (6-6), the rate of energy conversion to mechanical form is

$$f\dot{x} = \tfrac{1}{2} L_0'(I_0 + i)^2 \dot{x}$$

The stored magnetic energy is, of course, just the known expression

$$W_m = \int f \, dx = \tfrac{1}{2}(I_0 + i)^2 \int \frac{\partial L}{\partial x} \, dx = \tfrac{1}{2} L(I_0 + i)^2$$

[1] B. D. H. Tellegen, The Gyrator—A New Electric Network Element, *Philips Research Repts.*, **3**: 81 (1948).

Observe, therefore, that the rate of electrical energy input is twice the rate at which the energy is converted to mechanical form. Thus, half the electrical energy input is stored in the magnetic field of the transducer, the remaining half being converted to mechanical energy, in accordance with the 50-50 rule discussed in Chap. 2. Note also, that upon expanding the above expressions, the first terms become of the form $L_0' I_0^2 \dot{x}$, which denotes the energy stored in the mechanical spring, or compliance; the terms of the form $L_0' I_0 i \dot{x}$ (for negligible higher-order terms) are those which represent the converted energy which is able to do work on the mechanical load.

6-4. Multiply Excited Magnetic-field Transducer. The general approach to the study of a transducer with n independently excited

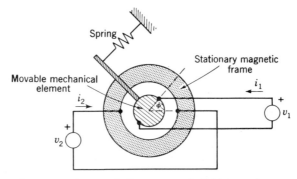

FIG. 6-11. A two-winding magnetic-field transducer.

windings is generally similar to that followed for the singly excited case. However, owing to larger numbers of generalized coordinates that exist, there is a higher degree of complexity, with one Lagrange equation for each generalized coordinate. In general, there is one Lagrange equation for each independent current plus one for the mechanical coordinate.

Consider the multiply excited transducer illustrated in Fig. 6-11. Coil 1 is the input winding; coil 2 is the constant-current excitation winding. The torque developed in this transducer movable element is countered by the spring, which is extended by an increasing torque. It is desired to analyze this device and to find an analog circuit which relates the potential and current at the input winding terminals with the displacement φ and torque T of the mechanical element. The self-inductances of all windings, and the mutual inductance between windings, not including the No. 1 winding, are assumed independent of the displacement φ.

The system kinetic energy may be written directly as

$$\mathfrak{I} = \tfrac{1}{2}J\dot{\varphi}^2 + \tfrac{1}{2}L_{11}i_1{}^2 + L_{12}i_1i_2 + \tfrac{1}{2}L_{22}i_2{}^2$$

and the potential energy is

$$U = \tfrac{1}{2}k\varphi^2$$

$$(6\text{-}14)$$

where J = inertia of mechanical element
φ = angular displacement of mechanical element
k = spring constant of restoring spring
L_{mn} = inductance between the mth and nth windings (if a multiply excited transducer with more than two windings is under survey)

For convenience, it will be assumed that electrical and mechanical dissipation may be neglected.

The results of writing a Lagrange equation for each coordinate are the equations

$$\frac{d}{dt}(L_{11}i_1 + L_{12}i_2) - v_1 = 0$$

$$\frac{d}{dt}(L_{21}i_1 + L_{22}i_2) - v_2 = 0$$

$$\frac{d}{dt}(J\dot{\varphi}) - i_1i_2\frac{\partial L_{12}}{\partial \varphi} + k\varphi = T$$

$$(6\text{-}15)$$

When expanded and rewritten, these expressions become

$$L_{11}\frac{di_1}{dt} + i_2\frac{\partial L_{12}}{\partial \varphi}\frac{d\varphi}{dt} = v_1$$

$$L_{21}\frac{di_1}{dt} + i_1\frac{\partial L_{21}}{\partial \varphi}\frac{d\varphi}{dt} = v_2$$

$$J\frac{d^2\varphi}{dt^2} + k\varphi - i_1i_2\frac{\partial L_{12}}{\partial \varphi} = T$$

$$(6\text{-}16)$$

A comparison of these equations with Eqs. (6-9) for the singly excited transducer reveals that they have the same form. Therefore, by defining the set of analogous quantities in the same manner as in Eqs. (6-10), namely,

$$C' = \frac{J}{\left(i_2\dfrac{\partial L_{12}}{\partial \varphi}\right)^2} \qquad L' = \left(i_2\frac{\partial L_{12}}{\partial \varphi}\right)^2\frac{1}{k} \qquad i = \frac{T}{\left(i_2\dfrac{\partial L_{12}}{\partial \varphi}\right)} \qquad v = \left(i_2\frac{\partial L_{12}}{\partial \varphi}\right)\dot{\varphi}$$

$$(6\text{-}17)$$

the input-output equations become

$$\frac{J}{\left(i_2 \dfrac{\partial L_{12}}{\partial \varphi}\right)} \frac{dv}{dt} + \frac{k}{\left(i_2 \dfrac{\partial L_{12}}{\partial \varphi}\right)} \int v \, dt - \left(i_2 \frac{\partial L_{12}}{\partial \varphi}\right) i_1 = T$$

$$L_{11} \frac{di_1}{dt} + \left(i_2 \frac{\partial L_{12}}{\partial \varphi}\right) \dot{\varphi} = v_1$$

(6-18)

These may be represented by the analog circuit equations

$$C' \frac{dv}{dt} + \frac{1}{L'} \int v \, dt - i_1 = i$$

$$L_{11} \frac{di_1}{dt} + v = v_1$$

(6-19)

The analog network specified by these equations is that illustrated in Fig. 6-12. Observe that the same lack of reciprocity of the mutual-interaction terms exists in the present case as in the singly excited case.

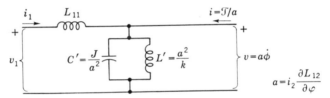

FIG. 6-12. The analog circuit for a multiply excited transducer.

Attention is called to the fact that the analog circuit of Fig. 6-12 is valid only when the electromechanical-conversion coefficient a is a constant over the operating range. This result may be achieved by restricting the displacements to small angles. It may also be achieved by designing the magnetic circuit to make $\partial L_{12}/\partial \varphi$ constant. It is of some interest to note that the so-called synchro, or selsyn, has been so designed that this restriction has been met. Also, a number of rotating electrical machines of the single-phase and the polyphase types have such a geometry that the conditions herein specified are approximated. However, in rotating machinery the mutual inductances vary sinusoidally with displacement, whence the conversion coefficient a is no longer a constant, and such devices cannot be treated by the analog technique.

To evaluate the rate of electrical energy input to winding 1 for a change of displacement φ at constant current, one proceeds directly from the first of Eqs. (6-16). The result, by maintaining i_1 constant during the displacement, is

$$v_1 i_1 = \left(i_2 \frac{\partial L_{12}}{\partial \varphi}\right) \dot{\varphi} i_1$$

Correspondingly, the rate of energy conversion into mechanical form is

$$T\dot\varphi = -i_1\left(i_2\,\frac{\partial L_{12}}{\partial\varphi}\right)\dot\varphi$$

Thus the energy to winding 1 is all converted into mechanical form. However, during the process, there is also an electrical energy input to winding 2, of an amount

$$v_2 i_2 = \left(i_1\,\frac{\partial L_{12}}{\partial\varphi}\right)\dot\varphi i_2$$

which is just equal to the energy input rate to winding 1. Thus the total electrical energy input is twice that converted to mechanical form, with half the energy being stored in the magnetic field.

6-5. Permanent-magnet Transducer. The study of transducers which incorporate permanent magnets in their structure is through the use of

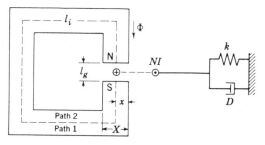

Fig. 6-13. A permanent-magnet transducer.

field quantities, owing to the special properties of the magnetic materials. That is, the appropriate energy functions will be expressed in terms of field quantities. Except for this feature, the procedure in analysis will be generally similar to that employed in discussing the transducers in the foregoing.

Consider the permanent-magnet transducer illustrated in Fig. 6-13, which comprises a coil of N turns which is part of a mechanical assembly which is free to move incrementally in the field of the permanent magnet when a current I is established in the coil. We wish first to examine the effect of the current in the coil on the magnetic circuit. This requires that we first examine some of the features of permanent-magnet materials.

A study of the characteristics of permanent magnets requires consideration of the hysteresis loop of the material. Actually, it is the section of the major hysteresis loop in the second quadrant of the BH diagram that is of particular interest. This portion of the curve is referred to as the demagnetization curve and is, of course, a characteristic of the material. Such a representative curve is given as $B_R a H_c$ of Fig. 6-14. It is usually desirable that permanent magnets have a high remanence B_R, but the coercive force H_c must be large also, so that the magnet is not easily demagnetized. That is, the material of the permanent magnet is of the so-called magnetically hard type.

In most applications, it is desired that magnetic stability prevail, in order that the magnetic characteristics may be maintained under normal operation conditions. Manufacturers and instrument makers often artificially age or mature their magnets by subjecting them to a temperature cycle. Of course, a natural aging process over several years is equally effective. In addition, magnetic stability is obtained generally by partially demagnetizing the material. Refer again to Fig. 6-14, which shows the effect of applying a negative external magnetic field corresponding to point a. This could be accomplished by placing the magnetic

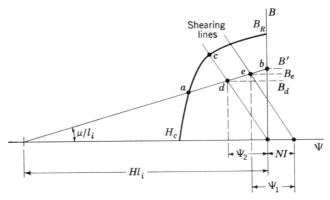

Fig. 6-14. The demagnetization curve for the permanent-magnet material.

material within a coil carrying a current. Thus the effect of the negative external field is to cause the material to move to point a on the demagnetizing curve. When the negative magnetizing field is removed, the flux density moves to point b. Successive applications and removal of the negative magnetizing field are accompanied by the operating point moving from point b to a and back along a minor hysteresis loop, which is shown in Fig. 6-14 as the straight line ab. Attention is called to the slope of the line ab, which is substantially the same as the slope of the demagnetizing curve at B_R, regardless of where point a is located on the original curve.

If there is no air gap and if the closed magnetic circuit is magnetized to some saturation value, then, with the removal of the magnetizing current, the flux density in the magnetic-core material is equal to the remanence B_R. If, however, a narrow air gap exists in the magnet circuit, the flux density has a smaller value, say the point c, which lies somewhere on the demagnetization curve, as shown in Fig. 6-14. To find the point c, it is necessary only to calculate the magnetic potential drop across the air gap. This is done by a direct application of the Ampère line integral, say around the dashed path of Fig. 6-13. Now, because no external magnetizing source is applied, $F = NI = 0$ and therefore

$$H_i l_i + H_g l_g = 0$$

or

$$H_i l_i = -H_g l_g \qquad (6\text{-}20)$$

Thus H_i and H_g are in opposite directions. If leakage is neglected, then B is uniform around the circuit. Also, if fringing in the air gap is neglected, then Eq. (6-20) may be written in the form

$$\frac{\mu_0 H_g}{H_i} = \frac{B}{H_i} = -\mu_0 \frac{l_i}{l_g} \qquad (6\text{-}21)$$

The ratio B/H_i, which specifies the permeability of the iron, gives the slope of a line called the *shearing line*, as shown in Fig. 6-14. The

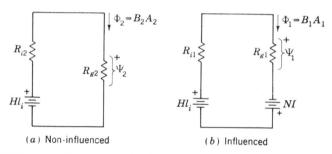

(a) Non-influenced   (b) Influenced

FIG. 6-15. The equivalent magnetic circuits of the two portions of the transducer.

intersection of this line with the demagnetization curve specifies the point c.

As already mentioned, it ordinarily would be desired that the permanent magnet be stabilized. This requires that a moderate demagnetizing field be applied to the iron, moving the operation point of the iron to a on the demagnetization curve. On removing the field, the iron moves to point d on the shearing line along the minor hysteresis loop. Now, just so long as any differences of H no greater than the values between points a and d are applied to the magnetic circuit, the iron will always return to d.

Return now to considerations of the permanent-magnet transducer illustrated in Fig. 6-13. When a current I is established in the coil, the magnetic circuit is influenced in the manner illustrated in Fig. 6-15. Figure 6-15a shows the equivalent magnetic circuit of that portion of the structure to the left of the broken line, whereas Fig. 6-15b shows the equivalent magnetic circuit of the portion of the structure to the right of this line. The differences of magnetic potential across the two portions of the gap are denoted as Ψ_1 and Ψ_2, respectively.

The energy that is stored in the transducer is that stored in the two portions of the field, which are specified by the distances $X - x$ and x, respectively. The permanent magnet itself can be considered as a source of magnetic potential, the internal reluctance of which is specified by $R_i = l_i/\mu A_i$, where l_i is again the mean length of the core, and where μ is the permeability of the magnetic material. The value of μ is specified by the minor hysteresis loop, which is approximated by the line ab, and is given by the relation $\mu = B/H$ of Fig. 6-14.

Also shown in Fig. 6-14 is the air-gap shearing line of the noninfluenced part of the air gap. The corresponding shearing line of the influenced part of the air gap is obtained by shifting the air-gap line by NI ampere-turns. The operating points are d and e, respectively. It is interesting to note from this figure that the flux densities B_d and B_e are not markedly different from each other; and the permanent magnet therefore tends to be a source of constant flux density in a magnetic circuit. That is, owing to the contribution of the magnetic potential by the coil, the permanent magnet will then tend to reduce its contribution to the magnetic potential in such a way as to maintain the flux density nearly constant. Conversely, a coil, with its changing current, produces a constant magnetic potential for a given current.

The magnetic energy in the magnetic field is the sum of that stored in each part of the magnetic material and the air gap. For unit depth, the energy stored in the portion of the field specified by $X - x$, which is the uninfluenced portion of the field, is

$$W_2 = \frac{1}{2}\frac{F^2}{R_i + R_g} = \frac{\frac{1}{2}(Hl_i)^2}{l_i/\mu_i(X - x) + l_g/\mu_0(X - x)}$$

or
$$W_2 = \frac{1}{2}(Hl_i)^2(X - x)\frac{1}{l_i/\mu_i + l_g/\mu_0} \qquad (6\text{-}22)$$

The stored energy in the influenced portion of the magnetic circuit is

$$W_1 = \frac{\frac{1}{2}(Hl_i + Ni)^2}{l_i/\mu_i x + l_g/\mu_0 x} = \frac{1}{2}(Hl_i + Ni)^2\, x \frac{1}{l_i/\mu_i + l_g/\mu_0}$$

which is
$$W_1 = \frac{1}{2}(H^2l_i^2 + 2Hl_iNi + N^2i^2)\, x \frac{1}{l_i/\mu_i + l_g/\mu_0} \qquad (6\text{-}23)$$

The total energy in the magnetic field is the sum of the foregoing expressions and becomes

$$W = W_1 + W_2 = \frac{1}{2}(H^2l_i^2 x + 2Hl_iNi x + N^2i^2 x)\frac{1}{l_i/\mu_i + l_g/\mu_0}$$

Note that the second factor is just the permeance of the magnetic circuit per unit cross-sectional area, which is written as

$$\mathcal{P} = \frac{1}{\mathcal{R}} = \frac{1}{l_i/\mu_i + l_g/\mu_0} \tag{6-24}$$

Hence the final expression for the energy stored in the magnetic field is

$$W = \frac{1}{2}(H^2 l_i^2 x + 2H l_i N i x + N^2 i^2 x)\mathcal{P} \tag{6-25}$$

The system kinetic energy may be written in the form

$$\mathfrak{I} = W + \frac{1}{2}M\dot{x}^2 \tag{6-26}$$

where due account is taken of the mechanical energy of the moving mass assembly. The potential energy for a system which provides a restoration to a position of equilibrium about which the incremental motion is to occur is

$$U = \frac{1}{2}kx^2 \tag{6-27}$$

For convenience, it will be assumed that electrical and mechanical dissipation may be neglected.

The results of writing a Lagrange equation for each coordinate are

$$\frac{d}{dt}\frac{1}{2}(2H l_i N x + 2N^2 i x)\mathcal{P} = v$$
$$\frac{d}{dt}(M\dot{x}) - \frac{1}{2}(2H l_i N i + N^2 i^2)\mathcal{P} + kx = f \tag{6-28}$$

When expanded and rewritten, these expressions become

$$N^2 x \mathcal{P} \frac{di}{dt} + (H l_i + N i)\mathcal{P} N \dot{x} = v$$
$$M\ddot{x} + kx - (H l_i + \frac{1}{2}N i)\mathcal{P} N i = f \tag{6-29}$$

Observe that, in order to establish a linear transducer, it is necessary that the control ampere-turns Ni be small compared with $H l_i$, the internal magnetic potential difference of the permanent magnet. Subject to these conditions, the equations reduce to the following:

$$N^2 \mathcal{P} i \dot{x} + N^2 x \mathcal{P} \frac{di}{dt} + H l_i \mathcal{P} N \dot{x} = v$$
$$M\ddot{x} + kx - H l_i \mathcal{P} N i = f \tag{6-30}$$

Note also that the quantity $H l_i \mathcal{P}$ is the flux density B_2, which is the value of the flux density in the noninfluenced portion of the air gap. Thus

$$H l_i \mathcal{P} = B_2$$

Also, $N^2 x \mathcal{P}$ is the self-inductance of the coil displaced x into the air gap, or

$$N^2 x \mathcal{P} = L$$

Then Eqs. (6-10) become

$$L\frac{di}{dt} + B_2N\dot{x} = v$$

$$M\ddot{x} + kx - B_2Ni = f$$

(6-31)

In these equations the term $a_2N\dot{x}$ is the familiar expression for the motional (Blv') emf; also B_2Ni is the familiar (Bli) expression for the force on a current in a magnetic field.   Note also the same lack of reciprocity of the mutual-interaction terms as for the other magnetic-field transducers.

Equations (6-31) have precisely the same form as Eqs. (6-9) and (6-16) for the singly excited and the multiply excited transducers.   By defining the quantities

$$C' = \frac{M}{(B_2N)^2} \qquad L' = \frac{(B_2N)^2}{k} \qquad i_2 = \frac{f}{B_2N} \qquad v_2 = B_2N\dot{x}$$

we may show, following the manner of Eqs. (6-10) and (6-19), that the analog circuit of the permanent-magnet transducer is that illustrated in Fig. 6-16.

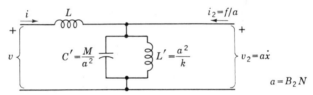

FIG. 6-16. The analog circuit of the permanent-magnet transducer.

The energy-flow aspects of the device can readily be checked by reference to Eqs. (6-29).   Thus, the rate of electrical energy input for a change in displacement x, while the current i is maintained constant, is

$$vi = (Hl_i + Ni)\mathcal{P}N\dot{x}i$$

Correspondingly, the power converted to mechanical form is

$$f\dot{x} = -(Hl_i + \tfrac{1}{2}Ni)\mathcal{P}Ni\dot{x}$$

Observe that the quantity $Hl_i\mathcal{P}Ni\dot{x}$ involves the characteristics of the permanent magnet.   Hence the first terms in both the foregoing expressions may be interpreted to mean that the permanent magnet stores and supplies an equal amount of energy.   The resulting terms show that the electrical power supplied is twice that converted into mechanical form, with the remaining half of the electrical energy being stored in the magnetic field.

6-6. Electric-field Transducer—Singly Excited. The electric-field transducer to be examined in some detail is the conventional capacitor microphone.   A diagrammatic representation of the essential elements of this device is given in Fig. 6-17a; the equivalent representation is given in Fig. 6-17b. The diaphragm translates the impinging sound-pressure waves into mechanical displacements, as for the singly excited magnetic-field transducer of Sec. 6-3. Owing to the manner of mounting of the diaphragm, a displacement caused by the impinging sound-pressure wave is translated into a mechanical displacement, which is equivalent to the motion of the mass M, with an elastic restoring force that is represented by the spring k. The damping of the motion of the diaphragm by the air cushion between it and the back plate is represented by the damping constant R_m.

In so far as the electrical circuit is concerned, it consists of the d-c polarizing potential source V, which supplies charge to the capacitor

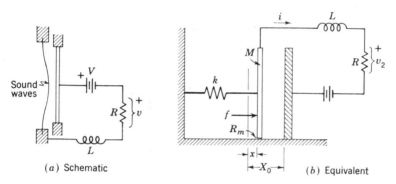

(a) Schematic   (b) Equivalent

Fig. 6-17. A capacitor microphone.

that is formed by the diaphragm and the backing plate through a resistor and inductor, as illustrated. As the diaphragm vibrates, the capacitance of the microphone varies instantaneously, causing a current variation in the electrical circuit. The resulting output potential $v(t)$ is assumed to be an electrical reproduction of the sound waves. As a first approximation, the capacitance is given by the expression

$$C = \frac{\epsilon A}{G_0 - X} \tag{6-32}$$

where X denotes the displacement of the diaphragm from the equilibrium position G_0 (the normal undisplaced position when there is no polarizing potential) due to the impinging sound-pressure waves, where A is the effective cross-sectional area of the capacitor, and where ϵ is the permittivity of the air in the space between the capacitor plates.

Two generalized coordinates are used to describe the system; the mechanical displacement X from the rest position of the mass M, and the total instantaneous charge Q on either of the two plates. The appropriate energy functions of the system are readily found. The kinetic energy includes the mechanical energy due to the motion of the diaphragm and the energy in the inductor,

$$\mathfrak{I} = \tfrac{1}{2}M\dot{X}^2 + \tfrac{1}{2}LI^2$$

The potential energy is specified with respect to the rest position G_0 and is

$$U = \tfrac{1}{2}kX^2 + \frac{Q^2}{2C}$$

This becomes, by combining it with the above expression for the capacitance,

$$U = \tfrac{1}{2}kX^2 + \frac{1}{2}\frac{G_0 - X}{\epsilon A}Q^2$$

Also, the dissipation energy function is

$$\mathfrak{F} = \tfrac{1}{2}R_m\dot{X}^2 + \tfrac{1}{2}RI^2$$

A Lagrange equation is now written for each of the generalized coordinates. The following equations result:

$$\frac{d}{dt}(M\dot{X}) + kX - \frac{1}{2}\frac{Q^2}{\epsilon A} + R_m\dot{X} = f$$

$$\frac{d}{dt}(L\dot{Q}) + \frac{G_0 - X}{\epsilon A}Q + R\dot{Q} = V \tag{6-33}$$

These are expanded and rewritten in the form

$$M\ddot{X} + R_m\dot{X} + kX - \frac{1}{2}\frac{Q^2}{\epsilon A} = f$$

$$L\ddot{Q} + R\dot{Q} + Q\frac{G_0 - X}{\epsilon A} = V \tag{6-34}$$

The charge Q is conveniently written in the form of a steady part Q_0 and a varying part q, or

$$\left. \begin{array}{l} Q = Q_0 + q \\ X = X_0 + x \end{array} \right\} \tag{6-35}$$

Also write

in which the displacement X is conveniently written as the sum of a steady-state displacement X_0, the displacement under electromechanical equilibrium conditions due to the polarizing potential V, and a variation x relative to this equilibrium value. Also, it will be assumed that the motion of the diaphragm is small, so that quantities of the second order, such as q^2, qx, etc., may be neglected. Then we have

$$Q^2 = (Q_0 + q)^2 \doteq Q_0^2 + 2Q_0q$$

and Eqs. (6-34) become

$$M\ddot{X} + R_m\dot{X} + kX - \frac{1}{2}\frac{Q_0^2 + 2Q_0 q}{\epsilon A} = f$$

$$L\ddot{Q} + R\dot{Q} + Q\frac{G_0 - X}{\epsilon A} = V \qquad (6\text{-}36)$$

Now, combining with the designated expressions for Q and X, and rearranging terms, we have

$$M\ddot{x} + R_m\dot{x} + kx - \frac{Q_0}{\epsilon A}q = f + \left[\frac{Q_0^2}{2\epsilon A} - kX_0\right]$$

$$L\ddot{q} + R\dot{q} + q\frac{G_0 - X_0}{\epsilon A} - \frac{Q_0}{\epsilon A}x = \left[V - \frac{Q_0(G_0 - X_0)}{\epsilon A}\right] \qquad (6\text{-}37)$$

The force terms in the brackets on the right vanish, since they express the equilibrium conditions which define Q_0 and X_0. That is,

$$X_0 = \frac{Q_0^2}{2k\epsilon A}$$

$$Q_0 = C_0 V = \frac{\epsilon A}{G_0 - X_0} V$$

The resulting expressions become

$$M\ddot{x} + R_m\dot{x} + kx - \frac{Q_0}{\epsilon A}q = f$$

$$L\ddot{q} + R\dot{q} + \frac{q}{C_0} - \frac{Q_0}{\epsilon A}x = 0 \qquad (6\text{-}38)$$

Observe in the present case that the final set of equations for the singly excited electric-field transducer indicates the reciprocity of the mutual-interaction terms, since they have the same coefficients and both have negative signs. This makes the electric-field transducer unlike the magnetic-field transducer, which did not satisfy the condition of reciprocity. It will be shown in Sec. 6-7 that these are general properties of the two classes of transducers.

To find the inverse analog circuit of the singly excited electric-field transducer, the following quantities are defined:

$$\frac{Q_0 x}{\epsilon A} = \frac{q_2}{C_0} \qquad a = \frac{Q_0 C_0}{\epsilon A} = \frac{Q_0}{G_0 - X_0}$$

$$L_2 = \frac{M}{a^2} \qquad R_2 = \frac{R_m}{a^2} \qquad C_2 = \frac{a^2}{k} \qquad v_2 = \frac{f}{a} \qquad (6\text{-}39)$$

Equations (6-38) may now be written in the form

$$L_2\frac{di_2}{dt} + R_2 i_2 + \frac{q_2}{C_2} - \frac{q}{C_0} = v_2$$

$$L_i\frac{di}{dt} + Ri + \frac{q}{C_0} - \frac{q_2}{C_0} = 0 \qquad (6\text{-}40)$$

These equations specify the two-loop network shown in Fig. 6-18. Observe that in the analog circuit the capacitance C_d appears in the second loop, with $C_d = C_2 C_0/(C_0 - C_2)$, in order to satisfy the requirements of Eqs. (6-40). For C_d to be positive, it is required that

$$C_0 - C_2 = \frac{\epsilon A}{G_0 - X_0} - \frac{1}{k}\left(\frac{Q_0}{G_0 - X_0}\right)^2 = \frac{\epsilon A}{(G_0 - X_0)^2}(G_0 - 3X_0) > 0$$

This is always satisfied in practice.

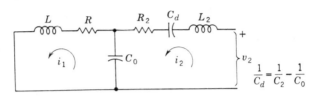

FIG. 6-18. The indirect analog circuit for the capacitor microphone.

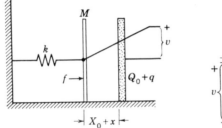

FIG. 6-19. A singly excited electric-field transducer.

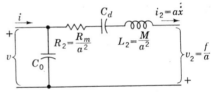

FIG. 6-20. The analog circuit for the electric-field transducer of Fig. 6-19.

The energy-flow balance of the device is examined with the aid of Eqs. (6-35). The electrical energy input for a change in displacement, while the charge q is maintained constant, is

$$V(Q_0 + q) = \frac{(Q_0 + q)^2}{\epsilon A}(G_0 - X_0 - x)$$

Correspondingly, the energy converted to mechanical form is

$$\int_0^t f\dot{x}\,dt = \int_0^t -\frac{1}{2}\frac{(Q_0 + q)^2}{\epsilon A}\dot{x}\,dt = -\frac{1}{2}\frac{(Q_0 + q)^2}{\epsilon A}(G_0 - X_0 - x)$$

As expected, for a displacement made at constant charge, one-half the energy supplied by the electric source is converted into mechanical form, the remaining half of the energy being stored in the electric field of the transducer.

A modification of the present problem which leads to substantially the same equations is illustrated in Fig. 6-19. In this case the excitation is provided electrically, with the diaphragm vibrations being a consequence of the excitation. This is the situation to be found in the electric-field loudspeaker. The analog electric circuit has the form shown in Fig. 6-20.

6-7. General Characteristics of Transducers. Refer again to Fig. 6-1, which illustrates the general features of transducers. The form illustrated, as already found, is the natural form for the singly excited device. For the multiply excited transducer, it is assumed that all currents in the magnetic-field device except that in the control conductor are held constant. Also, for the multiply excited electric-field transducer, it is assumed that all charges except that on the control conductor are held constant.

The several analyses which have been carried out in detail show that the electromechanical characteristics of the transducer in the region of linear operation can be described by a pair of equations of the form[1]

$$v = \alpha_{11}i + \alpha_{12}\omega$$
$$f = \alpha_{21}i + \alpha_{22}\omega \tag{6-41}$$

which, in matrix form, is

$$\begin{bmatrix} v \\ f \end{bmatrix} = \begin{bmatrix} \alpha_{11} & \alpha_{12} \\ \alpha_{21} & \alpha_{22} \end{bmatrix} \begin{bmatrix} i \\ \omega \end{bmatrix}$$

The electrical and mechanical variables, here denoted as i and ω, are symbols only and may represent charge, current, flux linkages, displacement, velocity (linear or angular), etc., respectively. The coefficients α will, in general, include derivative operators, integral operators, and constants but will be independent of the variables; they will depend on the geometry and any of the biases introduced in the electrical or mechanical circuits. Under the conditions of linear operation, the operation involves small electrical and mechanical displacement from the reference values; in fact, Eqs. (6-41) specify the relationships relative to the reference point.

The system equations [Eqs. (6-41)] have the same form as those used to describe the behavior of a two-port network. In the terminology of two-port network theory, the coefficients represent the following:

$\alpha_{11} = \left(\dfrac{v}{i}\right)_{\omega=0}$ = driving-point impedance looking into electrical terminals of transducer, with mechanical element clamped so that $\omega = 0$

$\alpha_{22} = \left(\dfrac{f}{\omega}\right)_{i=0}$ = mechanical impedance looking into mechanical element, with electrical-circuit current $i = 0$

$\alpha_{12} = \left(\dfrac{v}{\omega}\right)_{i=0}$ = potential v produced at open-circuited electrical terminals for unit incremental velocity ω applied to mechanical element

$\alpha_{21} = \left(\dfrac{f}{i}\right)_{\omega=0}$ = force f produced at clamped mechanical element ($\omega = 0$) for a unit current i

[1] A. Bloch, Electromechanical Analogies and Their Use for the Analysis of Mechanical and Electromechanical Systems, *J. IEE*, **92**: 157 (1949).

It is desired to examine the nature of these coefficients. This is conveniently done by considering the incremental variables to be sinusoidal functions of time.

Considerable useful information is possible if we suppose that the transducer is lossless.[1] For sinusoidal variables, Eqs. (6-41) become

$$V = A_{11}I + A_{12}\Omega$$
$$F = A_{21}I + A_{22}\Omega \tag{6-42}$$

where the coefficients are implicit complex functions of the frequency and the dependent and independent variables are now phasor quantities. The total average power input to the transducer at both the electrical and mechanical terminals is given by

$$P = \tfrac{1}{2}[VI^* + V^*I + F\Omega^* + F^*\Omega] \tag{6-43}$$

where * indicates the complex conjugate of the quantity. Combining Eqs. (6-42) and (6-43), there results

$$P = \tfrac{1}{2}(A_{11} + A_{11}^*)II^* + (A_{22} + A_{22}^*)\Omega\Omega^*$$
$$+ (A_{21} + A_{12}^*)I\Omega^* + (A_{12} + A_{21}^*)I^*\Omega \tag{6-44}$$

In order that P vanish for all values of I and Ω, since it was assumed that the transducer contained no dissipative elements, it is required that the following conditions be valid:

$$A_{11} + A_{11}^* = 0 \tag{6-45a}$$
$$A_{22} + A_{22}^* = 0 \tag{6-45b}$$
$$A_{21} + A_{12}^* = 0 \tag{6-45c}$$
$$A_{12} + A_{21}^* = 0 \tag{6-45d}$$

These conditions require the following:

$A_{11} + A_{11}^* = 0$; A_{11} can contain no real (i.e., resistive) part; therefore A_{11} must be a function of odd powers of frequency, only. Consequently, α_{11} must be a function only of odd powers of the derivative operator p

$A_{22} + A_{22}^* = 0$; A_{22} can have no real part, or α_{22} must be a function only of odd powers of the derivative operator p

$A_{21} + A_{12}^* = (A_{12} + A_{21}^*) = 0$; the imaginary parts of A_{12} and A_{21} must be equal; the real parts must be equal and opposite

It is observed that the conditions on the coefficients A_{11} and A_{22}, or correspondingly α_{11} and α_{22}, are those which apply for driving-point impedances of dissipationless networks. This means that the driving-point impedances are purely reactive.

To understand the conditions on the mutual terms A_{21} and A_{12}, it is

[1] E. M. McMillan, Violation of the Reciprocity Theorem in Linear Passive Electromechanical Systems, J. Acoust. Soc. Am., 18: 344 (1946).

best to return to considerations of the two types of transducers that have been studied in some detail. Consider first the electric-field transducer (crystal or capacitor types). In these devices the force is in phase with the charge on the conductor. Also, since the current is related to the charge by $I = j\omega Q$, the force is in time quadrature with the current. Consequently, the term A_{21} is imaginary, and, from Eq. (6-45c) or (6-45d), $A_{21} = A_{12}$ ($\alpha_{21} = \alpha_{12}$). Therefore α_{21} is a function of odd powers of the time-derivative operator p.

In the case of the magnetic-field transducer, the force is in phase with the current. Therefore A_{21} is real, and $A_{21} = -A_{12}$ ($\alpha_{21} = -\alpha_{12}$). This requires that α_{21} be a function of even powers of the operator p, plus, perhaps, a constant.

Now, the force f of Fig. 6-1 is that given in Eqs. (6-41) and is the force on the mechanical element by the mechanical restraint. Under steady-state conditions, it is equal and opposite to the internally produced force of the magnetic-field transducer due to positive current. It is equal and opposite to the internally produced force of the electric-field transducer due to positive charge. Hence the sign of the α_{21} term must be negative for the defined positive direction of force. The resulting equations then become:

For the magnetic-field transducer: $\quad \begin{bmatrix} v \\ f \end{bmatrix} = \begin{bmatrix} \alpha_{11} & \alpha_{12} \\ -\alpha_{21} & \alpha_{22} \end{bmatrix} \begin{bmatrix} i \\ \omega \end{bmatrix} \quad$ (6-46)

For the electric-field transducer: $\quad \begin{bmatrix} v \\ f \end{bmatrix} = \begin{bmatrix} \alpha_{11} & -\alpha_{12} \\ -\alpha_{21} & \alpha_{22} \end{bmatrix} \begin{bmatrix} i \\ \omega \end{bmatrix} \quad$ (6-47)

In summary, α_{11} and α_{22} are functions of odd powers of p for both the electric-field and the magnetic-field transducers. However, α_{12} and α_{21} are given in terms of a constant and even powers of p for magnetic-field transducers and in terms of odd powers of p for electric-field transducers. The presence of dissipation results in the appearance of constant terms in the expressions for the various α's.

The physical significance of the α coefficients that appear in these equations was discussed in connection with Eqs. (6-41). It is now desired to examine the measurements that might be made on a given transducer in order to be able to relate the actual transducer characteristics with the mathematical model that was studied. For this, we consider the specific case of a telephone receiver, such as that discussed in Sec. 6-3. The controlling system equations are specified by Eq. (6-46). Observe that it is no longer supposed that the system is lossless, but it is assumed that sinusoidal variables apply. Under these conditions, Eq. (6-46) is written in the form

$$\begin{aligned} E &= A_{11}I + A_{12}\dot{X} \\ F &= -A_{21}I + A_{22}\dot{X} \end{aligned} \qquad (6\text{-}48)$$

where the **A** coefficients are complex functions of the frequency and the dependent and independent variables are phasor quantities. Observe that the dependent variables are here written as **I** and **Ẋ** so as to conform to Eqs. (6-9).

Two sets of electrical driving-point-impedance measurements versus frequency are possible. One set of measurements is made with the mechanical element clamped, and this yields

$$\mathbf{Z}_{1f} = \frac{\mathbf{E}}{\mathbf{I}}\bigg)_{\dot{\mathbf{X}}=0} = \mathbf{A}_{11} \tag{6-49}$$

The second set of measurements is made with the diaphragm free, but with no applied mechanical force. From Eqs. (6-48) it follows that

$$\mathbf{Z}_{1c} = \frac{\mathbf{E}}{\mathbf{I}}\bigg)_{\mathbf{F}=0} = \mathbf{A}_{11} - \frac{\mathbf{A}_{12}\mathbf{A}_{21}}{\mathbf{A}_{22}} = \mathbf{A}_{11} + \frac{\mathbf{A}_{12}^2}{\mathbf{A}_{22}} \tag{6-50}$$

It is convenient to write this expression as

$$\left.\begin{aligned}\mathbf{Z}_{1c} &= \mathbf{Z}_{1f} + \mathbf{Z}_{1m}\\[4pt]\mathbf{Z}_{1m} &= \frac{\mathbf{A}_{12}^2}{\mathbf{A}_{22}}\end{aligned}\right\} \tag{6-51}$$

where

$\mathbf{Z}_{1m}$ may be interpreted as the contribution to the driving-point impedance due to the mechanical movement of the diaphragm and is therefore known as the *motional* impedance of the transducer.

Now, for the specific transducer under consideration, the explicit forms of the **A** factors are known from Eqs. (6-9). These are

$$\begin{aligned}\mathbf{A}_{11} &= R + j\omega L_{00}\\\mathbf{A}_{12} &= -\mathbf{A}_{21} = L_0' I_0\\\mathbf{A}_{22} &= R_m + j\omega M + \frac{k}{j\omega}\end{aligned} \tag{6-52}$$

The motional impedance is then given by the expression

$$\mathbf{Z}_{1m} = \frac{(L_0' I_0)^2}{R_m + j\left(\omega M - \dfrac{k}{\omega}\right)}$$

We wish now to show that this is the equation of a circle on a complex (R,X) plane. We proceed in this by noting that since $\mathbf{Z}_{1m}$ is a complex quantity, in general, it may be written as

$$\mathbf{Z}_{1m} = R_e - jX_e = \frac{(L_0' I_0)^2}{R_m^2 + (\omega M - k/\omega)^2}\left[R_m - j\left(\omega M - \frac{k}{\omega}\right)\right] \tag{6-53}$$

From this, by equating real and imaginary terms,

$$R_e = \frac{(L_0' I_0)^2 R_m}{R_m^2 + (\omega M - k/\omega)^2} \qquad X_e = \frac{(L_0' I_0)^2(\omega M - k/\omega)}{R_m^2 + (\omega M - k/\omega)^2} \tag{6-54}$$

Now combine these expressions by writing the first of these in the form

$$R_m{}^2 + \left(\omega M - \frac{k}{\omega}\right)^2 = (L_0'I_0)^2 \frac{R_m}{R_e}$$

and then combining this with the second, to get

$$X_e(L_0'I_0)^2 \frac{R_m}{R_e} = (L_0'I_0)^2 \left[(L_0'I_0)^2 \frac{R_m}{R_e} - R_m{}^2 \right]^{1/2}$$

Squaring both sides gives

$$X_e{}^2 - \left(\frac{R_e}{R_m}\right)^2 \left[(L_0'I_0)^2 \frac{R_m}{R_e} - R_m{}^2 \right] = 0$$

or

$$X_e{}^2 - (L_0'I_0)^2 \frac{R_e}{R_m} + R_e{}^2 = 0$$

This expression is written as

$$R_e{}^2 - \frac{(L_0'I_0)^2}{R_m} R_e + \left[\frac{(L_0'I_0)^2}{2R_m} \right]^2 + X_e{}^2 = \left[\frac{(L_0'I_0)^2}{2R_m} \right]^2$$

or, finally,

$$\left[R_e - \frac{(L_0'I_0)^2}{2R_m} \right]^2 + X_e{}^2 = \left[\frac{(L_0'I_0)^2}{2R_m} \right]^2 \tag{6-55}$$

This equation shows that the motional impedance is a circle of radius $(L_0'I_0)^2/2R_m$, with the center at $L_0'I_0/2R_m$, 0 on the real or resistance axis.

Actually, we have neglected the effect of eddy currents in our analysis. The eddy currents affect both the effective resistance and the effective mass of the system, with the result that the motional impedance is not a circle. However, in well-designed receivers the eddy currents are small, and the motional impedance does, in fact, approximate a circle, although its center does not lie on the real axis. A series of experimental results are contained in Figs. 6-21 to 6-23. In these, the damped and free driving-point-impedance measurements are used to deduce the motional impedance of the transducer. Observe from Fig. 6-23 that the motional impedance does approximate a circle, but with the center off the real axis.

The final general aspects of transducers are their representation in analog form and the appropriate two-port representation. This was accomplished in each detailed transducer study, and it is desired to obtain the analog forms corresponding to the electromechanical equations given by Eqs. (6-46) and (6-47). The direct analog is obtained by writing

$$f = bi \qquad \omega = \frac{v}{b}$$

and the inverse analog results by writing

$$f = av \qquad \omega = \frac{i}{a}$$

$$\tag{6-56}$$

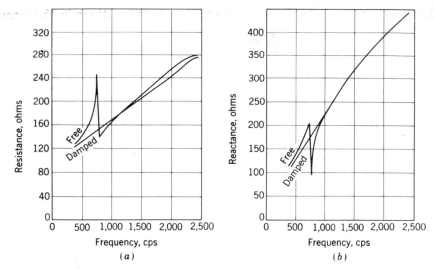

Fig. 6-21. Damped and free driving-point impedance of a telephone receiver. (a) Resistance; (b) reactance. (*Reprinted with permission from K. McIlwain and J. G. Brainerd, "High Frequency Alternating Currents," John Wiley & Sons, Inc., New York, 1939.*)

For the magnetic-field transducer, Eqs. (6-46) become, under the specified transformations,

Direct analog:

$$v_1 = \alpha_{11}\dot{i}_1 + \alpha_{12}\frac{v_2}{b}$$

$$i_2 b = -\alpha_{21}\dot{i}_1 + \alpha_{22}\frac{v_2}{b}$$

(6-57)

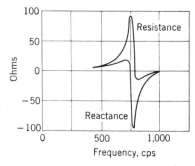

Fig. 6-22. Resistance and reactance components of the motional impedance of a telephone receiver. (*Reprinted with permission from K. McIlwain and J. G. Brainerd, "High Frequency Alternating Currents," John Wiley & Sons, Inc., New York, 1939.*)

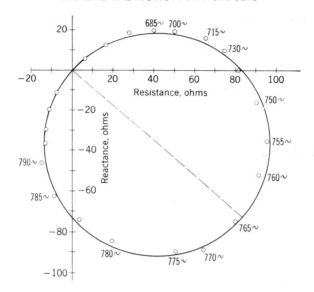

FIG. 6-23. The motional-impedance circle of a telephone receiver. (*Reprinted with permission from K. McIlwain and J. G. Brainerd, "High Frequency Alternating Current," John Wiley & Sons, Inc., New York, 1939.*)

These equations are solved simultaneously to find

$$v_1 = \left(\alpha_{11} + \frac{\alpha_{12}\alpha_{21}}{\alpha_{22}} \right) i_1 + b \frac{\alpha_{12}}{\alpha_{22}} i_2$$

$$v_2 = b \frac{\alpha_{21}}{\alpha_{22}} i_1 + \frac{b^2}{\alpha_{22}} i_2 \tag{6-58}$$

It is now recalled that the T-circuit representation of a two-port network,

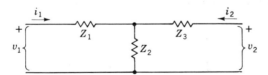

FIG. 6-24. The T-circuit form of a two-port network.

as illustrated in Fig. 6-24, is described in terms of the Z-system parameters noted,

$$v_1 = Z_{11}i_1 + Z_{12}i_2$$

$$v_2 = Z_{21}i_1 + Z_{22}i_2 \tag{6-59}$$

where, from the diagram,

$$Z_1 = Z_{11} - Z_{12}$$

$$Z_2 = Z_{12} = Z_{21} \tag{6-60}$$

$$Z_3 = Z_{22} - Z_{12}$$

These parameters become, for the direct analog specified by Eq. (6-50),

$$Z_1 = \alpha_{11} + \frac{\alpha_{12}\alpha_{21}}{\alpha_{22}} - b\frac{\alpha_{12}}{\alpha_{22}}$$

$$Z_2 = b\frac{\alpha_{12}}{\alpha_{22}} \tag{6-61}$$

$$Z_3 = \frac{b^2}{\alpha_{22}} - b\frac{\alpha_{12}}{\alpha_{22}}$$

For the special case when $b = \alpha_{12}$, the direct-analog representation attains the form illustrated in Fig. 6-25.

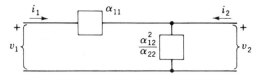

FIG. 6-25. The direct-analog representation of a magnetic-field transducer, with $b = \alpha_{12}$.

The inverse-analog representation of the magnetic-field transducer follows by subjecting Eq. (6-46) to the second transformations of Eqs. (6-56). The equations now become

$$v_1 = \alpha_{11}\dot{i}_1 + \frac{\alpha_{12}}{a}\dot{i}_2$$

$$v_2 = \frac{\alpha_{21}}{a}\dot{i}_1 + \frac{\alpha_{22}}{a^2}\dot{i}_2 \tag{6-62}$$

The appropriate parameters of the analog T circuit now have the form

$$Z_1 = \alpha_{11} - \frac{\alpha_{12}}{a}$$

$$Z_2 = \frac{\alpha_{12}}{a} \qquad Z_2' = -\frac{\alpha_{21}}{a} \tag{6-63}$$

$$Z_3 = \frac{\alpha_{22}}{a^2} + \frac{\alpha_{21}}{a}$$

These expressions show the lack of reciprocity of the mutual terms, which necessitates the use of the gyrator, as already discussed in Sec. 6-3. Although gyrators do exist as physical elements, they are not common network elements, and so Fig. 6-26, which gives the inverse-analog circuit, including such a gyrator, might well be considered as a less desirable analog than the direct analog.

For the electric-field transducer, attention is directed to Eq. (6-47).

For the direct analog, Eq. (6-47) is combined with the first of Eqs. (6-56). The resulting equations are the following:

$$v_1 = \alpha_{11}i_1 - \alpha_{12}\frac{v_2}{b}$$

$$i_2 b = -\alpha_{21}i_1 + \alpha_{22}\frac{v_2}{b}$$

which are solved simultaneously to yield the expressions

$$v_1 = \left(\alpha_{11} - \frac{\alpha_{12}\alpha_{21}}{\alpha_{22}}\right)i_1 - b\frac{\alpha_{12}}{\alpha_{22}}i_2$$

$$v_2 = b\frac{\alpha_{21}}{\alpha_{22}}i_1 + \frac{b^2 i_2}{\alpha_{22}}$$

(6-64)

Observe that these equations for the direct analog of the electric-field transducer show the same general lack of reciprocity as the inverse

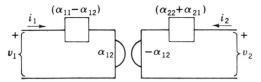

Fig. 6-26. The inverse-analog representation of a magnetic-field transducer, with $a = 1$.

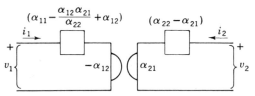

Fig. 6-27. The direct-analog representation of an electric-field transducer, with $b = \alpha_{22}$.

analog for the magnetic-field transducer. This means, therefore, that a gyrator is required in the network representation of the analog circuit specified by Eqs. (6-64). This network representation is given in Fig. 6-27.

For the inverse analog, Eq. (6-47) is combined with the second of Eqs. (6-56). The resulting equations are the following:

$$v_1 = \alpha_{11}i_1 - \frac{\alpha_{12}}{a}i_2$$

$$v_2 = \frac{-\alpha_{21}}{a}i_1 + \frac{\alpha_{22}}{a^2}i_2$$

(6-65)

These equations show the existence of reciprocity, and a network representation is illustrated in Fig. 6-28.

If it is again assumed that the transducer is lossless, then it is possible to make certain general statements concerning the nature of the circuit elements that appear in the various analog representations of the magnetic-field and electric-field transducers.   Clearly, since the transducers are assumed lossless, the circuit elements will consist only of capacitors and inductors.   Also, from the significance of the parameters, it is expected that α_{11}, which is the driving-point impedance of the transducer with the mechanical element clamped, would be an inductor for the magnetic-field transducer and would be a capacitor for the electric-field transducer.

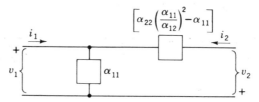

FIG. 6-28. The inverse-analog representation of an electric-field transducer, with $a = -\alpha_{12}/\alpha_{11}$.

FIG. 6-29. A complete system involving a transducer.

Correspondingly, since α_{22} denotes the mechanical driving-point impedance for $i = 0$, the mass and spring constant will appear as capacitor C and inductor L, or vice versa, depending on the analog representation.

6-8. Transducers in Systems.   Figure 6-1, which shows the general features of transducers, and also the figures for the several examples that have been examined in some detail make clear the fact that the transducer is a coupling device, coupling an electrical source to a mechanical system, or vice versa.   In general, therefore, there will be a driving source and a driven element.   Such a complete system, including the transducer, may be graphically represented, as shown in Fig. 6-29.

In ascertaining the complete performance of such a system, a reasonable procedure is to represent the transducer by an analog representation and to represent the mechanical load by an analog representation (as discussed in Chap. 4).   The complete representation of the system will then be of the form shown in Fig. 6-30, which might represent a magnetic-field transducer which couples to a mechanical load and which is driven from some electrical source.   The complete solution for the response of such a system is obtained by employing the known techniques of network analysis.

Attention is directed to the fact that for an adequate sensitivity to the input signal level, and for power output capabilities necessary to actuate the output circuit, the problems of proper impedance match for optimum power transfer and the problems of system bandwidth for operation over the prescribed frequency range become very important. The situation here is no different, of course, from that which is to prevail in any two-port coupling device.   The design is somewhat more

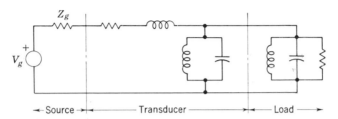

Fig. 6-30. The electric-circuit analog for the transducer and system of Fig. 6-29.

difficult than with simple electrical-network elements, since the characteristics of the transducer are functions of the size, materials, and design. The problems of mechanical physical realizability may impose considerable limits on the system and its frequency-response characteristics.

PROBLEMS

6-1. The accompanying sketch shows the important features of a singly excited magnetic transducer.   The constants of this transducer are the following:

Resistance of coil: 40 ohms
Inductance of coil: 0.1 mh
Mechanical resistance of moving element: 100 dynes/cm/sec
Mass of coil assembly: 0.2 g
Deflection of mechanical assembly per unit force: 2×10^{-6} cm/dyne
Flux density in air gap: 10^4 gauss
Length of coil winding: 100 cm
Find the apparent electrical impedance of the movable winding at a frequency of 150 cps.

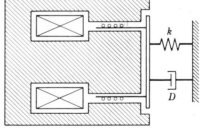

Fig. P6-1

6-2. Consider the singly excited magnetic transducer discussed in Sec. 6-3.   Let f, v, and R_m be zero.   The bias potential V is suddenly applied with the mass clamped. Find the various energies involved in reaching steady state and their steady-state values.   The mass is now unclamped.   Find the steady-state position of the mass. Explain in terms of energy as well as motion the actions in attaining this steady-state position.   At the instant that M is unclamped, what is the sign of di/dt and d^2i/dt^2?

6-3. Deduce the system equations of the electromechanical device illustrated. Assume that the iron is infinitely permeable, no fringing at the air gap, and no losses. The air-gap cross section is A, and the length of the air gap at equilibrium is G.

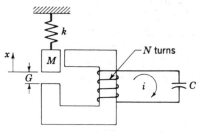

Fig. P6-3

6-4. The equations governing an electromechanical system are given below. Find an electrical analog for the system characterized by these equations. Make a table relating the mechanical constants to the electrical-circuit constants.

$$M\ddot{z} + kz - \frac{Q_0}{\epsilon A}q = f \qquad -\frac{Q_0}{\epsilon A}z + \frac{q}{C_0} = v$$

6-5. The essential features of a transducer are characterized by $C(x)$ and $L(x)$ in the circuit shown, where x is the displacement of the mechanical system, also as

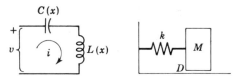

Fig. P6-5

illustrated. Find the equations governing the response of this electromechanical device.

6-6. A singly excited magnetic-field transducer is shown schematically in the accompanying figure. The relationship between current, flux linkages, and mechani-

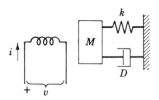

Fig. P6-6

cal displacement is found experimentally to be of the form

$$i = a\lambda^2(1 - bx^2)$$

(a) Find an expression for the mechanical force in the x direction as a function of λ and x.

(b) For an applied potential $v = V_m \sin \omega t$, find expressions for λ, x, and i.

6-7. Consider a multiply excited transducer that consists of three windings, two of which are excitation windings, the third being the signal winding. Assuming that the self-inductances of all windings and the mutual inductance of all windings not including the excitation winding are independent of displacement φ and that the currents in the excitation windings are constant, deduce the analog circuit relating the displacement φ and torque T of the mechanical elements with the potential v_1 and current i_1 at the terminals of the input winding. NOTE: This is an extension of the system considered in detail in Sec. 6-4.

6-8. A photoelectric transducer is shown schematically in the accompanying figure. The characteristics of the photocell have the form shown. The amplifier is assumed

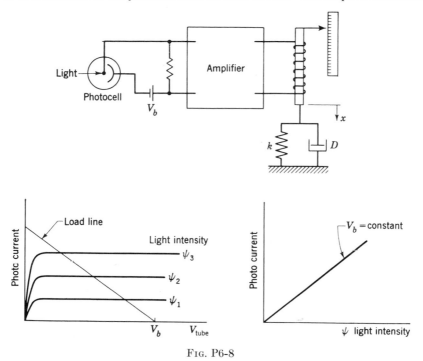

FIG. P6-8

to be a linear d-c amplifier, the output current being directly proportional to the input potential. The amplifier feeds a solenoid-operated output device, which is spring- and dashpot-loaded. The plunger of the solenoid is of iron. Find the equations for the motion of the solenoid plunger as the light is varied.

7

Rotary Power Converter

A very extensive literature has developed since 1910 which concerns itself with the many problems of rotating electrical machinery. Much of this work is oriented toward establishing the relation between the machine parameters and the steady-state load-performance characteristics of such machines. While some attention has been given to the transient performance of machinery under starting or fault conditions, the attention to transient problems has been much less extensive than that concerned with the steady-state load performance. There is interest in providing the background for more extensive studies in the device behavior, both because of general interest and also because of the needs which arise from the development of feedback control systems which utilize rotating electrical machines of various types in varied operating modes. It is desired to formulate the performance equations from a general point of view which will permit a complete analysis of the behavior of the machine.

As discussed in Sec. 1-5, two alternative general methods will be developed for discussing the complete performance characteristics of rotary power converters. Both methods assume idealized generalized machine models, but the details of the studies will differ somewhat. One approach assumes the Kron primitive machine for study. In this machine, the description proceeds essentially as a network problem, with considerations of the self-inductances of the various windings and the mutual inductances between windings, and with due regard for any motional electromotances (induced emfs) that are generated by the windings which may be moving relative to each other. The problem is complicated because the Kron machine is provided with a commutator which imposes special constraints on the fields. The success of the method stems from the applicability of the Kron model through mathematical transformations which will permit the analysis of many important practical machines in terms of certain stationary quantities that apply in the Kron machine. Later, these transformations are accounted for in relating the results in machine coordinates.

The second approach assumes the White and Woodson idealized machine. While the analysis ultimately proceeds on a network basis as for the Kron machine, initially the analysis proceeds from considerations of the instantaneous **E** and **H** fields in the air gap of the machine. These fields are related to the currents in the windings in the machine. Now the effect of space or time variations due to the fixed and moving windings appears in the expressions for the fields. The description of the behavior of the machine follows after the network parameters are derived from the field expressions. In order to be able to deduce expressions for the **E** and **H** fields, there are somewhat more rigid limitations on the machine geometry of the White and Woodson machine than is necessary in the Kron machine.

We shall begin our study of rotating-machine theory from a study of an elementary electrical-machine model. This model will gradually be extended to permit the discussion of the important types of d-c machines. This study will then permit a ready transition to the Kron machine, which will then provide the basis for the next step in our study.

7-1. The Magnetic Structure of Rotating Machines.[1] We first direct our attention to the magnetic structure and geometry of the typical rotating machine. The usual machine consists of two major structural elements of iron (usually high-quality magnetic steel), an outer stationary member and an inner rotating member which is mounted in bearings which are fixed to the stationary member. Windings are usually attached to each of these members.

In the case of d-c machines, owing to the need for a commutator, the rotating member is the armature winding, the stationary member being so constructed and wound as to make up the field assembly. Usually field poles are attached to the outer frame, or yoke, the winding direction of the field coils and the excitation being such as to produce alternate north and south magnetic fields. Figure 7-1 illustrates the general features of the d-c machine. A machine with isolated poles of the type illustrated is known as a salient-pole machine.

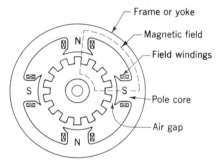

Fig. 7-1. Diagrammatic sketch of d-c machine.

Alternating-current machines may be of the salient-pole type, or they may be of the nonsalient-pole type, depending on the machine and its

[1] For more details see A. E. Fitzgerald and C. Kingsley, Jr., "Electric Machinery," 2d ed., McGraw-Hill Book Company, Inc., New York, 1961.

application.   The sketches of Figs. 7-2 show the general features of synchronous machines of the salient-pole and the nonsalient-pole types. In the latter case, the windings on the rotating, or field, member are such as to produce an effective north and south pole even though the field structure is cylindrical, without any projecting poles.

As indicated in Figs. 7-1 and 7-2, armature windings are almost always distributed uniformly over the entire surface for better utilization

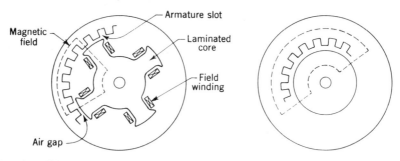

FIG. 7-2. Diagrammatic sketch of salient-pole and nonsalient-pole synchronous machine.

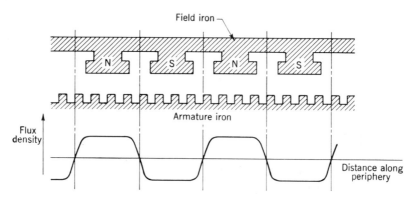

FIG. 7-3. Developed sketch of a d-c machine structure showing the air-gap flux distribution for the excitation of the field alone.

of space and material in the machine.   For such machines, the radial distribution in the air gap of the flux produced by the field structure may be pictured by a developed sketch of the machine.   A typical sketch of a d-c machine structure showing the air-gap flux distribution is given in Fig. 7-3.   It will be observed that the flux-density distribution shown approximates a square wave, a desirable flux distribution for the d-c machine.   In the case of most salient-pole a-c machines, the pole faces are usually shaped to provide a sinusoidal flux distribution. In a nonsalient-pole machine with a uniform air gap the field windings are ordinarily so distributed on the rotor surface as to yield an effective sinusoidal flux-density distribution.

7-2. Distributed Windings as Current Sheets. Suppose that the armature iron of Fig. 7-3 has windings placed in the slots. Figure 7-4a illustrates a *full*-pitch two-layer lap winding. A full-pitch winding is one in which the coil side in one slot, say under a north pole, has its return coil side in the same relative location under the south pole. Such windings progress from slot to slot until all slots are filled. Figure

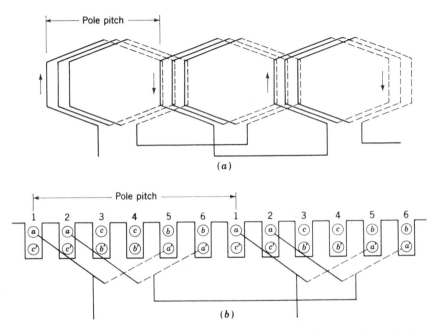

(a)

(b)

FIG. 7-4. (a) A developed sketch of a full-pitch two-layer lap winding with three slots per pole per phase; (b) a two-thirds-pitch lap winding with six slots per pole.

7-4b illustrates a two-layer winding for a three-phase machine, with six slots per pole and a coil pitch equal to two-thirds of the pole pitch. In this case, each slot contains coil sides belonging to different phases. This has an effect on the leakage reactance of the winding and on the resultant mmf of the winding.

If the winding is assumed to be finely distributed, then for a constant current in the windings, which are in the axial direction (and often, in fact, these are skewed slightly from the true axial direction), the effect approximates that of a uniform current sheet on the surface of the armature. Figure 7-5 illustrates the equivalent current sheet approximated by a winding distribution, such as that illustrated in Fig. 7-4a. Clearly, if there are N uniformly distributed conductors per pole, each carrying a current I, then there is a total current of NI amp per pole. The *linear* current density along the armature surface of radius b is then

$$J = \frac{NI}{\pi b} \qquad \text{amp/m} \qquad (7\text{-}1)$$

The analysis of the operation of a rotating machine requires a knowledge of the magnetomotance (mmf) distribution in the air gap, which is a plot of the magnetic potential difference along the air gap. To find the mmf distribution, one proceeds from a knowledge of the current distribution. This is accomplished by a direct application of the Ampère

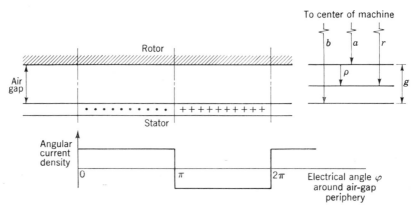

Fig. 7-5. The equivalent uniform current sheet on the armature surface, and the associated amplitude.

line integral, a path being chosen that crosses the air gap. If the reluctance of the path in the iron is assumed to be negligible compared with that in the air gap, then the mmf around the closed path can be assumed to be concentrated in the air gap. For the present purposes, the path is chosen as one pole pitch, or π radians, wide, the position of the path being taken at a number of points. Refer to Fig. 7-6, which illustrates the situation here being discussed. For the path shown in Fig. 7-6a, the total current linked is πJ, which is equal to the mmf acting on the path shown. The magnitude of the magnetic potential difference across the gap at each of the angles π and 2π is $\pi J/2$. For the path shown in Fig. 7-6b, the net current linked is 0, whence the magnetic potential difference across the gap at each of the angles $\pi/2$ and $3\pi/2$ is zero. For the path shown in Fig. 7-6c, a net current is linked, depending directly on the path displacement relative to the zero mmf position, thereby giving rise to a finite magnetic potential difference. The result is the triangular distribution shown in Fig. 7-6d.

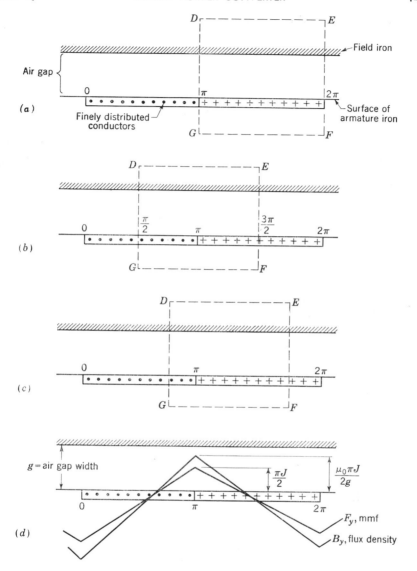

Fig. 7-6. The mmf paths and the mmf waves.

Recall that the flux, and so the flux density, depends on the mmf and the reluctance of the magnetic path.   For the uniform air gap shown, and saturation effects being neglected, the flux density is everywhere proportional to the mmf.   To find the proportionality factor, consider a path having an infinitesimal width at the point where the mmf is at its peak value.   From the fact that

$$\phi = \frac{F}{\Re} = \frac{F}{g/(\mu_0 l \, \Delta x)} = Bl \, \Delta x$$

then

$$\frac{\mu_0 F}{g} = B$$

or finally

$$\frac{B}{F} = \frac{\mu_0}{g} \tag{7-2}$$

The flux-density curve thus has the form illustrated in Fig. 7-6d.

As already noted, one very important current-sheet distribution in machine analysis is that with a sinusoidal variation along the periphery of the air gap.   For such a case, the important mmf and flux-density

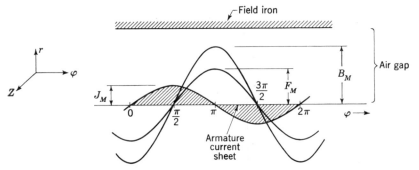

FIG. 7-7. The mmf and flux-density curves for a sinusoidal current sheet.

waveforms for the uniform-air-gap machine have the forms illustrated in Fig. 7-7.

7-3. The Rotary-coil Transformer.   Consider a two-winding structure which is so designed that one coil is fixed with respect to the magnetic structure and the second coil is so arranged that it can be rotated with respect to the fixed-coil assembly.   The device discussed may have the form illustrated in Fig. 7-8.   The mutual inductance between the two coils will vary with angle.   It will be a maximum when the flux linking the rotating coil is a maximum.   This case is essentially that of the two-winding transformer, and the movable coil is said to be oriented along the direct flux axis, hereafter referred to as the *direct axis*.   The mutual inductance will be zero when the flux linkages are zero, the situation that exists at $\varphi = \pi/2$ and $3\pi/2$, respectively.   This axis is referred to as the *quadrature axis*.

For the rotary-coil transformer shown, the reluctance of the magnetic path is independent of the orientation of the movable coil, and for a constant excitation current in the fixed winding, the flux in the iron circuit remains constant.   In this case the flux linking the movable coil follows a cosine law, and the mutual inductance is then of the form

$$M(\varphi) = M_d \cos \varphi \qquad (7\text{-}3)$$

A similar type of mutual-inductance variation applies if the coils are in air, in which case the magnetic circuit is also unaffected by the rotation.

With a lack of symmetry in the magnetic circuit, and this will exist if the reluctance of the magnetic circuit changes as the movable member changes its orientation, the self-inductance of the two windings L_1 and L_2 will also be functions of the angle φ. In many devices the design is such as to maintain the self-inductances constant. This is true in rotating machines with cylindrical rotating members and with the windings

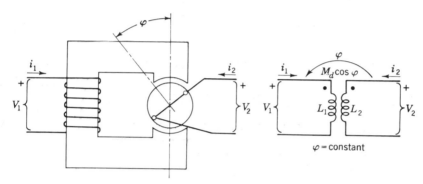

FIG. 7-8. Schematic and network representation of the two-winding movable-coil transformer.

uniformly distributed on the surface of the rotating member (the rotor) or in machines with cylindrical rotor and stator geometry (the nonsalient-pole machine).

For the simple transformer, $\varphi = 0$, and the mutual inductance is a maximum. For the movable-coil transformer with the movable assembly fixed at an angle φ, the controlling electrical equations are

$$v_1 = R_1 i_1 + L_1 \frac{di_1}{dt} + M_d \cos \varphi \frac{di_2}{dt}$$
$$v_2 = R_2 i_2 + L_2 \frac{di_2}{dt} + M_d \cos \varphi \frac{di_1}{dt} \qquad (7\text{-}4)$$

which may be written in matrix form as follows:

$$\begin{bmatrix} v_1 \\ v_2 \end{bmatrix} = \left\{ \begin{bmatrix} R_1 & 0 \\ 0 & R_2 \end{bmatrix} + \begin{bmatrix} L_1(\varphi) & M_d \cos \varphi \\ M_d \cos \varphi & L_2(\varphi) \end{bmatrix} p \right\} \begin{bmatrix} i_1 \\ i_2 \end{bmatrix} \qquad (7\text{-}5)$$

or more simply $\qquad [V] = [RI] + [Lp][I] \qquad (7\text{-}6)$

where $[R]$ and $[L]$ are the matrices specified in Eq. (7-5).

Suppose that the rotatable coil is being driven at some angular speed ω_m in the reference direction. Now, since $\varphi = \omega_m t$, a function of time, Eq. (7-6) must be modified. The general electrical equations must now be written

$$[V] = [RI] + p[LI] \tag{7-7}$$

where $[LI]$ gives the flux-linkage matrix of the system. When this expression is expanded, it has the form

$$[V] = \{[R] + [Lp]\}[I] + [pL][I] \tag{7-8}$$

which may conveniently be written as follows:

$$[V] = [R + Lp][I] + \left[\frac{\partial L}{\partial \varphi} \frac{\partial \varphi}{\partial t} \right][I] \tag{7-9}$$

Observe that the last term in this equation, which specifies the motional emf due to the coil movement, is different from zero when $[L]$ is a function of the angle φ. This expression is written in the form

$$[V] = [R + Lp][I] + [G\omega_m I] \tag{7-10}$$

where $\dot{\varphi}$, the speed of the machine, is written as ω_m. The quantity $[\partial L/\partial \varphi] \equiv G$ has the following complete form, assuming that L_1 and L_2 are independent of φ and that M varies sinusoidally with angle φ:

$$[G] \equiv \left[\frac{\partial L}{\partial \varphi} \right] = \begin{bmatrix} 0 & -M_d \sin \varphi \\ -M_d \sin \varphi & 0 \end{bmatrix} \tag{7-11}$$

This latter is the equivalent of the statement that the flux-density waves are assumed to be sinusoidally distributed around the circumference in each layer of the rotor.

Now refer to Eq. (7-10) when written explicitly for $\varphi = 0$ and $\varphi = \pm\pi/2$. These sets of equations become

$\varphi = 0$:

$$\begin{bmatrix} v_1 \\ v_2 \end{bmatrix} = \left\{ \begin{bmatrix} R_1 & 0 \\ 0 & R_2 \end{bmatrix} + \begin{bmatrix} L_1 & M_d \\ M_d & L_2 \end{bmatrix} p + \begin{bmatrix} 0 & 0 \\ 0 & 0 \end{bmatrix} \omega_m \right\} \begin{bmatrix} i_1 \\ i_2 \end{bmatrix}$$

and

$\varphi = \mp \dfrac{\pi}{2}$:

$$\begin{bmatrix} v_1 \\ v_2 \end{bmatrix} = \left\{ \begin{bmatrix} R_1 & 0 \\ 0 & R_2 \end{bmatrix} + \begin{bmatrix} L_1 & 0 \\ 0 & L_2 \end{bmatrix} p + \begin{bmatrix} 0 & \mp M_d \\ \mp M_d & 0 \end{bmatrix} \omega_m \right\} \begin{bmatrix} i_1 \\ i_2 \end{bmatrix} \tag{7-12}$$

These expressions show that the transformer potentials are a maximum when the motional potentials are zero, and vice versa. Hence the motional-emf factors are maxima when the mutual inductances are zero. Clearly from these expressions we see that:

1. The mutual inductance is a maximum when the two coils are aligned magnetically along the same axis.

2. The motional-emf coefficient is a maximum when the two coils are magnetically at right angles to each other.

3. The magnitudes of M and G are the same, for the two-winding system.

4. The sign of G is positive when $\varphi = -\pi/2$ and is negative when $\varphi = +\pi/2$.

In the light of the foregoing, Eq. (7-10) may be given diagrammatic representation relative to a coordinate system that is fixed with respect

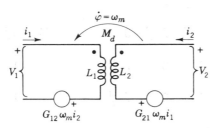

FIG. 7-9. The network representation of the rotating-coil transformer referred to the stationary coordinates, showing the presence of the motional emf in each winding.

to the stator. Figure 7-9 gives the appropriate equivalent network of the device. The motional-emf sources shown have a space-phase displacement of $\pi/2$ relative to the transformer potentials.

The foregoing properties of G and M permit the establishment of a rule for relating G with M. First we adopt the more elaborate notation G_{dq}^{rs} to denote the factor that relates the motional emf that appears in the (d,r) (direct axis, rotor) winding due to its rotation in the field produced by the (q,s) (quadrature axis, stator) winding. The G-M rule follows:

G_{dq}^{rs} is equal to the mutual inductance M_{qq}^{rs} between windings (q,s) and (q,r), the winding into which (d,r) goes after it has been moved by $\pi/2$ to align it along the (q,s) axis. The sign is positive when the motion is in the reference direction of rotation; the sign is negative when the motion is opposite to the reference direction for positive angle.

Note that in the general case, with the reference direction for positive angle being counterclockwise, the matrix G is found from the static matrix L by a transposition of all terms involving only rotor coordinates, and with $q \rightarrow -d$ and $d \rightarrow q$. For example, given the L matrix shown, which applies for a machine with double stator and double rotor windings along each axis, the appropriate G matrix has the form given.

$L =$

2d index → 1st index ↓	$s1 \atop d$	$s2 \atop d$	$s1 \atop q$	$s2 \atop q$	$r1 \atop d$	$r2 \atop d$	$r1 \atop q$	$r2 \atop q$
$s1 \atop d$	L_d^{s1}	M_d^s	0	0	M_d^{11}	M_d^{21}	0	0
$s2 \atop d$	M_d^s	L_d^{s2}	0	0	M_d^{12}	M_d^{22}	0	0
$s1 \atop q$	0	0	L_q^{s1}	M_q^s	0	0	M_q^{11}	M_q^{21}
$s2 \atop q$	0	0	M_q^s	L_q^{s2}	0	0	M_q^{12}	M_q^{22}
$r1 \atop d$	M_d^{11}	M_d^{12}	0	0	L_d^{r1}	M_d^r	0	0
$r2 \atop d$	M_d^{21}	M_d^{22}	0	0	M_d^r	L_d^{r2}	0	0
$r1 \atop q$	0	0	M_q^{11}	M_q^{12}	0	0	L_q^{r1}	M_q^r
$r2 \atop q$	0	0	M_q^{21}	M_q^{22}	0	0	M_q^r	L_q^{r2}

$G =$

2d index → 1st index ↓	$s1 \atop d$	$s2 \atop d$	$s1 \atop q$	$s2 \atop q$	$r1 \atop d$	$r2 \atop d$	$r1 \atop q$	$r2 \atop q$
$s1 \atop d$	0	0	0	0	0	0	0	0
$s2 \atop d$	0	0	0	0	0	0	0	0
$s1 \atop q$	0	0	0	0	0	0	0	0
$s2 \atop q$	0	0	0	0	0	0	0	0
$r1 \atop d$	0	0	$-M_q^{11}$	$-M_q^{12}$	0	0	$-L_q^{r1}$	$-M_q^r$
$r2 \atop d$	0	0	$-M_q^{21}$	$-M_q^{22}$	0	0	$-M_q^r$	$-L_q^{r2}$
$r1 \atop q$	M_d^{11}	M_d^{12}	0	0	L_d^{r1}	M_d^r	0	0
$r2 \atop q$	M_d^{21}	M_d^{22}	0	0	M_d^r	L_d^{r2}	0	0

As noted, the last term in Eq. (7-10) denotes the motional emf that results because the coil is rotating in the magnetic field. For this reason G is sometimes referred to as a motional inductance. The quantity G is often also referred to as the torque term, since it is directly involved in the expression for the electrical torque. To see this, it is necessary only to recall that the instantaneous energy stored in the magnetic field of two coupled coils is given by the expression

$$W_m = \tfrac{1}{2}L_1i_1{}^2 + \tfrac{1}{2}L_2i_2{}^2 + M_d \cos \varphi i_1 i_2 \quad (7\text{-}13)$$

which in matrix form is the expression

$$W_m = \frac{1}{2} \begin{bmatrix} i_1 & i_2 \end{bmatrix} \begin{bmatrix} L_1 & M_d \cos \varphi \\ M_d \cos \varphi & L_2 \end{bmatrix} \begin{bmatrix} i_1 \\ i_2 \end{bmatrix}$$

or, more compactly,

$$W_m = \tfrac{1}{2}[I_t L I] \quad (7\text{-}14)$$

where $[I_t]$ is the transpose of the matrix for $[I]$. But the torque by the electrical system is given by the expression

$$T_e = \frac{\partial W_m}{\partial \varphi}$$

so that

$$T_e = \frac{1}{2}\left[I_t \frac{\partial L}{\partial \varphi} I \right] = \frac{1}{2}[I_t G I] \quad (7\text{-}15)$$

In expanded form this becomes

$$T_e = \frac{1}{2} \begin{bmatrix} i_1 & i_2 \end{bmatrix} \begin{bmatrix} 0 & -M_d \sin \varphi \\ -M_d \sin \varphi & 0 \end{bmatrix} \begin{bmatrix} i_1 \\ i_2 \end{bmatrix}$$

which is

$$T_e = -i_1 i_2 M_d \sin \varphi \quad (7\text{-}16)$$

F i g . 7 - 1 0. To calculate the mutual inductance between the field winding and a concentrated coil on the surface of a cylindrical rotor.

It follows from this expression that, for i_1 and i_2 both positive (in the reference directions for current shown in Fig. 7-8), the torque is negative for angles in the range $0 \le \varphi = \omega_m t \le \pi$, which corresponds to generator action. It is positive for angles in the range $\pi \le \varphi = \omega_m t \le 2\pi$, which corresponds to motor action.

7-4. Concentrated and Distributed Windings. As already noted, the value of M between two concentrated coils will depend on the form of the actual magnetic-field distribution and the angle φ which the coil makes with the flux or direct axis. The case of the movable coil which is distributed over the surface of the rotor warrants detailed attention.

Refer to Fig. 7-10, which shows a single coil on the surface of the rotor of a machine. It is desired to deduce an expression for the mutual inductance between this winding and the windings of the magnetic assembly. It will be assumed that the permeability of the iron is large compared with that of the air. The flux lines will be straight lines

through the rotor.   For an air-gap flux density which is sinusoidal in the
angle φ, the flux linking the coil is

$$\psi = 2rlB_d \sin \varphi \qquad (7\text{-}17)$$

where r is the radius of the coil and l is the axial length of the rotor.
Suppose now that the winding on the rotor is uniformly distributed over
the surface of the rotor.   If there are Z conductors per radian, then
the flux linking the conductors contained within the increment of angle
$d\varphi$ is

$$d\psi = 2rlZB_d \sin \varphi \, d\varphi$$

and the total flux linking all the windings is

$$\psi = \int_0^\pi 2rlZB_d \sin \varphi \, d\varphi$$

which becomes
$$\psi = 4rlZB_d \qquad (7\text{-}18)$$

If the flux is produced by a current i_1 in the main magnetic circuit, then,
for no saturation of the iron,
$$B_d = K_f i_1$$
and the mutual inductance is
$$M_d = 4rlZK_f \qquad (7\text{-}19)$$

The flux linking the distributed assembly for any increment of angle
$d\varphi$ at the angle φ is

$$\psi = \int_\varphi^{\varphi+\pi} 2rlZB_d \sin \varphi \, d\varphi$$

which is, upon integration,
$$\psi = 4rlZB_d \cos \varphi$$
From this it follows that
$$M(\varphi) = M_d \cos \varphi \qquad (7\text{-}20)$$

This result shows that the mutual inductance between the field winding
and a uniformly distributed winding has exactly the same form as that
between a field winding and a single concentrated coil.   This is an
important conclusion, since it permits, in our subsequent discussions,
replacing distributed windings by equivalent concentrated windings.
In both cases, however, the orientation dependence must be taken into
account.

7-5. The Commutated Winding and M.   Since d-c machines and a
class of commutator a-c machines are very important, detailed attention
is essential to a winding structure which is provided with a commutator.
Consider first the case when the rotating element which is provided with
a single concentrated coil is also provided with a commutator, as illustrated in Fig. 7-11.   This is the elementary form of d-c generator.

Suppose that there is a sinusoidal flux-density distribution in the air gap. As the coil rotates, the motional emf that is induced in the rotor coil is a sinusoid. Now, because there is a moving contact between the commutator segments or commutator bars (these are usually of copper) and the fixed brushes (and these ordinarily are made of carbon), as the moving segment passes from one brush to the second, a reversal of polarity occurs; i.e., rectification takes place. The brushes are positioned at the point where the motional emf between the commutator segments is zero. The difference of potential between the brushes when the brush width just equals the spacing between the commutator segments will have the form illustrated in Fig. 7-12. Clearly, the mutual inductance between the movable winding and the main field winding will vary from zero to a maximum and will then reverse suddenly.

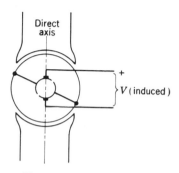

Fig. 7-11. A concentrated winding assembly with a commutator to which the coil ends are connected.

If, instead of a single coil, the rotor winding is uniformly distributed on the surface of the rotor with as many commutator segments as there are armature slots, with the windings in each slot being connected to a commutator bar (see Fig. 7-13), then, as the rotor revolves, polarity reversals will occur with each shift of the commutator bar under the brush. Of course, since the rotor winding is continuous, the entire winding will contribute to the output potential. Now the situation is more nearly that illustrated in Fig. 7-14. In this case, not only has a

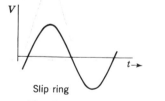

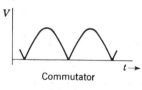

Fig. 7-12. The rectification effect of the commutator.

smoother potential been achieved, a desirable end in itself if a d-c output is desired, but what has also been achieved is a configuration which has lost any preferred orientation properties. As a result, the effective values of M_d and hence of the G factor are now constants which are independent of orientation. This means that in the d-c machine provided with a commutator the total effective $M(\varphi)$ and $G(\varphi)$ are constants, independent of position or time. This materially reduces the complexity of the analysis in these cases.

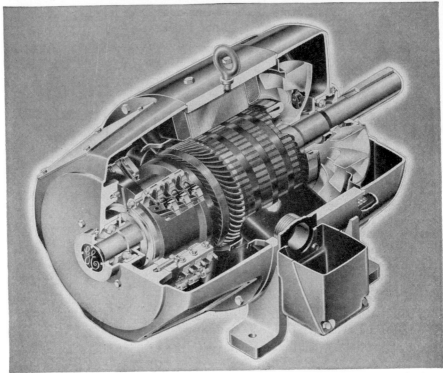

FIG. 7-13. Armature of d-c machine showing commutator. (*Courtesy of General Electric Co.*)

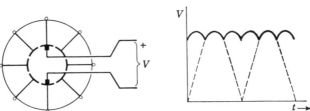

FIG. 7-14. A distributed winding equipped with a commutator, and the form of the output potential.

For the case of the rotating transformer with commutated rotor winding, the electrical equations [Eq. (7-10)] become, with subscript f denoting the fixed winding and a the rotor winding,

$$
\left.
\begin{aligned}
v_d &= v_f = (R_f + L_f p)i_f \\
v_a &= (R_a + L_a p)i_q + G_{af}^{rs}\omega_m i_f
\end{aligned}
\right\}
$$

which, in matrix form, is

$$
\left.
\begin{bmatrix} v_f \\ v_a \end{bmatrix} =
\begin{bmatrix} R_f + L_f p & 0 \\ G_{af}^{rs}\omega_m & R_a + L_a p \end{bmatrix}
\begin{bmatrix} i_f \\ i_a \end{bmatrix}
\right\}
$$

$$(7\text{-}21)$$

where R_f and L_f are the resistance and self-inductance of the fixed winding, R_a and L_a are the resistance and self-inductance of the rotor winding as measured along the quadrature axis, and G_{af}^{rs} $(= +M_f)$ is the motional-emf factor.   Note that, since the motional emf in the rotating winding and the potential $L_f p i_f$ in the fixed winding depend on the total flux regardless of its distribution, these equations are independent of the form of the flux distribution.

The discussion above is actually basic to the description of the operation of all rotating machines, as will be developed below.   It will first be applied to several important classes of d-c machinery.

7-6. The Separately Excited D-C Machine.   We shall first consider the separately excited d-c machine when operated as a generator, and then

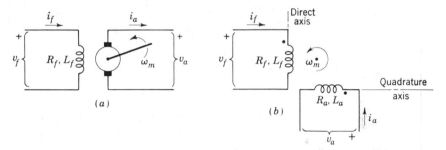

FIG. 7-15. The schematic diagram and the network representation of the separately excited d-c generator.

when operated as a motor.   A schematic diagram of the machine is given in Fig. 7-15a.

Generator Operation.   When a machine is used as a generator, the output quantities of interest are the armature potential, current, or power.   We shall confine our attention to the output potential.   The basic d-c machine comprises a single field system and a single set of brushes along the q axis.   This is precisely the machine considered in the foregoing section.   The subscripts in the notation specify f for field and a for armature, with ω_m denoting the rotational speed in the reference direction.   The general equations for the machine which is illustrated in network form in Fig. 7-15b have the form

$$\begin{bmatrix} v_f \\ v_a \end{bmatrix} = \begin{bmatrix} R_f + L_f p & 0 \\ G_{af}^{rs}\omega_m & R_a + L_a p \end{bmatrix} \begin{bmatrix} i_f \\ i_a \end{bmatrix} \tag{7-22}$$

For the separately excited machine the field excitation potential is independent of the armature potential, although the armature potential is a function of the field potential.   The explicit form of this relationship is to be found.   We thus consider the system performance under steady-state conditions of constant speed and constant load. This is done by referring to the reduced equations

$$\begin{bmatrix} v_{f0} \\ v_{a0} \end{bmatrix} = \begin{bmatrix} R_f & 0 \\ G_{af}\omega_m & R_a \end{bmatrix} \begin{bmatrix} i_{f0} \\ i_{a0} \end{bmatrix}$$

These equations are combined by eliminating the field current i_{f0}, to find

$$v_{a0} = \frac{G_{af}\omega_m}{R_f} v_{f0} + R_a i_{a0} \qquad (7\text{-}23)$$

But for a generator the positive direction for current is opposite to that chosen as the reference direction. Also, the direction of rotation is in the reference direction for $\dot{\varphi}$. Thus for the generator

$$\omega_m \rightarrow \omega_m, \text{ a constant}$$
$$i_{a0} \rightarrow -i_{a0}$$
$$G_{af} \rightarrow +M_d$$

Equation (7-23) now becomes the following operating equation:

$$v_{a0} = \frac{M_d\omega_m}{R_f} v_{f0} - R_a i_{a0} \qquad (7\text{-}24)$$

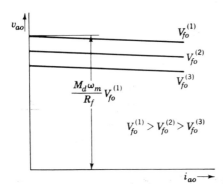

FIG. 7-16. The terminal characteristics of the separately excited d-c generator.

A plot of this expression, with v_f as a parameter, is given in Fig. 7-16. This plot gives the characteristics of the separately excited d-c generator.

The transient-response characteristics of the machine are somewhat more involved. Moreover, three cases of interest exist: (1) the load is considered to be small, with the machine being driven at constant speed; (2) the load is not negligible, under constant-speed conditions; and (3) the case under (2), but with the speed varying with load. All three cases are to be examined.

1. For the case when the load current is negligible, the matrix equation [Eq. (7-22)] becomes the following:

$$\begin{bmatrix} v_f \\ v_a \end{bmatrix} = \begin{bmatrix} R_f + L_f p & 0 \\ M_d\omega_m & R_a + L_a p \end{bmatrix} \begin{bmatrix} i_f \\ 0 \end{bmatrix} \qquad (7\text{-}25)$$

These equations lead directly to the following system response equation,

$$v_a = M_d\omega_m \frac{1}{R_f + L_f p} v_f$$

which may be written in the form

$$v_a = \frac{M_d\omega_m}{R_f} \frac{v_f}{1 + \tau_f p} \qquad (7\text{-}26)$$

where $\tau_f = L_f/R_f$ is the field-circuit time constant.

For the case when v_f is the step excitation corresponding to closing the switch to the field excitation source,

$$v_f = V_f \qquad \text{for } t \geq 0$$
$$v_f = 0 \qquad \text{for } t < 0$$

the response is the simple exponential form, having the explicit equation

$$v_a = \frac{M_d\omega_m}{R_f} V_f(1 - e^{-t/\tau_f}) \qquad (7\text{-}27)$$

The response characteristic specified by this equation has the form illustrated in Fig. 7-17. For practical machines the field time constant τ_f will range from approximately 0.2 sec for small machines (of the order of 1 kw) to perhaps 3 or 4 sec for large machines (of the order 100 to 500 kw).

2. For the case when the load current is not negligible, the complete expression specified by Eq. (7-22) must be evaluated. Now the system differential equation becomes

$$v_a = \frac{M_d\omega_m}{R_f} \frac{1}{1 + \tau_f p} v_f - (R_a + L_a p)i_a$$
$$(7\text{-}28)$$

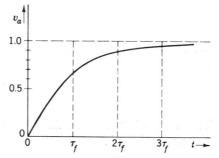

FIG. 7-17. The armature potential response of the separately excited d-c generator to a step-field excitation.

But an explicit relation exists between i_a and v_a which depends on the character of the load. For the case when the load is purely resistive,

$$i_a = \frac{v_a}{R_L}$$

and Eq. (7-28) reduces to the expression

$$v_a = \frac{M_d\omega_m}{R_f} \frac{1}{1 + \tau_f p} v_f - \frac{R_a + L_a p}{R_L} v_a$$

This is rearranged to the form

$$v_a = \frac{M_d\omega_m}{R_f} \frac{1}{1 + \tau_f p} \frac{1}{(R_L + R_a + L_a p)/R_L} v_f$$

which is
$$v_a = \frac{M_d R_L \omega_m}{R_f(R_L + R_a)} \frac{1}{(1 + \tau_f p)(1 + \tau_a' p)} v_f \qquad (7\text{-}29)$$

where $\tau_a' = L_a/(R_a + R_L)$ is the effective armature time constant.

Ordinarily the effective armature time constant is small compared with the field time constant because of the relatively small self-inductance of the armature winding and the relatively appreciable value of R_L under normal load conditions. Thus the effects due to the armature time constant can ordinarily be neglected, with the principal delay being that due to the field circuit.

3. In the case when the speed of rotation ω_m varies with load, the analysis becomes more involved because now the differential equations of the system become nonlinear, owing to the appearance therein of the term $M_d\omega_m i_f$. Two possible approaches now exist for the analysis. One approach would seek the solution to the nonlinear differential equations, when the explicit form of the variation of ω_m with i_a is known. The second method assumes that the variation of ω_m with i_a is not large, and a perturbation calculation is made to find the effect of the variation of ω_m about the constant value, say ω_{m0}. This is essentially the approach that was followed in our study of incremental transducers.

To indicate the approach that must be followed, use is made of the fact that since v_a is now a function of both ω_m and v_f, and this may be implicitly written $v_a = v_a(\omega_m,v_f)$, then for a variation about the normal operating values we may write

$$\Delta v_a = \frac{\partial v_a}{\partial v_f}\bigg)_{\omega_m} \Delta v_f + \frac{\partial v_a}{\partial \omega_m}\bigg)_{v_f} \Delta \omega_m \qquad (7\text{-}30)$$

These are, of course, the first-order terms in the Taylor expansion of the function $v_a(\omega_m,v_f)$. Observe that the first term on the right expresses precisely the situation discussed above in (2), with the result being that specified in Eq. (7-29). The variation about this known response is expressed by the second term of Eq. (7-30). The explicit variation is given by the expression

$$\frac{\Delta v_a}{\Delta \omega_m} = \frac{M_d R_L}{R_f(R_L + R_a)} \frac{1}{(1 + \tau_f p)(1 + \tau_a' p)} V_f \qquad (7\text{-}31)$$

which can be evaluated directly. The complete response is the sum of the responses specified by the solutions to Eqs. (7-29) and (7-31).

Motor Action. When a rotating machine is used as a motor, the output quantities of interest are speed, torque, or power, depending upon the application to which the machine is to be put. It is desired initially to establish the torque convention to be employed in this book. Refer to Fig. 7-18, which shows the rotating system. This figure shows that the application of a mechanical torque T_m *to* the shaft of the machine *in* the reference positive direction for ω_m results in mechanical power passing into the machine. Likewise, the application of a mechanical torque of electrical origin to the shaft in the reference positive direction for ω_m also results in mechanical power passing into the machine.   These torques are opposed or resisted by inertial and dissipative torques.   The torque balance requires that

$$T_e + T_m = Jp^2\varphi + Dp\varphi = Jp\omega_m + D\omega_m \qquad (7\text{-}32)$$

The convention here adopted draws an analogy between the electrical and mechanical quantities.   Thus, potential is applied to electrical terminals, and torque is applied to the shaft. Apart from the effect of losses, positive potential and current mean motoring action, and positive torque and speed mean generating action.

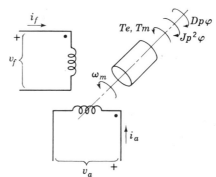

For a further view of this matter, consider that a closed surface encloses the machine.   The principle of conservation of energy may be invoked, and this requires that

Power into electrical ports
   + power into mechanical port
= power stored + power dissipated

Fig. 7-18. Schematic diagram of the d-c motor to establish the torque convention.

But the machine under survey contains two electrical ports and one mechanical port.   The controlling equations of the system are

$$v_f = (R_f + L_f p)i_f$$
$$v_a = M_{d}\omega_m i_f + (R_a + L_a p)i_a$$
$$T_m = Jp\omega_m + D\omega_m - T_e$$

Now multiply the first equation by i_f, the second by i_a, and the third by ω_m.   Add the resulting equations, and rearrange the terms as follows:

$$(v_f i_f + v_a i_a) + T_m \omega_m = (R_f i_f^2 + R_a i_a^2 + D\omega_m^2)$$
$$+ [i_f(L_f p i_f) + i_a(L_a p i_a) + \omega_m(Jp\omega_m)] + (M_{d}\omega_m i_f i_a - T_e \omega_m)$$

This equation is precisely in the form of the above statement of the principle of conservation of energy.   For exact correspondence, it is required that we write

$$- T_e \omega_m + M_{d}\omega_m i_f i_a = 0$$

from which it follows that

$$T_e = M_{d} i_f i_a \qquad (7\text{-}33)$$

This expression specifies that, if i_f and i_a are both positive (in the positive direction for current), then the mechanical torque of electrical origin is in the direction to cause rotation in the positive ω_m direction.   Observe that the presence of the commutator causes the factor $\frac{1}{2}$ that appears in the general expression given by Eq. (7-15) to be absent.

It is convenient to write

$$P_e = -\omega_m T_e = -\omega_m M_d i_f i_a \tag{7-34}$$

since this shows that P_e is derived from electrical power passing into the electrical terminals, whereas T_e is defined as a torque applied *to* the shaft.

For a motor i_f and i_a are in the positive reference direction, and T_e as specified by Eq. (7-33) is the mechanical torque converted from electrical form in the machine and produces rotation in the positive direction for ω_m. Since in the motor the applied torque causes mechanical power to flow *out* of the machine at positive speed, it is convenient to write

$$T_L = -T_m$$

where T_L is the load torque on the motor and is a positive number. The resulting torque equation for the motor is thus written

$$T_e - T_L = Jp\omega_m + D\omega_m \tag{7-35}$$

We wish to consider the operation of the motor under a variety of special operating conditions which are of practical importance. These are (1) field voltage control, with constant armature current, and (2) armature voltage control, with constant field current.

1. Field voltage control, with constant armature current. This method of control is used extensively in position control devices requiring small amounts of power. The analysis proceeds from Eqs. (7-22) and (7-32), with i_a now written I_a to denote that the armature current is constant. The controlling equations now under study are

and

$$\left.\begin{array}{c} \begin{bmatrix} v_f \\ v_a \end{bmatrix} = \begin{bmatrix} R_f + L_f p & 0 \\ M_d\omega_m & R_a + L_a p \end{bmatrix}\begin{bmatrix} i_f \\ I_a \end{bmatrix} \\ T_e = (Jp^2 + Dp)\varphi + T_L \end{array}\right\} \tag{7-36}$$

First we consider the mechanical equation, which becomes, under steady-state conditions,

$$T_{e0} = Jp^2\varphi_0 + Dp\varphi_0 + T_{L0}$$

But since, under steady-state conditions,

$$p^2\varphi_0 = 0 \qquad p\varphi_0 = \omega_{m0}$$

then we have that

$$T_{L0} = T_{e0} - D\omega_{m0} \tag{7-37}$$

This expression for torque is often used in precisely this form. We shall use this expression for specifying the steady-state speed.   Thus

$$\omega_{m0} = \frac{1}{D}(T_{e0} - T_{L0}) \tag{7-38}$$

The form of the variation specified by this equation is illustrated graphically in Fig. 7-19.   This curve shows that the speed is sensitive to torque variations.

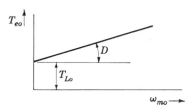

FIG. 7-19. Steady state speed-torque relation.

The transient response of the system can be deduced directly, although the relations become somewhat complicated.   From the first of Eqs. (7-36)

$$i_f = \frac{1}{R_f}\frac{1}{1 + \tau_f p}v_f \tag{7-39}$$

Also, the electrical torque is written

where
$$\left.\begin{array}{c} T_e = M_d I_a i_f = K_t i_f \\ K_t = M_d I_a \end{array}\right\} \tag{7-40}$$

Then, by combining Eqs. (7-39) and (7-40),

$$T_e = \frac{K_t}{R_f}\frac{1}{1 + \tau_f p}v_f \tag{7-41}$$

The general mechanical equation thus becomes

$$(Jp^2 + Dp)\varphi + T_L = \frac{K_t}{R_f}\frac{1}{1 + \tau_f p}v_f \tag{7-42}$$

From this equation we can write the relation between the rotational angle φ and the applied field potential and the mechanical load torque.   This is

$$\varphi = \frac{K_t}{R_f}\frac{1}{(1 + \tau_f p)(Jp^2 + Dp)}v_f - \frac{1}{Jp^2 + Dp}T_L$$

which is written in the form

$$\varphi = \frac{K_t}{R_f D}\frac{1}{p(1 + \tau_m p)(1 + \tau_f p)}v_f - \frac{1}{Dp(1 + \tau_m p)}T_L \tag{7-43}$$

where $\tau_m = J/D$ is the motor mechanical time constant.   Of course, if the speed response is of interest, we need recall only that $\omega_m = p\varphi$ and the controlling differential equation is

$$\omega_m = \frac{K_t}{R_f D} \frac{1}{(1 + \tau_m p)(1 + \tau_f p)} v_f - \frac{1}{D(1 + \tau_m p)} T_L \quad (7\text{-}44)$$

Equations (7-43) and (7-44) may be solved for two types of disturbances, both of which are of interest. These are (1) the response of the system to changes in applied field potential with constant load torque and (2) the response of the system to changes in load torque with constant field potential. Clearly from Eq. (7-44) a change in applied field potential Δv_f will be accompanied by a change in speed, for constant T_L, by an amount

$$\Delta \omega_m = \frac{K_t}{R_f D} \Delta v_f \quad (7\text{-}45)$$

The change in speed will be delayed by the field and mechanical time constants. Likewise, of course, an increase in T_L, for constant v_f, produces a decrease in speed, by an amount

$$\Delta \omega_m = \frac{1}{D} \Delta T_L \quad (7\text{-}46)$$

2. Armature voltage control, with constant field current. This method of control finds extensive application for large machines. The controlling equations become, in the present case, by writing $i_f = I_f$,

$$\begin{aligned} v_a &= M_d \omega_m I_f + (R_a + L_a p) i_a \\ T_e &= (M_d I_f) i_a = K_t' i_a \\ T_e &= (Jp^2 + Dp)\varphi + T_L = (Jp + D)\omega_m + T_L \end{aligned} \quad (7\text{-}47)$$

The field-circuit equation is not included in this set because it does not vary in time.

Under steady-state conditions, Eqs. (7-47) reduce to the following:

$$\begin{aligned} v_{a0} &= K_t' \omega_{m0} + R_a i_{a0} \\ T_{e0} &= K_t' i_{a0} \\ T_{e0} &= D\omega_{m0} + T_{L0} \end{aligned} \quad (7\text{-}48)$$

If the armature current i_{a0} is eliminated from these equations, the result may be written

$$T_{e0} = K_t' i_{a0} = \frac{K_t'}{R_a} (v_{a0} - K_t' \omega_{m0}) \quad (7\text{-}49)$$

Also, when this expression is combined with the last of Eqs. (7-48), the result is

$$T_{L0} = T_{e0} - D\omega_{m0} = \frac{K_t'}{R_a} v_{a0} - \left(\frac{K_t'^2}{R_a} + D\right) \omega_{m0} \quad (7\text{-}50)$$

This expression is solved for ω_{m0}. There results

$$\omega_{m0} = Av_{a0} - BT_{L0}$$

where $\qquad A = \dfrac{K'_t}{R_a(K'^2_t/R_a + D)} \qquad B = \dfrac{1}{K'^2_t/R_a + D}$ $\qquad$ (7-51)

A set of speed-torque curves specified by this equation, with v_{a0} and with T_{L0} as parameters, is contained in Fig. 7-20. Curves a show that the speed falls slightly as the load torque increases.

A physical explanation of this drooping characteristic is contained in Eqs. (7-48). From the first of these it is seen that the armature current actually depends on the difference between the applied voltage and the rotational emf. Under the conditions of no load, this difference

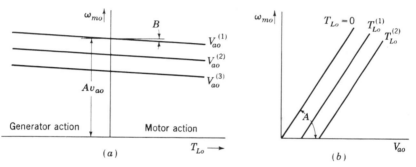

Fig. 7-20. (a) The speed-torque curves of a d-c machine, with v_{a0} as a parameter; (b) the speed-excitation curves, with torque as a parameter.

is very small, with a corresponding small armature current i_{a0}. The value of i_{a0} must be such that the electromagnetic torque produced by the machine is just sufficient to overcome the frictional and other losses. When a load is applied, the difference between the applied potential and the rotational emf must increase. The resulting armature current will increase and the machine will thereby produce sufficient torque for the load as well as for the losses. As a result, the speed must decrease. Ordinarily the change in speed for a considerable change in electrical torque is not large, and so the motor will operate at a reasonably constant speed over its full operating range.

The transient response of the motor is specified by the general equations [Eq. (7-47)]. These equations are combined into the following expression,

$$(Jp + D)\omega_m = -T_L + \frac{K'_t}{R_a(1 + \tau_a p)} (v_a - K'_t\omega_m)$$

which is solved for ω_m. The resulting expression is

$$\omega_m = \frac{K_t'}{R_a(1 + \tau_a p)\left[Jp + \left(D + \frac{K_t'^2}{R_a(1 + \tau_a p)}\right)\right]} v_a$$
$$- \frac{1}{Jp + \left[D + \frac{K_t'^2}{R_a(1 + \tau_a p)}\right]} T_L \quad (7\text{-}52)$$

This expression may be simplified, since the armature time constant τ_a is usually small compared with the motor effective mechanical time constant τ_m, which is defined below. The approximate equation thus becomes

$$\omega_m = \frac{K_t'}{R_a(Jp + D_e)} v_a - \frac{1}{Jp + D_e} T_L \quad \left.\right\}$$

where $\qquad D_e = D + \dfrac{K_t'^2}{R_a} \qquad\qquad\qquad (7\text{-}53)$

This expression is now written in the form

$$\omega_m = \frac{K_t'}{R_a D_e} \frac{1}{(1 + \tau_m p)} v_a - \frac{1}{D_e(1 + \tau_m p)} T_L \quad (7\text{-}54)$$

where $\quad \tau_m = \dfrac{J}{D_e} =$ effective mechanical time constant of motor

But note that the effective damping is primarily determined by the term $K_t'^2/R_a$, which arises from the electromagnetic effects of the rotation. The motor mechanical time constant, which is determined principally by this electromagnetic term, is reasonably small (of the order of 1 sec or less), with a corresponding rapid response to armature or load variations.

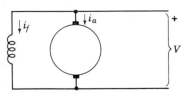

FIG. 7-21. The schematic diagram of the d-c shunt motor.

7-7. The Shunt Machine. In the shunt machine, the armature and field potentials are equal, since these windings are connected in parallel, as illustrated in Fig. 7-21. The controlling equations of this machine are now the following:

$$\begin{bmatrix} v_f \\ v_a \end{bmatrix} = \begin{bmatrix} v \\ v \end{bmatrix} = \begin{bmatrix} R_f + L_f p & 0 \\ G_{af}\omega_m & R_a + L_a p \end{bmatrix} \begin{bmatrix} i_f \\ i_a \end{bmatrix}$$
$$T_e = i_f M_d i_a$$
$$T_e = (Jp^2 + Dp)\varphi + T_L \qquad (7\text{-}55)$$

For convenience, we first examine the machine as a motor, and then as a generator. We shall find that in both cases the linear model will

lead to some difficulties in analysis.   These are resolved by recourse to
the experimental behavior of such machines.

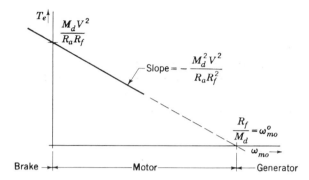

FIG. 7-22. The electrical torque vs. speed curve for the shunt motor.

Motor Operation.   For the case when v is the applied potential $(= V)$,
the equations yield for i_f and i_a

$$i_f = \frac{V}{R_f + L_f p}$$

$$i_a = \frac{-M_d \omega_m V}{(R_f + L_f p)(R_a + L_a p)} + \frac{V}{R_a + L_a p} \qquad (7\text{-}56)$$

Consider the expression for the electrical torque under steady-state
conditions.   Equations (7-56) reduce to

$$i_{f0} = \frac{V}{R_f}$$

$$i_{a0} = -\frac{M_d \omega_{m0} V}{R_f R_a} + \frac{V}{R_a} \qquad (7\text{-}57)$$

and the expression for the electrical torque becomes

$$T_{e0} = i_{f0} M_d i_{a0}$$

or $\qquad T_{e0} = \frac{V^2 M_d}{R_f}\left(-\frac{M_d \omega_{m0}}{R_f R_a} + \frac{1}{R_a}\right) = \frac{V^2 M_d}{R_f R_a}\left(1 - \frac{M_d \omega_{m0}}{R_f}\right) \qquad (7\text{-}58)$

A plot of this expression has the form illustrated in Fig. 7-22.   Also,
the no-load speed is that for which $T_{e0} \to 0$, or

$$M_d \omega_{m0} = R_f \qquad (7\text{-}59)$$

Actually this is a critical condition and requires further examination.
A complete explanation requires that the effects of saturation, as expressed
through the saturation curve of the machine (the open-circuit v_a, i_f curve,

with ω_m as a parameter), must be considered.   Figure 7-23 shows three magnetization curves of the d-c machine with rotor speed as a parameter. Also shown is the field resistance line.

Recall that the magnetization curve is a plot of the relation

$$v_a \ (= M_{d}\omega_m i_f) \text{ versus } i_f \qquad \text{for } i_a = 0, \text{ constant } \omega_m$$

As is evident from the figure, there is one particular speed at which $M_d\omega_m$ is equal to R_f, and it is at this value that the slope of the saturation curve and the R_f line are equal.   Also, it appears from the curves that at this speed the machine will not generate a potential equal to V.

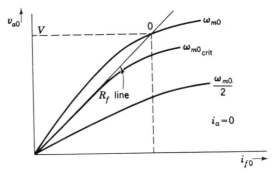

Fig. 7-23. Saturation curves of the d-c machine for three values of speed.   Also shown is the field resistance line.

In general, upon the application of a potential V to the armature' the machine will accelerate until it reaches such a speed that the generated emf is equal to the applied potential.   This occurs when the saturation curve crosses the R_f line for $v_a = V$, as illustrated in the figure.   Owing to the nonlinearity in the saturation curve, this may be taken to mean that M_d is a function of i_f.

The speed at which the motor operates under steady-state conditions of load is readily calculated from the second of Eqs. (7-56).   Thus since

$$i_{a0} = \frac{-M_{d}\omega_{m0}V}{R_f R_a} + \frac{V}{R_a}$$

from which $\qquad \omega_{m0} = \frac{R_f R_a}{M_d V}\left(\frac{V}{R_a} - i_{a0}\right) = \frac{R_f}{M_d}\left(1 - \frac{i_{a0}}{V/R_a}\right)$ (7-60)

because v_f is a constant, i_f is a constant and M_d assumes a single value, with $M_d\omega_{m0}$ representing the slope of the saturation curve for the field current being considered.   Hence, when the speed varies, for constant field current, the slope $M_d\omega_{m0}$ varies according to ω_{m0} but M_d remains constant.   But under operating conditions M_d is determined for no-load speed ω_{m00} by the crossover point of the ω_{m00} saturation curve and the R_f line, as illustrated in Fig. 7-22. At this point

$$M_d \omega_{m00} = R_f$$

This permits us to write Eq. (7-60) in the form

$$\omega_{m0} = \omega_{m00} \left(1 - \frac{i_{a0}}{V/R_a} \right) \qquad (7\text{-}61)$$

But since in general $V/R_a \gg i_{a0}$, the second term in the speed relation is small, even for rated armature current. The speed variations of the shunt machine with load are small, and the machine is considered as a substantially constant-speed machine.

Generator Operation. In the operation of the machine as a generator the speed is maintained constant at ω_{m0} and the no-load potential is established by the crossover of the saturation curve for ω_{m0} and the R_f line. The terminal potential drops with load, since from Eqs. (7-55) under steady conditions

$$\begin{aligned} v_{f0} &= v_{a0} = R_f i_{f0} \\ v_{a0} &= M_d \omega_{m0} i_{f0} - R_a i_{a0} \end{aligned} \qquad (7\text{-}62)$$

where $-i_{a0}$ is used for the armature current, owing to the prescribed reference direction for current. From these

$$v_{a0} = \frac{M_d \omega_{m0} v_{a0}}{R_f} - R_a i_{a0}$$

which leads to
$$v_{a0} = \frac{R_a}{M_d \omega_{m0}/R_f - 1} i_{a0} \qquad (7\text{-}63)$$

Actually, this equation is meaningless in the absence of saturation. For example, at the no-load point, by Eqs. (7-62)

$$v_{a0} = M_d \omega_{m0} i_{f0} = R_f i_{f0}$$

and v_{a0} given by Eq. (7-63) becomes infinite.

A more precise relation is possible if we assume that the saturation curve in the neighborhood of the crossover point is represented by a piecewise linear approximation, as illustrated in Fig. 7-24. This curve may be written explicitly as

$$v_{a0} = A + B i_{f0} \qquad (7\text{-}64)$$

Thus under the present approximation

$$v_{a0} = \left(A + \frac{B v_{a0}}{R_f} \right) - R_a i_{a0}$$

or
$$v_{a0} = \frac{A}{1 - B/R_f} - \frac{R_a i_{a0}}{1 - B/R_f} \qquad (7\text{-}65)$$

which may be written in the form

$$v_{a0} = V - \frac{R_a i_{a0}}{1 - B/R_f}$$ (7-66)

where V, the no-load potential, is

$$V = \frac{A}{1 - B/R_f}$$

This expression shows that the terminal potential will fall linearly with load current i_{a0}.

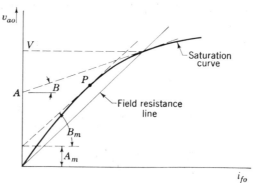

Fig. 7-24. Piecewise approximation to the saturation curve.

Actually, a minimum stable value of B exists; it is

$$B_m = R_f$$ (7-67)

as required by Eq. (7-66). When B_m has this value, the slope of the output-voltage curve becomes vertical. This sets a limit to i_{a0}. As seen in Fig. 7-24, B is the slope of the piecewise curve at the operating point, and B_m specifies the slope of the piecewise linear curve which is parallel to the field resistance line and to the saturation curve.

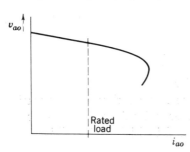

Fig. 7-25. The terminal characteristics of the shunt generator.

The foregoing discussion actually shows that, as a shunt generator is loaded beyond its normal capacity, the operating potential V continues to fall until the operating point on the saturation curve reaches point P, when no further increase in load current is possible. The form of the variation is illustrated in Fig. 7-25.

7-8. Cross-field Machines—The Amplidyne. In certain control applications which require rapid response of the output potential of a d-c generator with changes in excitation, it is found that the electrical time constants of the standard type of d-c machines are too great to meet the desired response requirements. The metadyne and the amplidyne generator, both of which are cross-field machines (that is, these machines are provided with brush sets in both the direct axis and the quadrature axis), have been developed to meet the requirements for

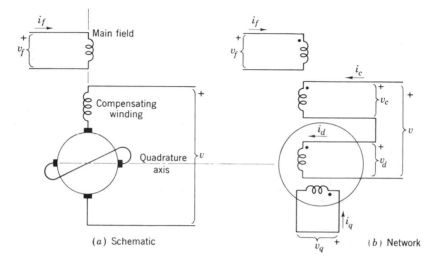

(a) Schematic   (b) Network

FIG. 7-26. The basic features of the amplidyne generator.

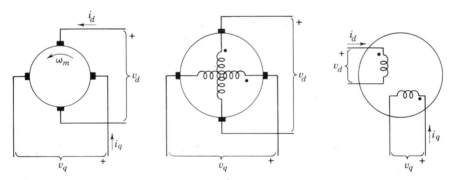

FIG. 7-27. The metadyne transformer crossed armature winding excitation.

rapid-response characteristics. The essential features of the amplidyne are shown in Fig. 7-26, which illustrates the general arrangement of the windings in their proper space-phase orientation. The metadyne is similar to this but lacks the compensating winding.

To understand the operation of the machine, we first examine the action of the rotor, with its two sets of brushes. Consider the situation illustrated in Fig. 7-27, with excitation to each brush pair. We may consider the stationary field windings to be missing or else that the

windings are not excited.   The iron structure of the stationary assembly
is required to provide the low-reluctance magnetic circuit.   This device
has been called a *metadyne transformer*, owing to the input-output
properties.

It is observed from the equivalent circuit that the two equivalent
windings bear precisely the same relation to each other as the windings
in the normal d-c machine.   The essential difference lies in the fact that
both windings are in motion, and each therefore has generated in it a
motional emf due to its motion in the other's quadrature field.   Thus,
instead of Eq. (7-22), the electrical equations now become

$$\begin{bmatrix} v_d \\ v_q \end{bmatrix} = \begin{bmatrix} R_d + L_d p & G_{dq}\omega_m \\ G_{qd}\omega_m & R_q + L_q p \end{bmatrix} \begin{bmatrix} i_d \\ i_q \end{bmatrix} \tag{7-68}$$

where G_{dq} and G_{qd} are the appropriate motional-emf factors for the two
windings.   If the air gap is uniform, the armature windings are equivalent
relative to the two sets of brushes and $L_d = L_q = L_r$; also $R_d = R_q = R_r$.
Also for a sinusoidal flux-density distribution in the air gap, and for the
specified reference direction for angle,

$$G_{dq}^{rr} = -G_{qd}^{rr} = -M_{dd}^{rr} = -L_d{}^r = -L_q{}^r \tag{7-69}$$

Thus Eq. (7-68) attains the form

$$\begin{bmatrix} v_d \\ v_q \end{bmatrix} = \begin{bmatrix} R_r + L_r p & -G_{qd}\omega_m \\ G_{qd}\omega_m & R_r + L_r p \end{bmatrix} \begin{bmatrix} i_d \\ i_q \end{bmatrix} \tag{7-70}$$

Observe from these equations, with i_q denoting the load current, that
the motional emf in the direct axis is zero for zero-load current.   Under
these conditions the performance equations are exactly the same as those
for the standard d-c generator.

Another feature of interest in cross-field machine operation   follows
from an examination of the torque equation given by Eq. (7-15).   Now
it follows that

$$T_e = [I_t G I] = \begin{bmatrix} i_d & i_q \end{bmatrix} \begin{bmatrix} 0 & -G_{qd}^{rr} \\ G_{qd}^{rr} & 0 \end{bmatrix} \begin{bmatrix} i_d \\ i_q \end{bmatrix} = 0 \tag{7-71}$$

which shows that no electromechanical energy conversion can take
place in such a cross-field machine.

An interesting property of the metadyne transformer is its ability
to generate a constant current under armature excitation.   To see this
requires that we note that in the absence of losses, and for zero energy
conversion,

$$v_d i_d = v_q i_q \tag{7-72}$$

Also, from the motional-emf equations

$$v_d = -G_{qd}^{rr}\omega_m i_q$$
$$v_q = G_{qd}^{rr}\omega_m i_d$$

Thus
$$i_q = \frac{v_d i_d}{G_{qd}^{rr}\omega_m i_d} = \frac{v_d}{\omega_m G_{qd}^{rr}} \tag{7-73}$$

which shows that the output current is a function of the input potential only and is independent of load. Thus the metadyne transformer converts d-c power at one voltage and current level to d-c power at a different voltage and current level.

Now return to considerations of the amplidyne which is illustrated in Fig. 7-26. In this case the q-axis armature winding is short-circuited so that in general $L_d \neq L_q$. The appropriate set of equations for this machine, which is essentially an extension of Eq. (7-70), is

$$\begin{bmatrix} v_f \\ v_c \\ v_d \\ v_q \end{bmatrix} = \begin{bmatrix} R_f + L_f p & M_{cf}p & M_{fd}p & 0 \\ M_{cf}p & R_c + L_c p & M_{cd}p & 0 \\ M_{fd}p & M_{cd}p & R_d + L_d p & \omega_m G_{dq}^{rr} \\ G_{qd}^{rf}\omega_m & G_{qd}^{rc}\omega_m & G_{qd}^{rr}\omega_m & R_q + L_q p \end{bmatrix} \begin{bmatrix} i_f \\ i_c \\ i_d \\ i_q \end{bmatrix} \tag{7-74}$$

where, by the G-M rule,

$$G_{dq}^{rr} = -L_q^r \qquad G_{qd}^{rf} = M_{fd} \qquad G_{qd}^{rc} = M_{cd} \qquad G_{qd}^{rr} = L_d^r$$

Steady-state Response. We first consider the machine characteristics under steady-state operation. In this case, with a slight change in notation, Eq. (7-74) reduces to the following form:

$$\begin{bmatrix} v_{f0} \\ v_{c0} \\ v_{d0} \\ 0 \end{bmatrix} = \begin{bmatrix} R_f & 0 & 0 & 0 \\ 0 & R_c & 0 & 0 \\ 0 & 0 & R_r & G_{dq}\omega_{m0} \\ G_{qf}\omega_{m0} & G_{qc}\omega_{m0} & G_{qd}\omega_{m0} & R_r \end{bmatrix} \begin{bmatrix} i_{f0} \\ i_{d0} \\ i_{d0} \\ i_{q0} \end{bmatrix} \tag{7-75}$$

It is desired to find an expression for the output potential. This is seen to be

$$v_{a0} = v_{c0} + v_{d0} \tag{7-76}$$

Now, from the fourth equation of Eq. (7-75)

$$i_{q0} = -\frac{G_{qf}\omega_{m0}}{R_r}i_{f0} - \frac{G_{qc} + G_{qd}}{R_r}\omega_{m0}i_{d0}$$

Combine this with the third equation of this set to get

$$v_{d0} = \left(R_r - G_{dq}\omega_{m0}^2 \frac{G_{qc} + G_{qd}}{R_r}\right)i_{d0} - \frac{G_{dq}G_{qf}}{R_r}\omega_{m0}^2 i_{f0}$$

This may be written, by the first equation of the set,

$$v_{d0} = \left[R_r - \frac{G_{dq}G_{qd}}{R_r} \omega_{m0}^2 \left(1 + \frac{G_{qc}}{G_{qd}} \right) \right] i_{d0} - \frac{G_{dq}G_{qf}}{R_r R_f} \omega_{m0}^2 v_{f0} \qquad (7\text{-}77)$$

Hence v_{a0} becomes

$$v_{a0} = \left[R_c + R_r - \frac{G_{dq}G_{qd}}{R_r} \omega_{m0}^2 \left(1 + \frac{G_{qc}}{G_{qd}} \right) \right] i_{d0} - \frac{G_{dq}G_{qf}}{R_r R_f} \omega_{m0}^2 v_{f0} \qquad (7\text{-}78)$$

This expression may be written in the following simple form, since $i_{d0} = -i_{a0}$,

$$\left. \begin{array}{l} v_{a0} = K_f v_{f0} - R i_{a0} \\[2mm] \text{where} \qquad K_f = - \dfrac{G_{dq}G_{qf}}{R_r R_f} \omega_{m0}^2 \\[4mm] \text{and} \qquad R = R_c + R_r - \dfrac{G_{dq}G_{qd}}{R_r} \omega_{m0}^2 \left(1 + \dfrac{G_{qc}}{G_{qd}} \right) \end{array} \right\} \qquad (7\text{-}79)$$

Now, the design of the machine is such that

$$G_{qc}\omega_m i_c = -G_{qd}\omega_m i_d$$

which is that

$$G_{qc} = -G_{qd} \qquad (7\text{-}80)$$

The result of this is that the demagnetizing influence of i_q on the main field flux, and hence on v_d, is fully compensated by the magnetizing effect produced by the compensating winding. Alternatively, it makes v_d less dependent on i_d, since it tends to reduce the effect of the armature self-inductance. For the connections shown, the potential drop due to armature reaction has been fully compensated. The typical output characteristic, specified by Eqs. (7-79), has the form illustrated in Fig. 7-28.

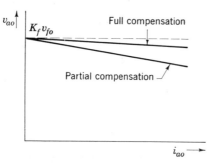

FIG. 7-28. Output characteristics of the compensated cross-field (amplidyne) generator.

Transient Response. The transient-response characteristics of the machine under the conditions of full compensation are now considered. The analysis begins from the sets of Eq. (7-74), although the second and third equations of the set are combined to give the output potential. The initial equations are now

$$\begin{aligned} v_f &= (R_f + L_f p)i_f - (M_{cf} + M_{fd})pi_a \\ v &= v_c + v_d = (M_{cf} + M_{fd})i_f \\ &\qquad - [(R_c + R_r) + (L_c + L_d + 2M_{cd})p]i_a + G_{dq}\omega_m i_q \\ 0 &= G_{qf}\omega_m i_f - \omega_m(G_{qc} + G_{qd})i_a + (R_r + L_q p)i_q \end{aligned} \qquad (7\text{-}81)$$

Now, for full compensation in accordance with Eq. (7-80), the compensating coil is considered to produce a flux that is equal though opposite to that of the armature coils. We assume therefore that the mutual flux linkage of each of these coils with the main field should be equal. Thus it is assumed that very approximately, at least,

$$M_{cf} = -M_{df} \tag{7-82}$$

Under these conditions, Eqs. (7-81) reduce to

where
$$\left. \begin{array}{l} v_f = (R_f + L_f p)i_f \\ v = -(R_e + L_e p)i_a + G_{dq}\omega_m i_q \\ 0 = G_{qf}\omega_m i_f + (R_r + L_q p)i_q \\ R_e = R_c + R_r \\ L_e = L_c + L_d + 2M_{cd} \end{array} \right\} \tag{7-83}$$

By combining the first and third of this set an expression for i_q results in terms of the applied field potential v_f,

$$i_q = -\frac{G_{qf}\omega_m}{R_r + L_q p}i_f = -\frac{G_{qf}\omega_m}{R_r(1 + \tau_q p)}\frac{1}{R_f(1 + \tau_f p)}v_f \tag{7-84}$$

where $\tau_q = L_q/R_r =$ quadrature-axis time constant
$\quad \tau_f = L_f/R_f =$ control-field time constant
This expression is combined with the second of Eqs. (7-83) to get

$$v + (R_e + L_e p)i_a = -\frac{G_{qf}G_{dq}\omega_m{}^2}{R_r R_f}\frac{1}{(1 + \tau_q p)(1 + \tau_f p)}v_f \tag{7-85}$$

which may be written as

$$v_g = \frac{K}{(1 + \tau_q p)(1 + \tau_f p)}v_f \tag{7-86}$$

where $v_g = v + (R_e + L_e p)i_a =$ generated potential
$\quad K = -G_{qf}G_{dq}\omega_m{}^2/R_r R_f$

The reason for writing Eq. (7-86) in terms of the amplidyne-generated potential rather than in terms of the terminal voltage of the machine is to be found in the fact that ordinarily the amplidyne is used to provide power to the armature of a d-c motor. Because of this, the load motor-armature-circuit electrical characteristics must also appear in the equations for the over-all amplidyne response characteristic. Thus by writing

$$v = v_{ma} + (R_{ma} + L_{ma} p)i_a$$

where

$$\left. \begin{array}{l} v_{ma} = \text{electromotance (counter emf) of motor armature} \\ R_{ma} = \text{armature resistance} \\ L_{ma} = \text{armature inductance} \end{array} \right\} \tag{7-87}$$

then we have that

$$v_g = v_{ma} + [(R_e + R_{ma}) + (L_e + L_{ma})p]i_a \qquad (7\text{-}88)$$

Observe that this is exactly of the same form as v_g in Eq. (7-87) except that the connected-motor characteristics are now included. But it is seen that the connected motor effectively changes the amplidyne-generated potential characteristics without otherwise affecting the equations, whence the description of the performance is still given by the first of Eqs. (7-87).

Equation (7-86) shows that the transient characteristic of the amplidyne is determined by two time constants. The quadrature-axis time constant is generally small, owing to the fact that this is a short-circuited winding, with a consequently low value of L_q. The control-field time constant is generally the dominant term, but even this is greatly reduced by feeding the field winding from a vacuum-tube amplifier with its large output terminal impedance, and the consequent reduction of τ_f due to the large combined circuit resistance. By the methods here discussed, the effective response of the amplidyne motor-generator set is roughly one-tenth that of the uncompensated machine.

REFERENCES

1. Fitzgerald, A. E., and C. Kingsley, Jr.: "Electric Machinery," 2d ed., McGraw-Hill Book Company, Inc., New York, 1961.
2. Jones, R. W.: "Electric Control Systems," 3d ed., John Wiley & Sons, Inc., New York, 1950.
3. Ku, Y. H.: "Electric Energy Conversion," The Ronald Press Company, New York, 1959.

PROBLEMS

7-1. Suppose that the coils of a magnetic device of the general type discussed in Sec. 7-3 are set for maximum mutual inductance. For small deviations θ, the mutual inductance varies according to the relation

$$M \doteq M_0 \left(\frac{\pi}{2} - \theta \right)$$

(a) If the current through one winding is i_1 and that in the second winding is i_2, find an expression for the torque between the two coils.

(b) If the device is used to measure current (a dynamometer ammeter), the two coils are connected in series. What is the deflection law of the device?

(c) If one coil is excited from the line and the second coil is carrying circuit current, to what is the reading of the device proportional?

7-2. The two-winding device of Prob. 7-1 is connected according to (c). The current coil is carrying the load current, and a step-function potential excitation is applied to the potential coil. Neglecting the time constants of the coils:

(a) Deduce an expression for the motion of the needle.

(*b*) What relation must exist among the system parameters for critical damping to exist?

7-3. Draw a developed diagram similar to Fig. 7-4 to show one phase of a two-phase lap winding for a machine of six poles with two coil sides per slot and four slots per pole. The coil pitch is eight slots (a full-pitch winding).

7-4. Consider a double-layer three-phase winding with nine slots per pole.

(*a*) Plot the stepped mmf curve at the instant when the current in one phase is a maximum, for the two cases: (1) the winding pitch is 100 per cent; (2) the winding pitch is 89 per cent.

(*b*) Draw a sine-wave approximation to the curve on each diagram, and estimate the greatest discrepancy between the two curves.

7-5. The accompanying figure is the developed view of a d-c machine that is provided with main field poles, finely distributed conductors on the armature, and compensating field windings in the pole faces. Observe that the brushes may be

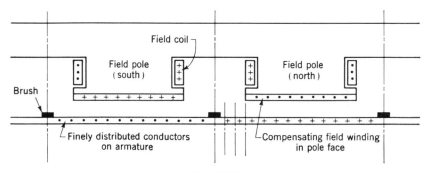

Fig. P7-5

moved. You are to sketch diagrams which will show the air-gap fields produced by each winding, and the combination of such fields, as follows:

(*a*) The main field flux-density distribution. Assume a linear variation from pole tip to pole tip in the interpolar space. What would the distribution be in the case of an ideal machine (one with infinite-permeability iron)? How might the distribution differ from the assumed linear variation, in the practical case?

(*b*) The armature mmf and flux-density distribution with only the armature excited. This is usually referred to as the "armature reaction" flux. Assume a constant flux density from pole tip to pole tip in the interpolar space. Assume also that the maximum flux density is one-third that due to the main field poles, as sketched in (*a*). The brushes are on the mechanical neutral. What would be the distribution in an ideal machine?

(*c*) The combined flux-density distributions due to (*a*) and (*b*).

(*d*) The combined flux-density distributions due to (*a*) and (*b*), but with the brushes at the ⅓ and ⅔ points between the neutral and the pole tip, in the direction of generator rotation. What approximation have you made to account for the changed reluctance of the magnetic circuit with the shift of the brushes?

(*e*) The mmf and flux-density distribution due to the compensating windings in the field pole surfaces. These windings carry armature current and are to provide the same ampere-turns per meter as the armature winding. Make the same assumptions concerning magnetic-circuit reluctance as in (*b*).

(*f*) The combined flux-density distributions due to (*a*), (*b*), and (*e*).

7-6. As the commutator segments slide past the brushes during the normal rotation of the armature of the d-c machine, a short circuit occurs in the coils, which are temporarily connected through the brushes, as illustrated in the sequence of diagrams of Fig. P7-6a. Because of the rapid reversal in current in the winding with changes

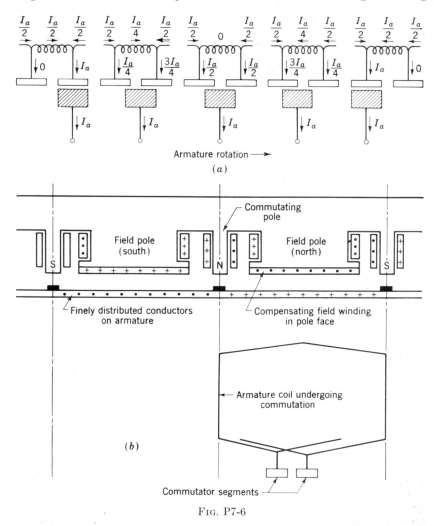

Armature rotation ⟶

(a)

Commutating pole

Field pole (south)

Field pole (north)

Finely distributed conductors on armature

Compensating field winding in pole face

Armature coil undergoing commutation

(b)

Commutator segments

Fig. P7-6

in coil position, a large $L\,di/dt$ potential results, and sparking occurs at the brush-contact surfaces. To reduce this sparking, a number of methods are possible. By design, the inductance is held to a minimum, and the resistive brush-contact voltage drop is significant compared with it. In the modern machines, narrow commutating poles (often called interpoles) are included between the main field poles. These introduce an additional flux density in the region or zone of the coil undergoing commutation. The resulting motional emf produced in the coil will very nearly compensate for the reactance potential. The polarity of the commutating poles is that of the main pole just ahead of it for a generator (in the direction of rotation) and just behind it for a motor. At one time it was common to shift the brushes in order to secure commutation. Basically the principle with brush shifting is the same as that using the commutating poles. Refer to Fig. P7-6b, and sketch the following diagrams:

(a) The main field flux-density distribution. Assume a linear variation from pole tip to pole tip in the interpolar space. With the iron of the commutating pole in the interpolar space, is this a better or a poorer approximation than for the comparable Fig. P7-5?

(b) The armature mmf and flux-density distribution, with only the armature excited. The brushes are in the mechanical neutral. Make reasonable approximations for the flux-density distribution curve for the region between pole tip and commutation pole.

(c) The compensating-winding flux-density distribution when only this winding is excited. These windings carry armature current and provide the same ampere-turns per meter as the armature winding.

(d) The commutating pole, when only this field is excited. Assume a field that is sharply defined by the commutating-pole width, and with an amplitude equal to 0.2 that of the main field flux density. The commutating pole carries armature current, the flux density usually being adjusted by adjusting the interpole air-gap length for optimum commutation.

(e) The combined flux-density distributions due to the contributions (a) through (d).

(f) Now consider a machine without compensating windings and without commutating poles. Combine the flux-density distributions due to the main field poles with that due to the armature winding, with the brushes on neutral, and at the $\frac{1}{3}$ and $\frac{2}{3}$ positions between neutral and next pole tip. Assume that the maximum flux density under the pole tip when the brushes are on neutral is one-third that due to the main field. Make reasonable approximations to account for the fact that the reluctance of the magnetic path will be different in each of the three brush positions. Is there a resultant flux density in the zone of the coil under commutation that would provide the same effect as that produced by the commutating pole?

7-7. A d-c machine that is being operated as a separately excited generator has the following parameters:

$$R_f = 30 \text{ ohms} \qquad R_a = 0.015 \text{ ohm} \qquad R_L = 0.315 \text{ ohm}$$
$$L_f = 30 \text{ henrys} \qquad L_a = 0.010 \text{ henry}$$

The armature is being driven at constant rated speed. Find i_f and v_L as functions of time after the 230-volt excitation is applied to the field terminals.

7-8. A separately excited d-c generator is excited at constant field potential and is operating unloaded. An armature short circuit is assumed to be applied suddenly. Assume that the speed remains constant. How does the armature current vary with time after the application of the short circuit? Assume that all system parameters remain constant, and that $\tau_a = 0.01$ sec, $\tau_f = 0.5$ sec, $V_f = 200$ volts, $M_{d}\omega_m/R_a R_f = 5.0$ are given.

7-9. A separately excited d-c motor is initially operating without external load at a constant speed of 1,800 rpm from a 220-volt source of excitation. Other pertinent data follow:

R_a, armature resistance: 4.45 ohms
$G_{af}i_{f0}$: 1.12 newton-m/amp
J, combined moment of armature plus load: 0.048 kg-m^2
D of mechanical load: 0.012 newton-m-sec/radian

Suppose that at time $t = 0$ an inertia load $J = 0.068$ kg-m² is suddenly applied to the motor shaft by means of a clutch. As a result the motor slows down, and then recovers its original speed.

(a) Find an electrical-analog representation of the system which will describe the operation of the machine.

(b) Deduce the minimum speed of the motor, the armature current at the instant of switching, and the speed-recovery time constant of the motor, following the application of the inertia load.

7-10. A separately excited d-c generator is supplying power to a resistive load. The field current is constant, but the driving source varies sinusoidally according to

$$\dot\varphi = \omega_{m0} + \Omega \sin \omega t$$

Under steady-state conditions, and neglecting R_a and L_a, deduce expressions for the following:

(a) The instantaneous load current i_a

(b) The instantaneous torque produced by the generator

(c) The instantaneous and average power converted from mechanical to electrical form

7-11. Consider two identical shunt motors which are to be excited simultaneously. These motors drive loads which are similar except that one has appreciably more inertia than the other. It is desired that these motors have the same transient response, with the same speeds at any instant. It is supposed that the fields are separately excited from the same power lines and that the armatures are supplied from the same bus, whose potential may be changed to adjust the speed of the machines. Is it possible to vary any of the motor parameters so as to make the transient responses of the two machines identical?

7-12. The accompanying diagram shows the Ward Leonard system for regulating the speed of a d-c motor. It provides armature voltage control, the field current to

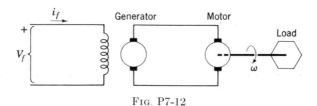

Fig. P7-12

the motor being maintained constant through separate connections, not shown. In this system the motor armature current is supplied by a generator which is driven at constant speed. Neglecting armature reaction in the two machines and considering the load torque to be of the form $D_L\omega + T_L$:

(a) Deduce the differential equation which relates the motor speed with the generator shunt-field excitation v_f and load torque T_L.

(b) What is the steady-state speed of the motor for constant V_f and T_L?

(c) Find the relation between the motor speed ω as a function of T_L, assuming a constant field excitation.

7-13. A Ward Leonard system that provides feedback through the series field of a d-c generator is illustrated in Fig. P7-13. The series field is connected so as to provide a cumulatively compounded generator (the resulting direct-axis field is in the same direction as the direct-axis field produced by the shunt-field winding). If the load torque is of the form $D_L\omega + T_L$:

(a) Deduce the differential equation which relates the motor speed with the generator shunt-field excitation v_f.

(b) What is the steady-state speed ω_{m0} for a specified $v_f = V_f$? Sketch the general form of the variation.

(c) Find the relation for the motor speed ω as a function of T_L, for constant field excitation.

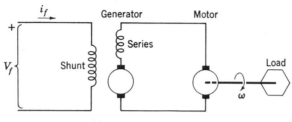

FIG. P7-13

7-14. An alternative form of Ward Leonard system is illustrated in Fig. P7-14. This figure shows the form which would be used in large systems where control of the generator output is by means of an exciter. Actually, the exciter-generator combination may be an amplidyne MG set. In small systems the generator would usually be self-excited. Over-all, therefore, the motor speed is controlled by the field excitation potential v of the exciter. A tachometer generator is coupled to the motor and provides a potential proportional to the speed. This tachometer potential is used as the reference for speed, the exciter potential being the difference between v_g and the adjustable v_1.

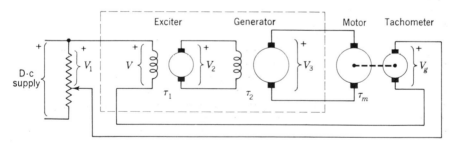

FIG. P7-14

In its normal operation the desired speed is set by adjusting v_1, and the output of the tachometer generator, in the closed-loop circuit, ensures that the speed will be maintained at the established value, independent of load. This latter follows because v is much smaller than v_1, so that, under any steady condition of operation, v_g cannot differ greatly from the reference v_1.

(a) Show that the following relation holds for the system illustrated,

$$v_g = \frac{K}{(1 + \tau_1 p)(1 + \tau_2 p)(1 + \tau_m p)} v$$

where K is a constant.

(b) Show also, since $v = v_1 - v_g$, that

$$v_g = \frac{K}{(1 + \tau_1 p)(1 + \tau_2 p)(1 + \tau_m p) + K} v_1$$

(c) Discuss what factors may cause the Ward Leonard system to fail to regulate, particularly at very slow speeds.

7-15. Two identical 20-hp 230-volt 75-amp d-c shunt machines are to be used as the generator and motor in a Ward Leonard system. The generator is driven at a constant speed of 1,200 rpm. The armature circuit resistance of each machine is 0.14 ohm. The magnetization curve of each machine at 1,200 rpm is:

I_f, amp.	1.2	1.4	1.6	1.8	2.0	2.4	2.8
V_g, volts.	167	190	209	227	241	262	272

(a) Determine the maximum and minimum values of generator field current needed for the motor to operate over the speed range from 300 to 1,500 rpm at full-load armature current. The motor field current is held constant at 1.5 amp.

(b) Compute the speed regulation of the motor for the conditions of maximum and minimum speed, as determined in (a).

(c) If the efficiencies of the machines of the system are: generator drive motor, 86 per cent; generator, 85 per cent; motor, 84 per cent, when the motor delivers 15 hp at 1,200 rpm, how much current is being supplied by the 230-volt line? What is the over-all efficiency of the system?

7-16. Consider that one of the shunt machines of Prob. 7-15 is operating under full load.

(a) If the resultant air-gap flux is increased by 8 per cent, what is the speed?

(b) If a 1.5-ohm resistor is connected in series with the armature, with the air-gap flux at its initial value, what is the speed?

(c) With the series resistor of (b) in the armature circuit, the resultant air-gap flux is again increased by 8 per cent. What is the speed?

7-17. Repeat Prob. 7-8 when the generator is self-excited.

7-18. A d-c generator is provided with a carbon-pile voltage regulator, as illustrated in the accompanying diagram. The output voltage is initially adjusted by setting the force (f_0), and so the position (x_0) of the regulator. The regulator operates by controlling the field current i_f so that V remains constant under all conditions of load. If, for example, V should tend to fall, the current through the solenoid coil will fall. As a result the solenoid plunger will move in such a way that the carbon-pile resistance is decreased (the carbon pile must be compressed to accomplish this). The current i_f now will increase, thereby restoring V to its controlled value.

Use the following terminology:

k_f = generator volts for unit field amperes i_f

k_m = force on regulator magnet per unit current i_r in regulator coil

x = displacement of solenoid plunger from its preset equilibrium position

R_r, L_r = resistance, inductance of regulator coil

R_f, L_f = resistance, inductance of generator field

k_r = spring constant of regulator

M_r = mass of moving parts of regulator

$V_r = V_r(x, i_f)$ = potential difference across the carbon pile and is a function of both displacement and field current

(a) Deduce an expression for the incremental change in field current for an incremental variation in the force setting of the regulator. Neglect the effects of armature resistance and inductance.

(b) Deduce an expression for the change in output potential ΔV for a change in load current Δi_L.

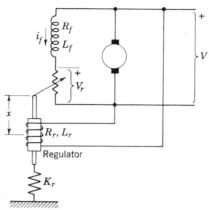

Fig. P7-18

7-19. A d-c shunt motor is driving a constant-torque load at its equilibrium speed ω_{m0}. The motor is to be stopped by dynamic braking, which is accomplished by instantaneously switching the armature terminals from the power line to a braking resistor R, as illustrated in the accompanying figure. The field remains excited at its normal value.

(a) Deduce an expression for the motor speed during the braking period. Neglect the effects of normal viscous damping.

(b) Find an electrical-analog representation of the machine under the specified operation.

(c) What should be the value of R in order that the motion be critically damped and thereby have the speed fall to zero in the minimum time?

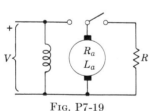

Fig. P7-19

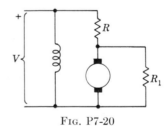

Fig. P7-20

7-20. The accompanying diagram illustrates a "shunted armature connection" for a d-c shunt motor. The use of both series and shunt resistors in the armature circuit improves the speed regulation $d\omega/dT$ over that possible with a series resistor alone.

(a) Deduce an expression for the steady-state speed-torque relation.

(b) Sketch on one diagram the speed-torque relations for (1) the shunt motor, $R = 0$, $R_1 = \infty$; (2) series resistor control, $R = R$, $R_1 = \infty$; (3) the shunted armature connection shown.

7-21. (a) A separately excited d-c motor that is operating under steady conditions with constant field excitation is supplying a load torque $T_L = D_L\omega$. A resistor R is connected in series with the armature. Suppose now that R is short-circuited by suitable switching so that the motor speed increases. Write the differential equation, determine the initial conditions, and sketch the variation of ω versus time, assuming that the response is overdamped.

(b) Find an electrical-analog representation of the machine under the specified operation.

(c) Suppose that a portion of R remains in the armature line. What value should this have if the time response after switching is to be critically damped?

7-22. A d-c shunt motor is operating with a resistor R in series with the armature and is driving a load whose torque is of the form $D_L\omega + T_L$. A resistor R_1 is switched in parallel with the armature to form the shunted armature connection of Fig. P7-20. Neglect the armature circuit inductance.

(a) Write the differential equation for motor speed which applies after the switching operation.

(b) Draw an electrical-analog representation of the machine.

(c) What are the initial conditions?

(d) What is the time constant of the system?

(e) Sketch the complete solution.

7-23. Develop the following expression for the total energy dissipated in the armature circuit of a d-c shunt motor as it accelerates from standstill to an angular velocity ω_1. The load torque T_L is constant.

$$\int_0^{t_1} R_a i_a{}^2 \, dt = \frac{J R_a{}^2 T_L{}^2}{(M_d I_f)^4} \log \frac{\omega_2}{\omega_2 - \omega_1} + J\omega_1{}^2 \left(\frac{\omega_2}{\omega_1} - \frac{1}{2} \right)$$

where ω_2 is the final (steady-state) velocity (with $\omega_1 < \omega_2$).

7-24. A d-c series motor is one in which the armature and the field winding are connected in series, and so both carry the same current.

(a) Deduce an expression for the steady-state load torque of the machine when the applied potential is V.

(b) Sketch the torque-speed curve.

(c) At what speed is the torque a maximum?

(d) For no load, what limits the speed of the motor?

7-25. A d-c series motor that is driving a particular load at 1,200 rpm is excited from a 230-volt source and draws an armature current of 16.3 amp. The torque to drive the load varies as speed $\omega^{1.8}$. What must be the input potential and current if the speed is to be 1,750 rpm? The resistance of the armature plus field, $R_a + R_f =$ 1.0 ohm.

7-26. A 20-hp 230-volt 80-amp series motor is running at full-load speed of 1,280 rpm. The machine, which has an armature plus field resistance of 0.40 ohm, is provided with a dynamic braking resistor of 1.8 ohms which is switched across the motor terminals in place of the power lines when the machine is to be brought to a halt.

(a) Draw an electrical-analog representation of the machine under the specified operation.

(b) What is the initial braking torque?

(c) How long will it take to stop the machine, which has $WR^2 = 3.1$ kg-m²?

7-27. Show that the total energy dissipated in the armature circuit resistance of the d-c series motor during the time that its speed changes from ω_1 to ω_2 is given by the expression

$$\int_{t_1}^{t_2} i_a{}^2 R_a \, dt = \frac{J R_a}{M_d} (\omega_2 - \omega_1) + \frac{T_L R_a}{M_d} (t_2 - t_1)$$

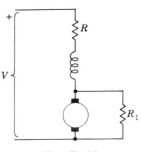

Fig. P7-28

7-28. The speed-torque curve for the series motor with "shunted-motor" connection, as illustrated in the accompanying diagram, is to be determined. Plot on one diagram the speed-torque curve for the following: the series motor; the series motor with series resistance added; the series motor with shunted-motor connection.

7-29. Consider a simple one-brush-pair d-c machine, but with the brush axis displaced from the direct axis by an angle α. The resulting mmf is equivalent to that of a machine with excitations from two currents

$$i_d = i_a \cos \alpha \qquad i_q = i_a \sin \alpha$$

Find the resulting expression for the torque of the machine, and show that it reduces, for $\alpha = 90°$, to Eq. (7-16).

7-30. It is required to deduce and plot the steady-state load characteristics of the cross-field d-c machine, without and with the compensating winding connected. Under conditions of no compensation the load condition is 200 volts and 50 amp. It is also given that

$$K_f = \frac{G_{dq}G_{qf}\omega_{m0}^2}{R_aR_f} = 20$$

$$K_c = \frac{G_{dq}G_{qd}\omega_{m0}^2}{R_r} = 10$$

$$R_r = R_c = 0.1 \text{ ohm}$$

7-31. A compound-wound d-c machine is one with a series winding and a shunt winding, both of which are in the direct axis, as shown in the accompanying diagram.

(a) Deduce expressions for the steady-state potentials v_{s0} and v_{a0}.

(b) Show that the effect of the series winding is to modify the armature resistance drop. What must be the relation to yield an effective zero armature resistance (a flat compounded machine)?

(c) Sketch the expected load characteristic v_{as0} versus i_{a0} under the conditions of (1) flat compounding; (2) differential compounding (the series field acts in opposition to the shunt field); (3) cumulative compounding (the series field acts to strengthen the main field).

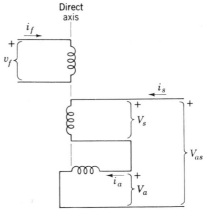

Fig. P7-31

8

Generalized Machine Theory

This chapter, which is a logical extension of the work of the foregoing chapter, will show that it is possible to unify the treatment of d-c machinery theory. This will be done through the introduction of the Kron *primitive* machine and then observing that any d-c machine is a special case of the general primitive machine. Of comparable importance is the fact that this same primitive machine can also be used to describe the behavior of a variety of a-c machines. The details of such special application to the study of a-c machine performance will be included below.

8-1. The Primitive Machine. The number of d-c machine types that have been examined in detail in the foregoing chapter has been relatively limited. However, it is relatively easy to extend the list to include the series and the compound machines (see Probs. 7-24 and 7-31), and also machines with interpoles (see Prob. 7-6) which have been introduced to improve the commutation of the machine. In all cases these machines reduce to sets of equivalent windings which are aligned along the direct and along the quadrature axis. That is, all d-c machines naturally lead to a *two-axis* formulation for their analysis.

Attention is now directed to the fact that a two-phase a-c machine also possesses an electrical geometry which is suggestive of the two-axis model, since the stator is essentially wound for two fields which are in electrical space quadrature. Moreover, it will be shown later in this chapter and also in Chap. 10, which continues with the field-theory formulation of Chap. 9, that the performance characteristics of machines with more than two phases (the n-m-phase machine will be studied in Chap. 11) can also be described in terms of a two-field theory. This would seem to indicate the possibility of a "generalized," or "primitive," two-pole machine which is approximately equivalent to the actual machine and which would be basic to the analysis of the performance characteristics of a variety of machines which are of general interest. Such a primitive machine was discussed by Kron,[1] who showed that with it the performance characteristics of a large number of conventional machine types, including d-c machines, synchronous machines without damper windings, and one-, two-, and three-phase induction machines, could be studied.

The Kron primitive machine with stationary axes is illustrated in Fig. 8-1. As drawn, this machine consists of a stationary salient-pole field winding in the direct axis; a field coil which is mounted magnetically at right angles to this axis in the quadrature axis; and a rotating armature winding brought out to a commutator. Two brush sets are provided which are magnetically perpendicular to each other, with one

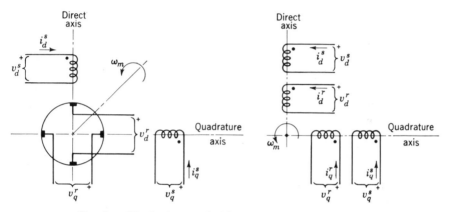

FIG. 8-1. The basic, or primitive, machine with four coils.

brush set in the direct axis and the other in the quadrature axis. Based on our studies in Chap. 7, the equivalent electrical network follows directly. Observe that the equivalent armature coils produce stationary fluxes only if the brushes are stationary. If the brushes are rotating, then the corresponding armature-coil fluxes will also be rotating. In the case of more complicated machines additional d and q windings can be added to both the stator and rotor configurations, as required by the complexity of the machine under study. Some machines may require fewer than four coils for their representation, as already found in discussing many d-c machines.

As discussed in relation to the amplidyne in Sec. 7-8, the two rotor windings represent the same set of rotor conductors, although the currents through each set of brushes produce fluxes along the designated axis. The two fluxes are assumed to be independent, so that the mmfs are additive. This means, of course, that saturation is neglected. Since

---

[1] G. Kron, "The Application of Tensors to the Analysis of Rotating Electrical Machinery," 2d ed., *General Electric Review*, Schenectady, N.Y., 1942.

the coils are mechanically identical, the electrical resistance will be the same for both coils. The inductances can differ since the magnetic reluctance in the two axes need not be the same, and in typical machines $L_d{}^r$ may be as much as 60 per cent larger than $L_q{}^r$. They will be the same in a machine with a uniform air gap.

A basic assumption in the Kron machine is that the mmf due to the currents in the windings of the actual machine, whatever the number of phases, can be developed by a two-winding system, if appropriately excited. Moreover, it is usually assumed that the mmf is sinusoidally distributed along the air gap, so that the combination of the direct-axis and quadrature-axis sinusoidal waves can represent this air-gap wave. Actually in many machines this assumption is not really true. However, the neglect of space harmonics is not so terribly drastic, since the effect of many harmonics can be included by modifying the values of the machine inductances. For this reason choosing the main flux as that corresponding to the fundamental sine-wave component of the flux-density curve is a generally good approximation. Some effects of the space harmonics may still exist, and these can often be accounted for by separate considerations. In the usual case, however, the model chosen is adequate.

The circuit equations for the machine of Fig. 8-1 can be written at once, as a simple extension of the work of Sec. 7-8. These are the following:

$$
\begin{bmatrix} v_d{}^s \\ v_q{}^s \\ v_d{}^r \\ v_q{}^r \end{bmatrix} =
\begin{bmatrix}
R_d{}^s + L_d{}^s p & 0 & M_d p & 0 \\
0 & R_q{}^s + L_q{}^s p & 0 & M_q p \\
M_d p & G_{dq}^{rs}\omega_m & R_d{}^r + L_d{}^r p & G_{dq}^{rr}\omega_m \\
G_{qd}^{rs}\omega_m & M_q p & G_{qd}^{rr}\omega_m & R_q{}^r + L_q{}^r p
\end{bmatrix}
\begin{bmatrix} i_d{}^s \\ i_q{}^s \\ i_d{}^r \\ i_q{}^r \end{bmatrix}
\quad (8\text{-}1)
$$

where the notation distinguishes between direct (d) and quadrature (q) quantities and between stator (s) and rotor (r) quantities. The mutual inductance between direct-axis windings is denoted M_d, and the mutual inductance between quadrature-axis windings is denoted M_q. An application of the G-M rule of Sec. 7-3 permits the G factors to be written in terms of appropriately chosen M's. Thus G_{dq}^{rs} must correspond to the mutual inductance between coils (d,r) and (q,s) when the rotor coil is moved by $\pi/2$ to align these coils along the same axis. In this case

$$
G_{dq}^{rs} = -M_q
$$

Similarly, all other G factors are found by moving the rotor forward through $\pi/2$. There result

$$
\begin{aligned}
G_{dq}^{rs} &= -M_q \\
G_{dq}^{rr} &\doteq -L_q{}^r \\
G_{qd}^{rs} &= M_d \\
G_{qd}^{rr} &\doteq L_d{}^r
\end{aligned}
\qquad (8\text{-}2)
$$

The signs are consistent with the reference directions shown in Fig. 8-1.

The electrical equations may now be written in the form

$$
\begin{bmatrix} v_d{}^s \\ v_q{}^s \\ v_d{}^r \\ v_q{}^r \end{bmatrix} =
\begin{bmatrix}
R_d{}^s + L_d{}^s p & 0 & M_d p & 0 \\
0 & R_q{}^s + L_q{}^s p & 0 & M_q p \\
M_d p & -M_q \omega_m & R_d{}^r + L_d{}^r p & -L_q{}^r \omega_m \\
M_d \omega_m & M_q p & L_d{}^r \omega_m & R_q{}^r + L_q{}^r p
\end{bmatrix}
\begin{bmatrix} i_d{}^s \\ i_q{}^s \\ i_d{}^r \\ i_q{}^r \end{bmatrix}
\tag{8-3}
$$

which may be written in the form

$$[V] = [R + Lp + G\omega_m]\,[I]$$

where $[R] = \begin{bmatrix} R_d{}^s & 0 & 0 & 0 \\ 0 & R_q{}^s & 0 & 0 \\ 0 & 0 & R_d{}^r & 0 \\ 0 & 0 & 0 & R_q{}^r \end{bmatrix}$ $[L] = \begin{bmatrix} L_d{}^s & 0 & M_d & 0 \\ 0 & L_q{}^s & 0 & M_q \\ M_d & 0 & L_d{}^r & 0 \\ 0 & M_q & 0 & L_q{}^r \end{bmatrix}$

$$
[G] = \begin{bmatrix}
0 & 0 & 0 & 0 \\
0 & 0 & 0 & 0 \\
0 & -M_q & 0 & -L_q{}^r \\
M_d & 0 & L_d{}^r & 0
\end{bmatrix}
\tag{8-4}
$$

The expression for the electrical torque produced by the generalized machine is now to be found. Because of the constraints imposed on the electrical system by the commutators, it will be found that Eq. (7-15) is not valid in the present case, although exactly this form of equation less the factor $\frac{1}{2}$ does apply. We proceed in a manner that exactly parallels the development in Sec. 7-6.

The total electrical power into the electrical ports of the machine is given by

$$P = v_d{}^s i_d{}^s + v_q{}^s i_q{}^s + v_d{}^r i_d{}^r + v_q{}^r i_q{}^r$$

which, in matrix form, is

$$
P = \begin{bmatrix} i_d{}^s & i_q{}^s & i_d{}^r & i_q{}^r \end{bmatrix}
\begin{bmatrix} v_d{}^s \\ v_q{}^s \\ v_d{}^r \\ v_q{}^r \end{bmatrix} = [I_t V]
\tag{8-5}
$$

This expression is now combined with Eq. (8-4) to get

$$P = [I_t][R + Lp + G\omega_m][I] \tag{8-6}$$

Observe that this expression implicitly assumes that L is independent of time or of angle. This is a valid condition for the Kron machine, since the presence of the commutator, as discussed in Sec. 7-5, ensures that the M and G factors are independent of orientation. This expression shows that the power into the electrical ports comprises heating losses, energy storage in the magnetic field, and mechanical energy variations, since upon expansion

$$P = \left[I_t R I + I_t L \frac{dI}{dt} + I_t G I \omega_m \right] \tag{8-7}$$

Also, from Eq. (7-32), the power into the mechanical port is

$$T_m \omega_m = \omega_m (J p \omega_m + D \omega_m - T_e) \tag{8-8}$$

We now invoke the principle of conservation of energy. This requires that

Power into electrical ports + power into mechanical port
$$= \text{power dissipated} + \text{power stored}$$

But by Eqs. (8-7) and (8-8) it follows that

$$P + T_m \omega_m = ([I_t R I] + D \omega_m{}^2) + \left(\left[I_t L \frac{dI}{dt} \right] + \omega_m J p \omega_m \right) + \omega_m([I_t G I] - T_e) \tag{8-9}$$

Observe that this equation is in precisely the form of the statement of conservation of energy. For exact correspondence, it is required that we write

$$T_e = [I_t G I] \tag{8-10}$$

It is observed that this is a generalization of Eq. (7-33), which was used for the d-c machine.

In its expanded form, the electrical torque becomes

$$T_e = [I_t G I] = \begin{bmatrix} i_d{}^s & i_q{}^s & i_d{}^r & i_q{}^r \end{bmatrix} \begin{bmatrix} 0 & 0 & 0 & 0 \\ 0 & 0 & 0 & 0 \\ 0 & -M_q & 0 & -L_q{}^r \\ M_d & 0 & L_d{}^r & 0 \end{bmatrix} \begin{bmatrix} i_d{}^s \\ i_q{}^s \\ i_d{}^r \\ i_q{}^r \end{bmatrix}$$

or
$$T_e = i_d{}^r(M_q i_q{}^s + L_q{}^r i_q{}^r) - i_q{}^r(M_d i_d{}^s + L_d{}^r i_d{}^r)$$

which is
$$T_e = -i_d{}^r M_q i_q{}^s + i_q{}^r M_d i_d{}^s - i_d{}^r i_q{}^r (L_q{}^r - L_d{}^r) \tag{8-11}$$

In those machines for which $L_q{}^r = L_d{}^r$, the condition which is met when the machine is provided with a smooth air gap, the third torque term vanishes. This torque term, which is known as the reluctance torque, results because the reluctance in the direct and in the quadrature axes is different, in general.

The foregoing equations, even though they stem from our work in Chap. 7 for the d-c machines, must be recognized to possess limitations that arise from the assumed sinusoidal space variation of the air-gap flux. In the case of practical commutator machines the assumed sinusoidal space variation never occurs, owing to the actual form of the current distribution. The results obtained, which consider only the fundamental component of current, are of the correct form. This means that the magnitudes of the G factors and of the coefficients of the time-derivative terms may actually differ from each other. A more accurate analysis must take into account the effects of higher harmonic components on these factors.

In the application of the foregoing general machine to the analysis of the performance of particular types of machines, it is necessary only to impose appropriate constraints to effect the adaptation of the generalized machine to the particular machine under survey. Examples of the techniques involved will be given in what follows.

8-2. Moving to Fixed-axis Transformation. To employ the primitive machine in the description of the operation of a-c machines of the two-phase variety, it is necessary to show that the a-c machine can be described in the d-q time- and space-invariant reference system. This may be accomplished by showing that an appropriately excited stationary two-phase set of a-c fields results in a field that rotates relative to a reference frame that is fixed with respect to the stationary windings. Correspondingly, of course, a two-phase system on a rotating structure also results, in general, in a field that rotates relative to the fixed frame of reference. With this done, it is then possible to show that such rotating fields can be expressed in terms of the d-q coordinates. Following this, we can describe the performance of the machine in the d-q system of coordinates and then later relate the performance to the moving reference frame. We now consider this matter.

Suppose that the equations of the machine are initially specified relative to a fixed stator and moving rotor frame of reference. The variables in this machine frame of reference are designated as the a-b variables. We now wish to show, for example, that a real transformation exists which will transform the rotor equations in the a-b variables into a new set of stationary-axes equations, defined as $(v_d{}^r, i_d{}^r)$ and $(v_q{}^r, i_q{}^r)$, which are time- and space-invariant. To deduce the transformation, we consider the flux relations that exist in the machine, as shown in Fig. 8-2. For a balanced two-phase winding, the individual phase fluxes will combine to produce an over-all flux of constant magnitude that is rotating with respect to the two-phase winding at the time frequency of the phase fluxes. The phase fluxes relative to the a-b axes, which are mutually perpendicular to each other, are given by

$$\begin{aligned}
\phi_a &= \phi_m \cos(\omega t + \varphi_0) \\
\phi_b &= \phi_m \sin(\omega t + \varphi_0)
\end{aligned} \tag{8-12}$$

where φ_0 is the reference phase angle with respect to some specified time reference.

We now wish to find the resultant flux at any instantaneous space angle φ measured with respect to the d axis, which is chosen as the reference. The resultant flux is specified by the relation

$$\phi = \phi_a e^{j\varphi} + \phi_b e^{j(\varphi + \pi/2)} = e^{j\varphi}(\phi_a + \phi_b e^{j\pi/2})$$

which is $$\phi = e^{j\varphi}(\phi_a + j\phi_b)$$

It follows from this that the magnitude of the flux is

$$\phi = \sqrt{\phi_a^2 + \phi_b^2} = \phi_m \tag{8-13}$$

This shows that the magnitude of the resultant flux is a constant and equal to the unit of flux for the phase fluxes.

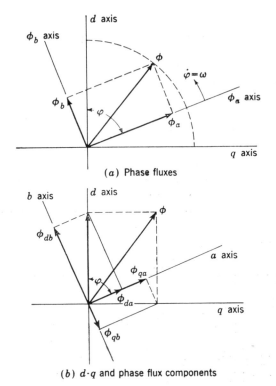

(a) Phase fluxes

(b) d-q and phase flux components

FIG. 8-2. Flux vector relations for the two-phase system.

Time and space portraits of the situation are illuminating and are given in Figs. 8-3 and 8-4. Figure 8-4 shows the flux waves of the individual phases, and the resultant flux at the three times t_1, t_2, and t_3 of Fig. 8-3. Observe that the net effect of the time variation of phase fluxes is a progressive shift of the resultant flux to the right, a 45° change in time phase being accompanied by a 45° change in space phase. Thus, as time passes, the flux wave moves uniformly in space, although the amplitude of the resultant flux remains constant, a 1-cycle time change being accompanied by a 360-electrical-degree space change.

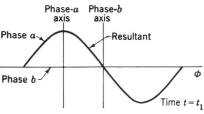

Now, relative to the d-q reference frame, the direct-axis flux is made up of contributions from the two phase fluxes. For any electrical angle φ between the two reference frames, as shown in Fig. 8-2,

$$\phi_d = \phi_a \cos \varphi + \phi_b \sin \varphi \quad (8\text{-}14)$$

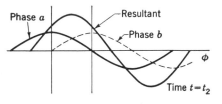

Similarly, the quadrature-axis flux ϕ_q has the following form:

$$\phi_q = -\phi_a \sin \varphi + \phi_b \cos \varphi \quad (8\text{-}15)$$

But in the a-b system the fluxes

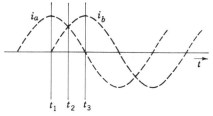

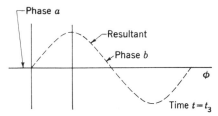

Fig. 8-3. Balanced two-phase a-c currents.

Fig. 8-4. Component and resultant flux distribution due to the currents of Fig. 8-3 in two-phase windings.

are related to the corresponding currents, and we may therefore write

$$i_d = i_a \cos \varphi + i_b \sin \varphi$$
$$i_q = -i_a \sin \varphi + i_b \cos \varphi$$

or in matrix form

$$\begin{bmatrix} i_d \\ i_q \end{bmatrix} = \begin{bmatrix} \cos \varphi & \sin \varphi \\ -\sin \varphi & \cos \varphi \end{bmatrix} \begin{bmatrix} i_a \\ i_b \end{bmatrix} \quad (8\text{-}16)$$

The corresponding inverse relations which transform from the d-q stationary coordinate system into the a-b rotating coordinate system are

$$\begin{bmatrix} i_a \\ i_b \end{bmatrix} = \begin{bmatrix} \cos \varphi & -\sin \varphi \\ \sin \varphi & \cos \varphi \end{bmatrix} \begin{bmatrix} i_d \\ i_q \end{bmatrix} \quad (8\text{-}17)$$

The potentials in the windings transform in exactly the same way as the

currents; hence

$$\begin{bmatrix} v_d \\ v_q \end{bmatrix} = \begin{bmatrix} \cos \varphi & \sin \varphi \\ -\sin \varphi & \cos \varphi \end{bmatrix} \begin{bmatrix} v_a \\ v_b \end{bmatrix} \qquad (8\text{-}18)$$

Clearly, what has been accomplished in the foregoing is to show that transformations are possible which will permit the performance characteristics of the machine to be specified in either the *a-b* or the *d-q* system. Results obtained in one system can easily be transformed into the other

FIG. 8-5. Stator of a synchronous machine. (*Courtesy of Westinghouse Electric Corporation.*)

by using the appropriate transformation relations. This means, therefore, that we can study the transformed machine in the stationary-axes *d-q* system and then transform the results to describe the system operation in the *a-b*, or machine, coordinate system.

8-3. The Two-phase Synchronous Machine. We consider for analysis the two-phase synchronous machine under balanced load conditions. Such a machine has a single winding on one magnetic member, which is excited with d-c current, and has a two-phase winding on the other magnetic member (see Figs. 8-5 and 8-6). Ordinarily the a-c windings are rigidly attached to the stationary stator, and the d-c winding, which produces a constant magnetic field, is mounted on bearings so that it may be rotated. For convenience in analysis we shall assume that the d-c field is stationary in space and that the a-c windings rotate with respect to this stationary frame of reference. Since only the relative motion between rotor and stator is of importance, interchanging the roles of the fixed and the stationary assemblies will not invalidate the analysis to follow.

When a synchronous machine is operated as an alternator, the d-c field is rotated by an external source of power. This generates motional electromotances in the stationary armature conductors. For the two-phase machine here being considered, the output power is two-phase, the rotational frequency being specified by the mechanical speed of the d-c

Fig. 8-6. Two-pole nonsalient-pole synchronous rotor. (*Courtesy of Westinghouse Electric Corporation.*)

field, the number of pairs of poles on the rotor, and the effective number of poles for which the stator windings have been wound. In such a machine an increasing electrical output power reflects itself immediately through the air-gap fields to the rotor, and so to the external mechanical driving source.

When the machine is operated as a synchronous motor, two-phase a-c power is applied to the stator windings and the rotor is d-c-excited. The a-c excitation of the stator produces a rotating field of constant amplitude. If the d-c field is rotating in the direction, and at the synchronous speed, of the a-c-excited stator windings, magnetic locking occurs between these fields and the rotor continues to turn. In fact, as the rotor is loaded externally, the machine continues to rotate at synchronous speed, although a phase displacement occurs between the center line, or axis, of the a-c-produced rotating field and the d-c field axis. Should the magnetic lock be broken, whether owing to loss of excitation or because of overload, the net average torque generated becomes zero and the motor will stop. Evidently, therefore, a synchronous motor is not self-starting, and auxiliary methods must be employed to bring the rotor up to synchronous speed and magnetic lock before loading is possible.

A number of methods have been devised for starting synchronous motors. One of the simplest is to provide "damper windings" which are attached to the rotor pole faces (see Fig. 8-7). These damper windings serve, when starting, as squirrel-cage windings, and the machine starts as an induction motor. (The induction motor is discussed in Sec. 8-4.) When the machine gets up to speed, magnetic locking takes place and the machine operates as a synchronous machine. The damper

Fig. 8-7. Salient-pole synchronous rotor and damper windings. (*Courtesy of Westinghouse Electric Corporation.*)

windings serve, during normal operation of the motor, to reduce hunting (oscillations of the rotor about the average speed).

In order that the volt-ampere equations in the d-q coordinates for the generalized machine shall apply to the synchronous machine under survey, the following constraints must be imposed:

$i_d{}^s = i^s$ for the d-c excitation current

$i_q{}^s$, $v_q{}^s$ do not exist, since the q winding is absent

$v_d{}^s = -V^s = \text{const}$ (the sign is so chosen as to obtain the conventional representation for the machine)

$\omega_m = \omega^r$ for the machine to operate as a synchronous device, with the synchronous speed of the rotor being specified by $\omega^r = \omega^s/n$, with $n = p/2$, one-half the number of poles (or the number of pairs of poles)

Subject to these constraints the general equations [Eq. (8-3)] become

$$\begin{bmatrix} -V^s \\ v_d{}^r \\ v_q{}^r \end{bmatrix} = \begin{bmatrix} R_d{}^s + L_d{}^s p & M_d p & 0 \\ M_d p & R_d{}^r + L_d{}^r p & -L_q{}^r \omega_m \\ M_d \omega_m & L_d{}^r \omega_m & R_q{}^r + L_q{}^r p \end{bmatrix} \begin{bmatrix} i^s \\ i_d{}^r \\ i_q{}^r \end{bmatrix} \quad (8\text{-}19)$$

The general dynamic d-q equivalent circuit of the machine, as specified by these equations, has the form illustrated in Fig. 8-8.

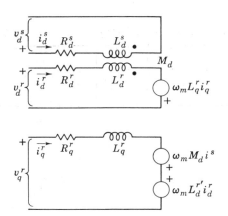

FIG. 8-8. The dynamic equivalent circuit of the two-phase synchronous machine.

The first of Eqs. (8-19), which is that of the fixed-excitation winding, is of little interest and may be eliminated. The following equations result:

$$\begin{bmatrix} v_d{}^r - \dfrac{M_d p}{R_d{}^s + L_d{}^s p} V^s \\ v_q{}^r + \dfrac{M_d \omega_m}{R_d{}^s + L_d{}^s p} V^s \end{bmatrix}$$
$$= \begin{bmatrix} R_d{}^r + \left(L_d{}^r - \dfrac{M_d{}^2 p}{R_d{}^s + L_d{}^s p} \right) p & -L_q{}^r \omega_m \\ + \left(L_d{}^r - \dfrac{M_d{}^2 p}{R_d{}^s + L_d{}^s p} \right) \omega_m & R_q{}^r L_q{}^r p \end{bmatrix} \begin{bmatrix} i_d{}^r \\ i_q{}^r \end{bmatrix} \quad (8\text{-}20)$$

The quantity

$$\left(L_d{}^r - \dfrac{M_d{}^2 p}{R_d{}^s + L_d{}^s p} \right) p \equiv L_d{}^{r\prime} p \quad (8\text{-}21)$$

is known as the "direct-axis transient reactance" of the machine. Observe that $L_q{}^r$ is not affected by the transient conditions.

Some insight into the significance of the transient reactance is possible by considering the fluxes linking the windings of the machine. This is possible by noting that the flux-linkage matrix is

$$
\begin{bmatrix} \psi_d{}^s \\ \psi_d{}^r \\ \psi_q{}^r \end{bmatrix} = \begin{bmatrix} L_d{}^s & M_d & 0 \\ M_d & L_d{}^r & 0 \\ 0 & 0 & L_q{}^r \end{bmatrix} \begin{bmatrix} i^s \\ i_d{}^r \\ i_q{}^r \end{bmatrix}
\tag{8-22}
$$

The direct-axis and quadrature-axis field-flux relations may be represented by the transformer equivalent circuit shown in Fig. 8-9. Use is made in this circuit of the relation between the field-flux variations and

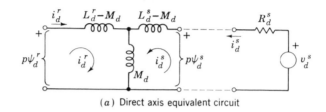

(a) Direct axis equivalent circuit

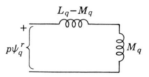

(b) Quadrature axis equivalent circuit

FIG. 8-9. The direct- and quadrature-axis equivalent circuits of the two-phase synchronous machine.

the applied field potential. The direct-axis operational impedance is to be examined. This is, by setting $v_d{}^s = 0$,

$$
L_d{}^{r\prime}p = (L_d{}^r - M_d)p + \cfrac{1}{\cfrac{1}{M_d p} + \cfrac{1}{(L_d{}^s - M_d)p + R_d{}^s}}
$$

This may be expanded to the form

$$
L_d{}^{r\prime}p = (L_d{}^r - M_d)p + \frac{M_d L_d{}^s p^2 - M_d{}^2 p^2 + M_d p R_d{}^s}{L_d{}^s p + R_d{}^s}
$$

or $\quad L_d{}^{r\prime}p = L_d{}^r p - \dfrac{L_d{}^s M_d p^2 + M_d p R_d{}^s - (M_d L_d{}^s p^2 - M_d{}^2 p^2 + M_d p R_d{}^s)}{L_d{}^s p + R_d{}^s}$

which reduces to

$$
L_d{}^{r\prime}p = L_d{}^r p - \frac{M_d{}^2 p^2}{L_d{}^s p + R_d{}^s}
$$

which is written in the form

$$
L_d{}^{r\prime}p = \left(L_d{}^r - \frac{M_d{}^2 p}{R_d{}^s + L_d{}^s p} \right) p
$$

which is seen to be precisely the form of Eq. (8-21).

The direct-axis transient reactance is the effective reactance to sudden changes in excitation applied to the direct axis. Attention is called to the fact that as used here the term "reactance" must be understood in a broad operational sense, not the usual restricted sense of sinusoidal excitation. Note that, if the field resistance may be neglected, then Eq. (8-21) reduces to

$$L_d{}^{r'}p = \left(L_{d^r} - \frac{M_d{}^2}{L_{d^s}}\right)p \qquad (8\text{-}23)$$

In this form $L_d{}^{r'}p$ is the transient reactance in the direct axis which applies under the condition of fast transients, such as short circuits. In the general case the transient reactance to fast transients is much smaller than that for slow transients.

The quadrature-axis impedance does not vary under transient conditions and remains

$$L_q{}^{r'}p = L_q{}^r p \qquad (8\text{-}24)$$

It is of considerable interest to study the steady-state performance of the machine. This is accomplished by setting the derivative terms in Eq. (8-19) to zero, since, for steady operation at synchronous speed, the axis voltages and currents are all constants, independent of time. Under these conditions, the appropriate set of equations becomes

$$\begin{aligned}
v_{d0}^r &= R^r i_{d0}^r - L_q{}^r \omega^r i_{q0}^r \\
v_{q0}^r &= M_d \omega^r i^s + L_d{}^r \omega^r i_{d0}^r + R^r i_{q0}^r \\
-V^s &= R_d{}^s i^s
\end{aligned} \qquad (8\text{-}25)$$

Also, the torque output of the synchronous machine is, by the proper adaptation of Eq. (8-11),

$$T_e = i_q{}^r M_d i_d{}^s - i_d{}^r i_q{}^r (L_q{}^r - L_d{}^r) \qquad (8\text{-}26)$$

The total power in the d-q axes is then

$$P_{dq} = \omega^r [i_q{}^r M_d i_d{}^s - i_d{}^r i_q{}^r (L_q{}^r - L_d{}^r)]$$

which is written in the form

$$P_{dq} = [i_q{}^r V_q + i_d{}^r i_q{}^r (X_d{}^r - X_q{}^r)]$$

where $X_d{}^r = \omega^r L_d{}^r$, direct-axis synchronous reactance
 $X_q{}^r = \omega^r L_q{}^r$, quadrature-axis synchronous reactance $\qquad (8\text{-}27)$
 $V_q = M_d \omega^r i_d{}^s$, generated potential due to $i_d{}^s$

To determine the performance characteristics of the machine in machine coordinates, we employ Eq. (8-17) for the transformations from the d-q to the a-b system of coordinates. The transformation equations are given explicitly as

$$v_a{}^r = v_d{}^r \cos \omega^r t - v_q{}^r \sin \omega^r t$$
$$i_a{}^r = i_d{}^r \cos \omega^r t - i_q{}^r \sin \omega^r t \tag{8-28}$$

It is observed that the first of these may be written in the form

$$v_a{}^r = \text{Re } (v_d{}^r e^{j\omega^r t} + j v_q{}^r e^{j\omega^r t})$$
$$= \text{Re } [(v_d{}^r + j v_q{}^r) e^{j\omega^r t}]$$

This is now written as

$$v_a{}^r = \text{Re } (\sqrt{2}\, \mathbf{V}^r e^{j\omega^r t})$$

where

$$\mathbf{V}^r = \frac{1}{\sqrt{2}} (v_d{}^r + j v_q{}^r) \tag{8-29}$$

In an exactly similar way, it follows that

$$v_b{}^r = \text{Im } (\sqrt{2}\, \mathbf{V}^r e^{j\omega^r t}) \tag{8-30}$$

We shall find the following quantities of importance in our further considerations:

$$\mathbf{V}_0{}^r = \frac{1}{\sqrt{2}} (v_{d0}^r + j v_{q0}^r) = V_{0d}^r + j V_{0q}^r$$

$$\mathbf{I}_0{}^r = \frac{1}{\sqrt{2}} (i_{d0}^r + j i_{q0}^r) = I_{0d}^r + j I_{0q}^r \tag{8-31}$$

Suppose that we now substitute for v_{d0}^r and v_{q0}^r the values that are specified by Eqs. (8-25). This gives

$$\mathbf{V}_0{}^r = \frac{1}{\sqrt{2}} [(R^r i_{d0}^r - L_q \omega^r i_{q0}^r) + j(M_d \omega^r i^s + L_d{}^r \omega^r i_{d0}^r + R^r i_{q0}^r)]$$

$$= \frac{1}{\sqrt{2}} [R^r (i_{d0}^r + j i_{q0}^r) + j\omega^r L_d{}^r i_{d0}^r - \omega^r L_q{}^r i_{q0}^r + j\omega^r M_d i^s]$$

which is

$$\mathbf{V}_0{}^r = R^r \mathbf{I}_0{}^r + j X_d{}^r I_{0d}^r - X_q{}^r I_{0q}^r + \mathbf{V}_{q0}$$

This expression is written finally as

$$\mathbf{V}_0{}^r = R^r \mathbf{I}_0{}^r + j(X_d{}^r - X_q{}^r) I_{0d}^r + j X_q{}^r \mathbf{I}_0{}^r + \mathbf{V}_{q0} \tag{8-32}$$

From Eqs. (8-29) and (8-30) this equation contains information about both phase potentials simultaneously. Since by a proper choice of phase it may be either $v_a{}^r$ or $v_b{}^r$, then this equation can be interpreted as that for either phase.

It is observed from Eq. (8-32) that the expression includes a term $+j(X_d{}^r - X_q{}^r) I_{0d}^r$, which accounts for saliency, since this quantity reduces to zero for the smooth-air-gap machine, in which $L_d{}^r = L_q{}^r$. This saliency factor can often be quite appreciable, since in the typical machine $X_d{}^r$ will be approximately 60 per cent larger than $X_q{}^r$. The space-flux diagram of Eq. (8-22) in the d-q axis and the phasor diagram of the rotor potential for Eq. (8-32) are illustrated in Fig. 8-10.

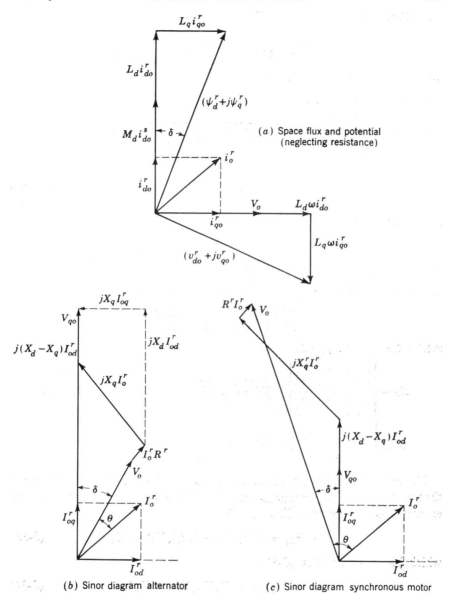

(a) Space flux and potential
(neglecting resistance)

(b) Sinor diagram alternator

(c) Sinor diagram synchronous motor

FIG. 8-10. (a) The space flux; (b, c) sinor diagrams for the two-phase salient-pole machine.

Example 8-3.1. A salient-pole alternator is operated at full load and 0.8 power factor lagging. The angle between the motional emf V_{q0} and the current $I_0{}^r$ is 60°, and the magnitude of V_{q0} is 2 per unit. The resistance drop is 0.02 per unit. Find the direct- and quadrature-axis currents and the direct- and quadrature-axis reactances.

Solution. From Fig. 8-10b, the direct and quadrature currents are

$$I_d = I_0 \sin(\theta + \delta) = 1 \sin 60 = 0.866 \text{ p.u.}$$
$$I_q = I_0 \cos(\theta + \delta) = 1 \cos 60 = 0.500 \text{ p.u.}$$

With I_0 as the axis of reference, then

$\mathbf{V}_0 = 0.800 + j0.600$ p.u.
$\mathbf{R'I}_0 = 0.02 + j0$ p.u.
$\mathbf{V}_{q0} = 2.00 \underline{/\theta + \delta} = 2 \times (0.500 + j0.866) = 1.00 + j1.732$ p.u.
$\mathbf{I}_q = I_q \underline{/\theta + \delta} = 0.5(0.500 + j0.866) = 0.250 + j0.433$ p.u.

$$\mathbf{I}_d = I_d \left/ \theta + \delta - \frac{\pi}{2} \right. = -jI_d \underline{/\theta + \delta}$$

$$= -j0.866(0.500 + j0.866) = 0.750 - j0.433 \text{ p.u.}$$

Hence from Eq. (8-32), the angles of the components of the phasors in this equation being carefully noted,

$$1.00 + j1.732 = 0.02 + jX_d(0.750 - j0.433)$$
$$+ jX_q(0.250 + j0.433) + (0.80 + j0.60)$$

or $0.18 + j1.132 = (0.433X_d - 0.433X_q) + j(0.750X_d + 0.25X_q)$

Equating real and imaginary terms gives the two equations

$$0.433X_d - 0.433X_q = 0.180$$
$$0.750X_d + 0.250X_q = 1.132$$

Solving for X_d and X_q yields

$$X_d = \frac{\begin{vmatrix} 0.180 & -0.433 \\ 1.132 & 0.250 \end{vmatrix}}{\begin{vmatrix} 0.433 & -0.433 \\ 0.750 & 0.250 \end{vmatrix}} = \frac{0.180 \times 0.250 + 0.433 \times 1.132}{0.433 \times 0.250 + 0.750 \times 0.433} = 1.236 \text{ p.u.}$$

$$X_q = \frac{\begin{vmatrix} 0.433 & 0.180 \\ 0.750 & 1.132 \end{vmatrix}}{\Delta} = \frac{0.433 \times 1.132 - 0.750 \times 0.180}{\Delta} = 0.820 \text{ p.u.}$$

We wish to study the power *per phase* of the machine. It is noted that under balanced conditions the phase powers are equal in the machine coordinates. Now from Eqs. (8-27)

$$P_0 = \tfrac{1}{2}P_{dq} = \tfrac{1}{2}[i_q{}^r V_q + i_d{}^r i_q{}^r (X_d{}^r - X_q{}^r)] \tag{8-33}$$

which becomes, by Eqs. (8-31),

$$P_0 = I^r{}_{0q} V_{q0} + I^r{}_{0d} I^r{}_{0q}(X_d{}^r - X_q{}^r) \tag{8-34}$$

This same result follows from the basic relation that $P = \text{Re}(\mathbf{VI}^*)$, with the appropriate $\mathbf{V}$ being given by Eq. (8-32) and the appropriate $\mathbf{I}$ being specified by Eqs. (8-31). Observe from this that even in the absence of d-c excitation, when $V_q = 0$, a machine power is possible. Such a "reluctance" power is the basis of operation of a variety of reluctance motors.

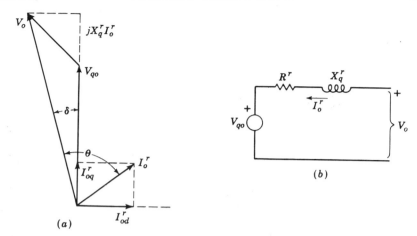

FIG. 8-11. (a) The sinor diagram for the nonsalient-pole synchronous motor, rotor resistance being neglected; (b) the equivalent-circuit representation.

For the case of the round-rotor machine, armature resistance being neglected, $X_d{}^r = X_q{}^r$, and Eq. (8-34) reduces to

$$P_0 = I_{0q}^r X_{q0} \qquad (8\text{-}35)$$

Now from Fig. 8-10b, which is modified to conform to the present conditions as illustrated in Fig. 8-11, and with δ denoting the angle, in electrical degrees, between V_{q0} and $V_0{}^r$, we see that

$$V_0{}^r \sin \delta = I_{0q}^r X_q{}^r \qquad (8\text{-}36)$$

Thus Eq. (8-35) becomes

$$P_0 = \frac{V_0{}^r V_{q0}}{X_q{}^r} \sin \delta \qquad (8\text{-}37)$$

This is the so-called "power-angle characteristic" of the round-rotor machine. A typical curve is plotted in Fig. 8-12. It is observed from

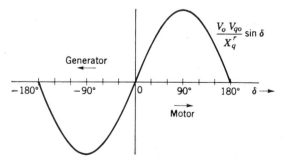

FIG. 8-12. The power-angle characteristic of the nonsalient-pole machine.

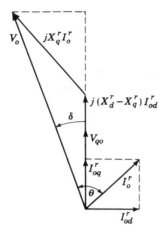

FIG. 8-13. The sinor diagram for the salient-pole synchronous machine.

this figure that the torque is zero for $\delta = 0$, or when the potential V_0 is aligned along the quadrature axis. Since the phase current is not zero, this implies reactive power flow. Positive power corresponds to motor operation. Observe that beyond $\delta = \pi/2$ the power decreases with increasing angle, thereby leading to unstable operation. Negative δ leads to negative torque, and so to generator operation. For increasing load δ will increase. The maximum load is reached for $-\pi/2$. Beyond this value, the rotor will break out of synchronism and will come to a halt.

For the general salient pole machine, the armature resistance again being neglected, the situation is somewhat more complicated than that of the nonsalient-pole machine. Now from Fig. 8-13, which is a modification of Fig. 8-10b, we can write

$$V_{q0} - V_0{}^r \cos \delta = -I_{0d}^r X_d{}^r$$
$$V_0{}^r \sin \delta = I_{0q}^r X_q{}^r \tag{8-38}$$

These expressions are combined with Eq. (8-34) to give

$$\begin{aligned} P_0 &= \frac{V_0{}^r V_{q0}}{X_q{}^r} \sin \delta - \frac{(V_{q0} - V_0{}^r \cos \delta)(V_0{}^r \sin \delta)}{X_d{}^r X_q{}^r}(X_d{}^r - X_q{}^r) \\ &= \frac{V_0{}^r V_{q0}}{X_q{}^r} \sin \delta - V_0{}^r V_{q0} \sin \delta \left(\frac{1}{X_q{}^r} - \frac{1}{X_d{}^r}\right) \\ &\qquad\qquad\qquad\qquad + V_0{}^{r2} \sin \delta \cos \delta \left(\frac{1}{X_q{}^r} - \frac{1}{X_d{}^r}\right) \end{aligned}$$

which becomes

$$P_0 = \frac{V_0{}^r V_{q0}}{X_d{}^r} \sin \delta + \frac{V_0{}^{r2}}{2}\left(\frac{1}{X_q{}^r} - \frac{1}{X_d{}^r}\right) \sin 2\delta \tag{8-39}$$

This expression contains two terms, the first of which corresponds to the cylindrical structure, the second term being essentially a reluctance term which becomes zero for the cylindrical geometry. The resulting power-angle characteristic is illustrated in Fig. 8-14.

In the case of the synchronous motor for a given power output the power factor at which the machine operates can be controlled over very wide limits by controlling the d-c excitation, and so the motional emf V_{q0} of the machine. The general features of the situations possible are illustrated in Fig. 8-15a. Attention is called to the fact that Fig. 8-15a has been drawn for the particular case of constant V and constant power.

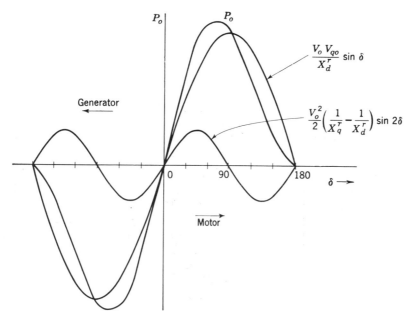

Fig. 8-14. Power-angle characteristic of the salient-pole synchronous machine.

Observe from these figures that both the power angle δ and the power-factor angle θ vary with the d-c excitation I_f or, correspondingly, with V_q. A sketch showing the variation of I versus I_f (or V_q), with P as a parameter, as deduced from these figures, is given in Fig. 8-15b. Owing to the shape of this curve, it is known as a V curve of the synchronous machine. Actually, a series of such curves may be drawn for different values of P, and the data for drawing these may be obtained experimentally or may be deduced from appropriately drawn phasor diagrams.

Example 8-3.2. Consider a salient-pole synchronous alternator having the following per-unit parameters: $X_d = 1.00$ p.u., $X_q = 0.60$ p.u., $R^r = 0$. Compute $\mathbf{V}_{q0}$ on a per-unit basis when the alternator delivers rated kva at 0.80 power factor lagging and rated terminal voltage. Check the results against the power-angle equation of the machine.

Solution. Refer to Fig. 8-3.2-1, which is Fig. 8-10b redrawn with V_0 as reference and $R^r = 0$. It is now found that

$$\mathbf{V}_0 = 1.00\underline{/0}, \text{ the reference phasor}$$
$$\mathbf{I}_0 = 0.80 - j0.60 = 1.00\underline{/-36.9°}$$
$$jX_q\mathbf{I}_0 = j0.60(0.80 - j0.60) = 0.36 + j0.48$$

Note now that

$\mathbf{V}' = \mathbf{V}_0 + jX_q\mathbf{I}_0 = (1.00 + j0) + (0.36 + j0.48) = 1.36 + j0.48 = 1.44\underline{/19.4}$

Also $I_{0d} = I_0 \cos(36.9 + 19.4) = I_0 \cos 56.3 = 1.00 \times 0.832 = 0.832$

Finally $\mathbf{V}_{q0} = \mathbf{V}' + j(X_d - X_q)I_{0d} = (1.44 + 0.40 \times 0.832)\underline{/19.4} = 1.77\underline{/19.4}$

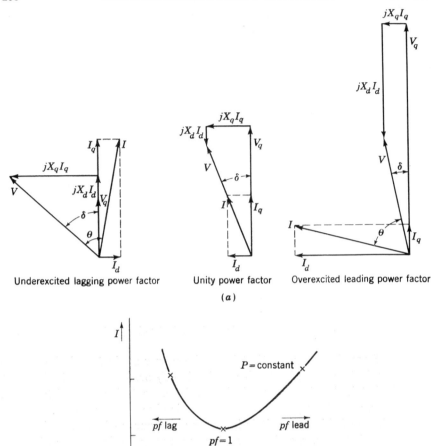

Underexcited lagging power factor   Unity power factor   Overexcited leading power factor

(a)

(b)

Fig. 8-15. (a) Effect of excitation on the power factor of a salient-pole synchronous motor for constant V and constant power; (b) the V curve that results from these constructions.

To check the power, use Eq. (8-39). Now

$$P = \frac{1.00 \times 1.77}{1.00} \sin 19.4 + \frac{1.00^2}{2} \left(\frac{1}{0.60} - \frac{1}{1.00} \right) \sin 38.8$$

$$= 1.77 \times 0.332 + \frac{0.667 \times 0.626}{2} = 0.587 + 0.209 = 0.796 \text{ p.u.}$$

as compared with the specified 0.80 p.u.

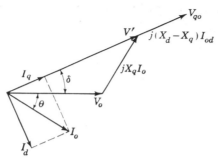

Fig. 8-3.2-1

8-4. The Two-phase Induction Machine.

As another example of the use of the primitive machine in a-c machine analysis, the two-phase

Fig. 8-16. F/A type of three-phase CW wound-rotor induction motor with enclosing covers removed.   (*Courtesy of Westinghouse Electric Corporation.*)

induction machine (see Fig. 8-16) under balanced load conditions is studied.   Such a machine is provided with two stator windings which are space-phased by 90 electrical degrees.   The rotor of the squirrel-cage machine comprises a series of closely spaced bars on the rotor surface with short-circuiting end rings (see Fig. 8-17).   The rotor of the wound-rotor machine is provided with two windings which are also space-phased by 90 electrical degrees. In the wound-rotor machine slip rings are often provided in order to permit the addition of external resistance in the rotor circuit for improved starting torque (see Fig. 8-18), a matter to be discussed later. The analysis to follow is valid for both the squirrel-cage and the wound-rotor machines.

Fig. 8-17. Two-pole squirrel-cage motor rotor. (*Courtesy of Westinghouse Electric Corporation.*)

Fig. 8-18. Stator of medium-size three-phase CW wound-rotor induction motor. (*Courtesy of Westinghouse Electric Corporation.*)

Physically the operation of the induction machine depends on the fact that, upon the application of two-phase excitation to the two-phase stator windings, a rotating magnetic field is produced thereby, as discussed in Sec. 8-2. In the case of the induction generator the rotor is driven at slightly greater than synchronous speed, with the result that a current is induced in the rotor windings, the frequency of the rotor currents being given by the difference between the applied excitation frequency and the rotational frequency of the rotor. This difference frequency is known as the *slip* frequency and is negative in this case. The reaction of the rotor currents in the stator windings is to generate electrical power. Note that the external excitation is required in order to establish the output frequency. Observe that, if the rotor turns at synchronous speed, there is no relative motion of rotor conductors and field. In this case no motional emf is induced, and no rotor currents will result.

When the induction machine is operating as a motor, the power is supplied from the power lines. Now the rotor speed is slightly less than the synchronous speed of the excitation source, the difference between them increasing with increasing load. That is, with increased load on the motor, the slip increases by such an amount that the rotor conductor current resulting from the induced motional emf is sufficient to provide the power demanded by the load. A maximum torque capability exists for the induction motor, and beyond this the machine will come to a halt.

Observe that in the induction machine the fields produced by the stator windings rotate at synchronous speed relative to a fixed reference. Also, the fields of the rotor move at slip frequency relative to the rotor. However, since the rotor moves at slip frequency behind the stator fields, then within the air gap the rotor fields move at the same frequency as the stator field. This means that the rotor fields are moving at synchronous speed relative to the fixed reference.

The procedure to be followed in the analysis initially requires the application of the two-phase transformations to the machine coordinates in order to establish a set of stationary-axes d-q coordinates. Since the stator and the rotor are each two-phase windings, or the equivalent in the case of the squirrel-cage machine, the transformed machine is precisely the primitive machine of Sec. 8-2. Owing to the symmetry of the machine, and the fact that a cylindrical structure is used, the constraints to be imposed on the general primitive machine are the following:

$$\begin{aligned}
v_d{}^r &= v_q{}^r = 0 &&\text{since } v_a{}^r = v_b{}^r = 0 \\
R_d{}^r &= R_q{}^r = R^r \\
R_d{}^s &= R_q{}^s = R^s \\
L_d{}^r &= L_q{}^r = L^r \\
L_d{}^s &= L_q{}^s = L^s \\
M_d &= M_q = M
\end{aligned} \tag{8-40}$$

Subject to these constraints, the general equations [Eq. (8-3)] become

$$\begin{bmatrix} v_d{}^s \\ v_q{}^s \\ 0 \\ 0 \end{bmatrix} = \begin{bmatrix} R^s + L^s p & 0 & M p & 0 \\ 0 & R^s + L^s p & 0 & M p \\ M p & -M\omega & R^r + L^r p & -L^r \omega \\ M\omega & M p & L^r \omega & R^r + L^r p \end{bmatrix} \begin{bmatrix} i_d{}^s \\ i_q{}^s \\ i_d{}^r \\ i_q{}^r \end{bmatrix} \tag{8-41}$$

Also, the electrical torque produced by the machine is obtained by the proper adaptation of Eq. (8-11). This is

$$T_e = (i_q{}^r M i_d{}^s - i_d{}^r M i_q{}^s) = M(i_q{}^r i_d{}^s - i_d{}^r i_q{}^s) \qquad (8\text{-}42)$$

It is convenient to determine the performance characteristics of the machine in machine coordinates. The procedure for accomplishing this is precisely that followed in the foregoing section, and we therefore define the quantities

$$\mathbf{V}^s = \frac{v_d{}^s + j v_q{}^s}{\sqrt{2}} \qquad \mathbf{I}^s = \frac{i_d{}^s + j i_q{}^s}{\sqrt{2}} \qquad \mathbf{I}^r = \frac{i_d{}^r + j i_q{}^r}{\sqrt{2}} \qquad (8\text{-}43)$$

Observe that $\mathbf{V}^s$ and $\mathbf{I}^s$ are at angular frequency ω^s and that $\mathbf{I}^r$ is of angular frequency $\omega = \omega_m$. By using these quantities, the expression for torque T_e specified by Eq. (8-42) may be written as

$$T_e = 2 \operatorname{Im} (M \mathbf{I}^r \mathbf{I}^{s*}) \qquad (8\text{-}44)$$

It is desired to ascertain the speed-torque variation of the machine.

To continue with the analysis, the matrix set [Eq. (8-41)] is expanded. This yields the four equations

$$\begin{aligned}
v_d{}^s &= (R^s + L^s p) i_d{}^s + M p i_d{}^r \\
v_q{}^s &= (R^s + L^s p) i_q{}^s + M p i_q{}^r \\
0 &= M p i_d{}^s - M \omega i_q{}^s + (R^r + L^r p) i_d{}^r - L^r i_q{}^r \\
0 &= M \omega i_d{}^s + M p i_q{}^s + L^r \omega i_d{}^r + (R^r + L^r p) i_q{}^r
\end{aligned} \qquad (8\text{-}45)$$

The first two of these equations are combined to yield

$$v_d{}^s + j v_q{}^s = (R^s + L^s p)(i_d{}^s + j i_q{}^s) + M p(i_d{}^r + j i_q{}^r)$$

which may now be written in the form

$$\mathbf{V}^s = (R^s + L^s p)\mathbf{I}^s + M p \mathbf{I}^r \qquad (8\text{-}46)$$

Correspondingly, combining the second two equations gives

$$0 = M(p + j\omega) i_d{}^s + M(jp - \omega) i_q{}^s$$
$$+ [R^r + L^r(p + j\omega)] i_d{}^r + [j(R^r + L^r p) - L^r \omega] i_q{}^r$$

which is $\quad 0 = M(p + j\omega)(i_d{}^s + j i_q{}^s) + [R^r + L^r(p + j\omega)](i_d{}^r + j i_q{}^r)$

This expression may be written

$$M(p + j\omega)\mathbf{I}^s + [R^r + L^r(p + j\omega)]\mathbf{I}^r = 0 \qquad (8\text{-}47)$$

Equations (8-46) and (8-47) are combined to find an expression for the current $\mathbf{I}^r$. We may now write

$$\mathbf{I}^r = \frac{\begin{vmatrix} R^s + L^s p & \mathbf{V}^s \\ M(p + j\omega) & 0 \end{vmatrix}}{\begin{vmatrix} R^s + L^s p & M p \\ M(p + j\omega) & R^r + L^r(p + j\omega) \end{vmatrix}}$$

$$= \frac{-M(p + j\omega)\mathbf{V}^s}{(R^s + L^s p)[R^r + L^r(p + j\omega)] - M^2 p(p + j\omega)}$$

This expression may be rearranged to the form

$$I^r = \frac{-M(p + j\omega)V^s}{R^sR^r + (L^sL^r - M^2)p(p + j\omega) + R^sL^r(p + j\omega) + R^rL^sp} \quad (8\text{-}48)$$

Now, the ω that appears in these equations is the machine speed, which for motor action is written $\omega \to -n\omega_m$ when referred to the excitation frequency, where n is the number of pole pairs in the machine. Also, the derivative operator $p \to j\omega^s$ under steady-state operation for a sinusoidal excitation function $V^s \cos \omega^s t = \text{Re } (V^s e^{j\omega^s t})$. Therefore the important factors that appear in Eq. (8-48) have the following forms:

$$p \to j\omega^s$$
$$p + j\omega \to j(\omega^s - n\omega_m) = js\omega^s \quad (8\text{-}49)$$
$$p(p + j\omega) \to -\omega^s(\omega^s - n\omega_m) = -s(\omega^s)^2$$

where

$$s \equiv \frac{\omega^s - n\omega_m}{\omega^s}$$

The quantity s is known as the slip factor, with $s\omega^s$ actually representing the slip frequency, the difference between the synchronous speed of the stator field (which is specified by the excitation frequency ω^s/n) and the mechanical speed of rotation of the machine ω_m. If $s = 0$, then the rotor speed is exactly the synchronous speed and there is no relative motion between the rotor conductors and the rotating stator field. In consequence, no motional emfs exist in the rotor windings, and as a result no rotor winding currents exist; therefore no torque is developed. When $s = 1$, the rotor speed is zero (locked rotor) and the induced emf in the rotor is at the primary excitation frequency ω^s/n. For any value of s, the rotor currents have the frequency $s\omega^s/n$.

An important characteristic of the induction machine is its speed-torque curve. To find this, we proceed from Eq. (8-44). Combine Eq. (8-44) with Eq. (8-47) to get, by dividing the expression by 2 for the contribution to the torque per phase, and with both currents referred to the primary frequency,

$$T_e = n \text{ Im } \left\{ I^r \left[\frac{R^r + L^r(p + j\omega)}{p + j\omega} I^r \right]^* \right\}$$
$$= n \text{ Im } \left(|I^r|^2 \frac{R^r - jL^r s\omega^s}{-js\omega^s} \right)$$
$$= n \text{ Im } \left[|I^r|^2 \left(\frac{jR^r}{s\omega^s} + L^r \right) \right]$$

from which, by Eq. (8-49), there results

$$T_e = \frac{|I^r|^2 R^r}{s\omega^s/n} = \frac{|I^r|^2 (1 - s)R^r}{\omega_m} \quad (8\text{-}50)$$

This expression may be interpreted to show that the effective load into which the rotor currents flow, and which is the apparent power sink which accounts for the energy converted between the electrical and mechanical systems, is $(1 - s)R^r/s$. This result is consistent with Eqs. (8-46) and (8-47), which can be given network representation by an equivalent circuit. This can be seen if the equations are written, in the light of Eqs. (8-49), in the form

$$\mathbf{V}^s = (R^s + j\omega^s L^s)\mathbf{I}^s + j\omega^s M \mathbf{I}^r$$

$$0 = j\omega^s M \mathbf{I}^s + \left(\frac{R^r}{s} + j\omega^s L^r\right)\mathbf{I}^r \qquad (8\text{-}51)$$

Two equivalent networks for the two-phase balanced induction machine are given in Fig. 8-19. Observe that these networks show the equivalent

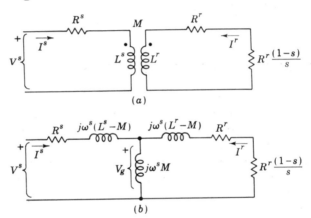

Fig. 8-19. Equivalent circuits per phase for the balanced two-phase induction machine.

load as $R^r(1 - s)/s$ but otherwise have forms identical with those of the transformer, as illustrated in Fig. 3-21. This induction-machine–transformer similarity is often helpful in an understanding of the induction-machine equivalent circuits.

It is possible to make another important observation concerning Fig. 8-19. Equations (8-46) and (8-47), on which this network is based, contain information about both phases simultaneously, through Eqs. (8-29) and (8-30). Since by a proper choice of phase the equations may apply to either phase a or phase b, then these equations can be interpreted as those for either phase. Consequently, Fig. 8-19 may be considered to show the network equivalents of the machine per phase when the potentials and currents are taken to be the phase quantities. In fact, in the case of the three-phase machine, and in the general case of the n-phase machine, the equivalent circuits are precisely those above.

For the balanced system it is necessary only to multiply the power and torque equations by the number of phases for the complete system output.

Example 8-4.1. A 5-hp four-pole 60-cps two-phase wound-rotor induction motor draws 4,400 watts from the line. The core loss is 250 watts; the stator copper loss is 290 watts; the rotor copper loss is 90 watts; friction and windage losses are 70 watts. Determine (a) power transferred across the air gap; (b) mechanical power in watts developed by the rotor; (c) mechanical output power in watts; (d) efficiency; (e) slip; (f) torque in newton-meters.

Solution. (a) Power across the air gap:

$$4,400 - 250 - 290 = 3,900 \text{ watts}$$

(b) Power developed by rotor:
$$3,900 - 90 = 3,810 \text{ watts}$$

(c) Power output:
$$3,810 - 70 = 3,740 \text{ watts}$$

(d) Efficiency:

$$\frac{3,740}{4,400} \times 100 = 84.2\%$$

(e) Slip. Solve for s from the expression for the power

$$P = I^2 R^r \frac{(1-s)}{s}$$

or

$$s = \frac{I^2 R^r}{P + I^2 R^r} = \frac{90}{3,810 + 90} = 0.023$$

(f) Torque. From the fact that $P = \omega_m T_e$, then

$$T = \frac{3,740}{2\pi \times {}^{120}\!/_{4}(1 - 0.023)} = \frac{3,740}{60\pi \times 0.977} = 20.3 \text{ newton-m}$$

We proceed, in finding the speed-torque curve, by rewriting the expression for I^r given by Eq. (8-48) in the form

$$I^r = \frac{-j\omega^s M V^s}{[R^r R^s/s - (\omega^s)^2 (L^s L^r - M^2)] + j\omega^s (L^s R^r/s + R^s L^r)} \tag{8-52}$$

The magnitude of the current I^r is

$$I^r = \frac{\omega^s M V^s}{\sqrt{[R^s R^r/s - (\omega^s)^2 (L^s L^r - M^2)]^2 + (\omega^s)^2 (L^s R^r/s + R^s L^r)^2}} \tag{8-53}$$

This expression is combined with Eq. (8-50), from which

$$T_e = \frac{n\omega^s M^2 (R^r/s)(V^s)^2}{[R^r R^s/s - (\omega^s)^2 (L^s L^r - M^2)]^2 + (\omega^s)^2 (L^s R^r/s + R^s L^r)^2} \tag{8-54}$$

This expression shows that the electromagnetic torque varies as the square of the stator voltage.

Example 8-4.2. A squirrel-cage induction motor would develop 2 p.u. torque if connected directly across the power lines and would take 7.0 p.u. current. A compensator (a tapped autotransformer) having 0.4 p.u. and 0.6 p.u. taps is available for starting the motor.   Neglecting compensator losses and exciting current, determine, for each tap setting, the per-unit (a) line current, (b) starting torque.

Solution.   (a) From Eq. (8-53) the motor current $I^s \propto I^r = kV^s$ for $s = 1$.   Thus, from the specified data, I^s p.u. $= 7V^s$ p.u.

For $V = 0.4$ p.u., $I = 0.4 \times 7 = 2.8$ p.u.
For $V = 0.6$ p.u., $I = 0.6 \times 7 = 4.2$ p.u.

(b) The starting torque is given by Eq. (8-54) and for $s = 1$ is of the form $T_e = k(V^s)^2$.   But $k = 2T_e/(V^s)^2$, so that T_e p.u. $= 2(V^s$ p.u.$)^2$.

For $V = 0.4$ p.u., $T_e = 0.32$ p.u.
For $V = 0.6$ p.u., $T_e = 0.72$ p.u.

It is of interest to illustrate the significance of the various parameters on the starting torque, the maximum torque, and the speed at which the maximum torque occurs.   We first examine the speed, or, equivalently, the slip, at which the maximum torque occurs.   To find this requires that we consider the partial derivative $\partial T_e / \partial s$, with s_{max} being that value of s which makes this derivative zero.   Thus, by considering

$$\frac{\partial T_e}{\partial s}\bigg|_{s_{max}} = 0$$

there results, on solving for s_{max},

$$s_{max} = \pm R^r \sqrt{\frac{(R^s)^2 + (\omega^s L^s)^2}{(\omega^s L^r R^s)^2 + (\omega^s)^4 (L^r L^s - M^2)^2}} \qquad (8\text{-}55)$$

The torque at this value of slip is obtained by combining this expression for s_{max} with Eq. (8-54).   The result is

$$T_{emax} = \pm \frac{\frac{n}{2} M^2 (V^s)^2}{\sqrt{[(L^r R^s)^2 + (\omega^s)^2 (L^s L^r - M^2)^2][(R^s)^2 + (\omega^s L^s)^2]} + R^s \omega^s M^2} \qquad (8\text{-}56)$$

Observe from this expression and Eq. (8-55) that the slip at which the maximum torque occurs is linear with rotor resistance R^r.   But since these two variables occur in Eq. (8-54) only as a ratio, the maximum torque is independent of rotor resistance.   This means that, while the shape of the torque-speed curve can be controlled by rotor resistance, its maximum value cannot.

A typical torque-speed curve for the machine is shown in Fig. 8-20a.   The starting torque, which is that for $s = 1$ (or $\omega_m = 0$), can have any value between zero and the maximum value given by Eq. (8-56).   The starting torque can be varied between these limits by changing the rotor resistance R^r.   Note that, as illustrated in Fig. 8-20b, increases in R^r will lower the slope of the torque-speed curve between $s = 0$ and $s = s_{max}$, which is the region of normal operation.   Such a reduction in slope will make the speed more sensitive to torque changes.   For this reason, in the case of the wound-rotor machine, if an external resistor is used for improved starting torque, it is removed from the circuit after the machine is brought up to speed.

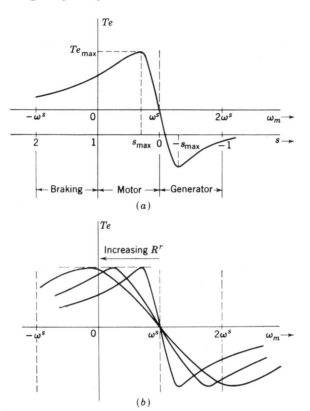

Fig. 8-20. Torque-speed curve of a balanced two-phase induction machine. (a) No added R^r; (b) effect of increasing R^r.

Example 8-4.3.   Find the slip at which the torque is a maximum, and the maximum torque possible by the induction motor specified in Example 8-4.2.

Solution.   The value of s_{max} is

$$s_{max} = 0.08 \sqrt{\frac{0.07^2 + (0.30 + 6.33)^2}{[(0.3 + 6.33) \times 0.07]^2 + (6.63 \times 6.63 - 6.33^2)^2}} = 0.13$$

At this slip, the torque is, from Eq. (8-53),

$$T_{e_{max}} = \frac{\dfrac{1}{2} \dfrac{1}{120\pi} 6.33^2 \left(\dfrac{115}{\sqrt{3}} \sqrt{2}\right)^2}{\sqrt{[(0.07 \times 6.63)^2 + (6.63^2 - 6.33^2)](0.07^2 + 6.63^2)} + 0.07 \times 6.33^2}$$

$$= \frac{6.33^2 \times 115^2}{360\pi(\sqrt{180} + 2.8)} = \frac{(6.33 \times 115)^2}{360\pi \times 16.2} = 28.9 \text{ newton-m/phase}$$

Hence the total torque is
$$T_{e_{\max}} = 3 \times 28.9 = 86.7 \text{ newton-m}$$

An examination of Fig. 8-20a shows that the torque-speed variation in the region of normal operation near synchronous speed ($s = 0$) is nearly linear. In fact, an approximate expression for the torque-speed variation in the region of small s is readily obtained from the general expression for T_e, given by Eq. (8-54). The result is directly

$$T_e = \frac{n\omega^s M^2 (R^r/s)(V^s)^2}{(R^r R^s/s)^2 + (\omega^s)^2 (L^s R^r/s)^2}$$

which is written in the following form,

$$T_e = \frac{nM^2(V^s)^2 s\omega^s}{R^r[(R^s)^2 + (\omega^s L^s)^2]} \tag{8-57}$$

which shows that the torque-speed variation is, in fact, a linear one.

Suppose that Eq. (8-57) is combined with the mechanical equation of the machine. There results

$$T_L = J\frac{d\omega_m}{dt} + D\omega_m - \frac{nM^2(V^s)^2(\omega^s - n\omega_m)}{R^r[(R^s)^2 + (\omega^s L^s)^2]} \tag{8-58}$$

We now define the electrical damping constant as

$$D_e = \frac{nM^2(V^s)^2}{R^r[(R^s)^2 + (\omega^s L^s)^2]} \tag{8-59}$$

Equation (8-58) may now be written in the form

$$T_L + D_e\omega^s = J\frac{d\omega_m}{dt} + (D + nD_e)\omega_m \tag{8-60}$$

This is a linear differential equation with constant coefficients and is one that may be solved readily. Note that the term $D_e\omega^s$ in Eq. (8-60) is a constant which determines the speed at which the motor will run when the applied torque T_L is zero. It follows from Eq. (8-60) that the motor speed under steady-state conditions and no-load torque is

$$\omega_{m0} = \frac{D_e}{D + nD_e}\omega^s \tag{8-61}$$

Observe that, when the mechanical damping D is zero, the motor runs at synchronous speed, because no average power is required to keep the rotor turning.

As shown in Fig. 8-20a, there is a region defined by $1 \leq s \leq 2$ which is referred to as the braking region, where the torque opposes the rotation and mechanical energy is converted into electrical energy. The difference between the braking region and the generator region arises because, in the braking region, the converted energy is dissipated in the rotor circuits as I^2R losses, whereas in the generator region the converted energy is supplied to the stator electrical source.

The foregoing discussion has not taken into account the losses that occur in the iron of the machine due to eddy current and hysteresis effects. The procedure adopted in discussing this matter is precisely that used in discussing the comparable question in the power transformer in Sec. 3-12; and the equivalent network of the device is modified in such a way that these iron losses are taken into account. Thus, from the known fact that the hysteresis and eddy-current losses depend

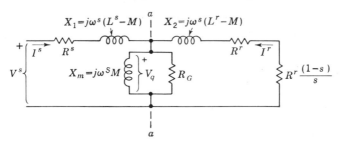

$X_1 = j\omega^s(L^s - M) \qquad X_2 = j\omega^s(L^r - M)$

Fig. 8-21. The equivalent circuit per phase of the balanced induction machine, with provision for the iron losses.

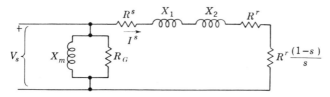

Fig. 8-22. The approximate equivalent circuit of the balanced induction machine.

on the flux density, and since V_q also depends on this same quantity, we then add a conductance G across the points of potential difference V_q. G is so chosen that the power loss $V_q^2 G$ equals that due to the eddy-current and hysteresis losses. When this is done, the equivalent circuit of Fig. 8-19b is altered to the form illustrated in Fig. 8-21.

Now, if it is recognized that the current through the shunt inductance, and this represents the magnetizing current to establish the mutual flux between stator and rotor, and also that the current through the resistance $R_h \ (= 1/G)$, which represents the iron losses, are both small compared with the total stator and rotor currents, $\mathbf{I}^s$ and $\mathbf{I}^r$, respectively, then we may move the parallel circuit across the input terminals from its noted position, without serious error. This established the approximate equivalent circuit of the induction motor which is illustrated in Fig. 8-22. This approximate equivalent circuit makes the calculations involved in numerical computation less involved than those based on the exact equivalent circuit of Fig. 8-21. In most cases, and especially under conditions of load, the results are quite adequate for most engineering purposes. If, for example, one wished to calculate the torque of the machine from the approximate equivalent circuit, one would combine Eq. (8-47) with the value of I^r deduced from Fig. 8-16.

Example 8-4.4. A three-phase 60-cps 115-volt six-pole induction motor has the following parameters per phase relative to the primary (see Fig. 8-21):

$$R_1 = 0.07 \text{ ohm} \qquad R_2 = 0.08 \text{ ohm} \qquad G = 1/R_G = 0.022 \text{ mho}$$
$$X_1 = 0.30 \text{ ohm} \qquad X_2 = 0.30 \text{ ohm} \qquad -B = 1/X_m = 0.158 \text{ mho}$$

For a slip of 2 per cent, find the following: primary current, power factor, electromotance, secondary current, power output, torque, input power, efficiency.

Solution

Effective load resistance:

$$R_L = \frac{1 - 0.02}{0.02} \times 0.08 = 3.92 \text{ ohms/phase}$$

Impedance to right of aa:

$$\mathbf{Z}_{aa}^r = R_L + (R_2 + jX_2) = 3.92 + (0.08 + j0.30) = 4.00 + j0.30 = 4.01\underline{/4.3^\circ}$$

Admittance to right of aa:

$$\mathbf{Y}_{aa}^r = \frac{1}{\mathbf{Z}_{aa}^r} = 0.249\underline{/-4.3^\circ} = 0.248 - j0.0187 \text{ mho}$$

Admittance to left of aa:

$$\mathbf{Y}_{aa}^l = (0.248 - j0.0187) + (0.022 - j0.158) = 0.270 - j0.177$$
$$= 0.324\underline{/-32.4}$$

Total input impedance:

$$\mathbf{Z} = (R_1 + jX_1) + \frac{1}{\mathbf{Y}_{aa}^l} = (0.07 + j0.30) + \frac{1}{0.270 - j0.177}$$
$$= 0.268 + j1.96 = 3.325\underline{/36.2}$$

Primary current, with input potential as reference:

$$\mathbf{I}_1 = \frac{115/\sqrt{3}\ \underline{/0}}{3.325\underline{/36.2}} = 20\underline{/-36.2} = 16.1 - j11.9 \text{ amp}$$

Power factor:

$$\cos 36.2 = 0.805$$

Primary electromotance:

$$\mathbf{V}_g = 66.5 - (16.1 - j11.9)(0.07 + j0.30)$$
$$= 61.8 - j3.9 = 61.8\underline{/-3.7}$$

Secondary current:

$$\mathbf{I}_2 = \mathbf{V}_g \cdot \mathbf{Y}_{aa}^r = 61.8\underline{/-3.7} \times 0.249\underline{/-4.3} = 15.4\underline{/-8.0}$$

Power output, total:

$$P = 3I_2^2 R_L = 3 \times 15.4^2 \times 3.92 = 2,790 \text{ watts}$$

Torque:

$$T_e = \frac{P}{\omega_m} = \frac{2,790}{2(1 - 0.02) \times 60 \times \%} = \frac{2,790}{123} = 22.7 \text{ newton-m}$$

Power input:

$$P_i = \sqrt{3} \, V_L I_L \cos \theta = \sqrt{3} \, 115 \times 20 \times 0.805 = 3,210 \text{ watts}$$

Efficiency:

$$\eta = \frac{2,790}{3,210} \times 100 = 87\%$$

8-5. Two-phase Servomotors. The braking region, illustrated in Fig. 8-20a, is of importance practically, and two-phase servomotors,

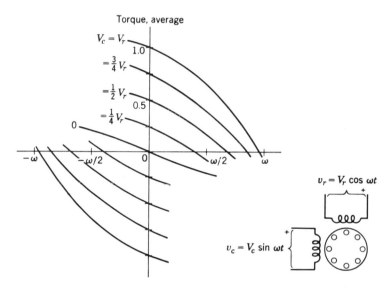

Fig. 8-23. Torque-speed characteristics of a two-phase servomotor.

which are widely used in position-control systems, have been designed to operate in this region. Such machines, and these are of low power rating because of the heating that occurs in them, are designed to have the maximum torque occur at a slip of about $s = 1.5$. This ensures that the torque-speed curve will have a negative slope, and so a stable operating region, in the neighborhood of zero speed, $s = 1$.

As used in automatic position-control systems, one winding of the stator of the servomotor, which may be called the reference phase, is excited by a constant-amplitude a-c potential. An adjustable potential which is 90° out of phase with respect to this reference potential is applied to the second, or control, winding. By varying the amplitude of the control potential, the speed or torque of the motor can be made to change. By reversing the phase sense of the control potential, the direction of the motor will reverse. The motor characteristics are symmetrical in the two directions and have the form illustrated in Fig. 8-23.

The two-phase servomotor provides a rugged device for converting an a-c signal of varying amplitude and phase into a shaft velocity or torque. However, because of the normally unbalanced excitation, a torque that pulsates at second harmonic of the applied excitation frequency is produced. This necessitates, if these pulsations are not to appear in the mechanical system that is coupled to the servomotor, that

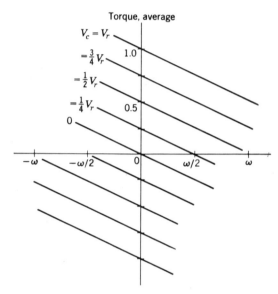

FIG. 8-24. Linearized torque-speed curves of a two-phase servomotor.

the mechanical time constant be large compared with the pulsation period.

Ordinarily in a position-control system the servomotor operates near zero speed. But it is noted from Fig. 8-23 that the curves are nearly linear parallel curves in this region. For this reason, and in the interests of simplifying the subsequent analysis by avoiding nonlinearities, it is the usual practice to linearize the torque-speed curves and to draw them as parallel, equally spaced lines, as shown in Fig. 8-24. From Eq. (8-54) the curves are specified approximately:

$$\left. \begin{array}{ll} \text{Intercept:} & \left. T_e \right|_{\omega_m=0} \doteq \dfrac{n\omega^s M^2 V_c V_r}{R^r[(R^s)^2 + (\omega^s L^s)^2]} = K_v V_c \\[18pt] \text{Slope:} & \left. \dfrac{\partial T_e}{\partial \omega_m} \right|_{\omega_m=0} \doteq \dfrac{-(n/2)M^2 V_r^2}{R^r[(R^s)^2 + (\omega^s L^s)^2]} = -K_\omega \end{array} \right\} \quad (8\text{-}62)$$

From these it follows that

$$\omega_m \bigg|_{T_e=0} = 2\omega^s \frac{V_c}{V_r} \tag{8-63}$$

The resulting linearized set of torque-speed characteristics is given by the equation

$$T_e\bigg)_{av} = K_v V_c - K_\omega \omega \tag{8-64}$$

The average torque is used because the torque that pulsates at the second harmonic of the electrical frequency will cause no appreciable response in the mechanical system, owing to its inherent long time constant compared with the pulsation period. Such a linearized approximation is adequate in analyzing the relative stability of a position-control system.

8-6. Single-phase Induction Motor. It is of interest that the two-phase induction motor, if running with a moderate or light load, will continue to run if one of the phase excitations is opened. That is, the machine will continue to run as a single-phase motor with, in fact, reasonably similar operating characteristics. As will be shown, however, the single-phase induction motor has no starting torque and the motor must be provided with some auxiliary starting device.

The single-phase induction motor is not unlike the polyphase machine in design, except that the stator is wound with only one winding, which is here considered to be in the direct axis. Such a machine has a lower capacity than a polyphase motor of the same weight and dimensions. Electrically the significant difference between the two types is that, in the polyphase machine, the air-gap mmf is of constant amplitude and rotates at a uniform speed. In the single-phase machine, the air-gap mmf is stationary in space but oscillates periodically in time.

The procedure in analysis closely parallels that previously employed, except that now, since only a single winding exists on the stator, the equation for $v_q{}^s$ in the general set given by Eq. (8-3) is suppressed. Thus, for the nonsalient-pole machine, the starting point is the set of Eqs. (8-41) and (8-42) appropriately modified. These equations are

$$\begin{bmatrix} V^s \\ 0 \\ 0 \end{bmatrix} = \begin{bmatrix} R^s + L^s p & Mp & 0 \\ Mp & R^r + L^r p & -L^r \omega \\ M\omega & L^r \omega & R^r + L^r p \end{bmatrix} \begin{bmatrix} i^s \\ i_d{}^r \\ i_q{}^r \end{bmatrix} \tag{8-65}$$

and

$$T_e = M i_q{}^r i^s \tag{8-66}$$

Now suppose that the second and third of the electrical set of equations are considered. These equations are

$$\begin{aligned} -Mpi^s &= (R^r + L^r p)i_d{}^r - L^r \omega i_q{}^r \\ -M\omega i^s &= L^r \omega i_d{}^r + (R^r + L^r p)i_q{}^r \end{aligned} \tag{8-67}$$

It follows from these equations that

$$i_q{}^r = \frac{\begin{vmatrix} R^r + L^rp & -Mpi^s \\ L^r\omega & -M\omega i^s \end{vmatrix}}{\begin{vmatrix} R^r + L^rp & -L^r\omega \\ L^r\omega & R^r + L^rp \end{vmatrix}} = \frac{-M\omega(R^r + L^rp) + MpL^r\omega}{(R^r + L^rp)^2 + (L^r\omega)^2} i^s$$

or

$$i_q{}^r = \frac{-M\omega R^r i^s}{[R^r + L^r(p + j\omega)][R^r + L^r(p - j\omega)]} \tag{8-68}$$

This expression is combined with Eq. (8-66) to give, for the torque,

$$T_e = \frac{-M^2\omega R^r}{[R^r + L^r(p + j\omega)][R^r + L^r(p - j\omega)]} (i^s)^2 \tag{8-69}$$

Now from Eqs. (8-67) we may write the pair of equations

$$\begin{aligned} 0 &= M(p + j\omega)i^s + [R^r + L^r(p + j\omega)](i_d{}^r + ji_q{}^r) \\ 0 &= M(p - j\omega)i^s + [R^r + L^r(p - j\omega)](i_d{}^r - ji_q{}^r) \end{aligned} \tag{8-70}$$

and by defining the quantities

$$\mathbf{I}^r = \frac{i_d{}^r + ji_q{}^r}{\sqrt{2}} \qquad \mathbf{I}^* = \frac{i_d{}^r - ji_q{}^r}{\sqrt{2}} \tag{8-71}$$

then the product of the two expressions of Eqs. (8-70) has the form

$$M^2(p + j\omega)(p - j\omega)(i^s)^2 = [R^r + L^r(p + j\omega)][R^r + L^r(p - j\omega)]|I^r|^2 \tag{8-72}$$

The combination of Eqs. (8-69) and (8-72) yields the expression, when the rotor current is referred to the stator frequency,

$$T_e = 2n|I^r|^2 R^r \frac{\omega}{(p + j\omega)(p - j\omega)} \tag{8-73}$$

But for an excitation function $V^se^{j\omega^s t}$, and for motor action, when $\omega \to -\omega_m$, then

$$\begin{aligned} p &\to j\omega^s \\ p + j\omega &\to j(\omega^s n\omega_m) = js\omega^s \\ p - j\omega &\to j(\omega^s + n\omega_m) = j(2 - s)\omega^s \end{aligned} \tag{8-74}$$

and Eq. (8-73) becomes

$$T_e = 2n|I^r|^2 R^r \frac{n\omega_m}{s\omega^s(2 - s)\omega^s} = \frac{2|I^r|^2 R^r}{\omega_m} \frac{(1 - s)^2}{s(2 - s)} \tag{8-75}$$

Suppose that Eq. (8-75) is written in the form

$$T_e = \frac{2|I^r|^2 R^r}{\omega_m} \left(\frac{1 - s}{s} - \frac{1}{2 - s} \frac{1 - s}{s} \right)$$

or

$$= \frac{2|I^r|^2 R^r}{\omega_m} \frac{1 - s}{s} - \frac{2|I^r|^2 R^r}{\omega_m(2 - s)} \frac{1 - s}{s} \tag{8-76}$$

This expression may be given a very significant interpretation, if it is recognized that s denotes the slip in the direction of rotation of the motor (the ω_m direction) and that $2 - s$ denotes the slip in the opposite, or $-\omega_m$, direction. The first term, which is exactly of the form of Eq. (8-50), may be interpreted as the torque produced by a two-phase field,

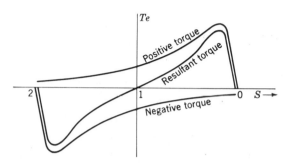

FIG. 8-25. Resultant torque due to oppositely rotating component fields.

with its graphical representation in Fig. 8-19a. The second term is the corresponding one for a two-phase field in the opposite direction. The resultant is the difference between the torques produced by the two fields. This has the form illustrated graphically in Fig. 8-25. This figure shows that the single-phase induction motor produces no average torque at $s = 1$ ($\omega_m = 0$), whence the machine is not self-starting. Observe also that the torque falls to zero at a speed just less than $s = 0$.

The foregoing results permit an interesting and important interpretation. They indicate that a pulsating field of the type which is here being considered can be resolved into two two-phase fields, one of which rotates at ω^s, the second of which rotates at $-\omega^s$. This so-called "rotating-field" theory not only finds application in this instance but also is the basis for discussing amplitude modulation in

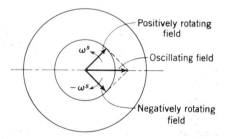

FIG. 8-26. The decomposition of an oscillating field into two oppositely rotating fields.

the electronics domain. The diagram of Fig. 8-26 illustrates the decomposition of the oscillating field into two oppositely rotating fields each of half amplitude.

The rotating-field description of the single-phase induction motor may be given network representation by appropriately extending Fig. 8-19 for the polyphase induction machine. At standstill the amplitudes of the forward and backward resultant air-gap flux waves are both equal to half the amplitude of the pulsating field, as just discussed above. In Fig. 8-27a the portion of the equivalent circuit representing the effects of the air-gap flux is split into two equal portions to represent the effects of the forward and backward fields, respectively.

When the machine is running, the effects of the forward and backward fields are different. The rotor currents induced by the forward field are of slip frequency, and the resulting mmf waves produced by these rotor currents travel forward at slip speed with respect to the rotor or at synchronous speed with respect to the stator. The resultant of the forward waves of stator and rotor mmf creates a resultant forward

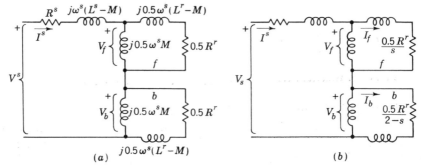

FIG. 8-27. Equivalent circuits for a single-phase induction motor. (a) Rotor blocked, showing the effects of the forward and backward fields; (b) running condition.

wave of air-gap flux which generates an electromotance V_f in the stator winding. Hence, as viewed from the stator, the effect is like that in a polyphase motor and can be represented by an impedance $0.5R^r/s + 0.5j\omega^s(L^r - M)$ in parallel with $0.5j\omega^s M$, as in the portion of the equivalent circuit of Fig. 8-27b, which is labeled f. The factors 0.5 arise from the decomposition of the pulsating stator mmf into the forward and backward components.

Now consider the backward field which has a slip of $2 - s$ with respect to the speed of the rotor. The backward field induces rotor currents with the frequency $(2 - s)f$, which, for small slips, are of almost twice stator frequency. As viewed from the stator, the rotor mmf waves of the backward-field rotor currents travel at synchronous speed, but in the backward direction. These internal reactions, as viewed from the stator, are like that of a polyphase motor whose slip is $2 - s$ and are shown in the portion of the equivalent circuit of Fig. 8-27b, which is labeled b. As with the forward field, the factors 0.5 arise from the resolution of the pulsating stator mmf into the forward and backward components. The electromotance V_b is that generated in the stator winding by the resultant backward field.

The equivalent circuit specified by Fig. 8-27b is in accordance with the results specified by Eqs. (8-70). This may be shown most easily by finding the relation between $\mathbf{V}^s$ and $\mathbf{I}^s$ from Eqs. (8-71) and then comparing it with the results deduced from the circuit of Fig. 8-27b.

The equivalent circuit of Fig. 8-27b may be used to compute the stator current, power input, and power factor, for any assumed value of slip and for specified applied voltage and motor impedances. An important general result, which is that illustrated in Fig. 8-25 for the resultant torque of the machine, follows directly from the equivalent-circuit representation. Thus, when the motor is running at a small slip, the reflected effect of the rotor resistance in the forward field, $0.5R^r/s$, is much larger than its standstill value, whereas the corresponding effect in the backward field, $0.5R^r/(2 - s)$, is much smaller than its standstill value. As a result, the electromotance V_f is much larger than its standstill value, while the backward-field factor V_b is much smaller than its standstill value. Hence the forward air-gap flux wave increases, while the backward flux wave decreases. The resulting effect is to produce an average torque in the forward direction. Moreover, the oppositely rotating waves cause torque pulsations at twice stator frequency, although they produce no average torque.

Example 8-6.1. At a slip of 0.05 the forward and backward components of current of a single-phase induction motor, when referred to the armature, are 29.5 and 31.4 amp, respectively. The rotor resistance referred to the armature is 0.30 ohm. Find the power output and torque, if the synchronous speed is 20 rps.

Solution

Power output due to forward current:

$$\frac{29.5^2 \times 0.150}{0.05} = 2,610 \text{ watts}$$

Power output due to backward current:

$$-\frac{31.4^2 \times 0.150}{2 - 0.05} = -75.8 \text{ watts}$$

Resultant power output:

$$2,610 - 76 = 2,534 \text{ watts}$$

Forward torque:

$$\frac{2,610}{40\pi(1 - 0.05)} = 21.9 \text{ newton-m}$$

Backward torque:

$$\frac{76}{40\pi(1 - 0.05)} = 0.9 \text{ newton-m}$$

Resultant torque:

$$21.9 - 0.9 = 21.0 \text{ newton-m}$$

Since, as noted, the single-phase induction motor is not self-starting, such machines must be provided with some auxiliary scheme for starting. Among the important starting methods are: (1) Providing a split-phase winding (a winding in quadrature with the main stator winding) which is excited through a large capacitance from the single-phase line. The capacitor introduces a substantial phase advance in the current and so provides a current in quadrature with the main field excitation. In essence, then, the machine is started as an effective two-phase machine. Ordinarily the capacitor, which is of special electrolytic design, must be switched out of the circuit after start, since such capacitors are not designed for continuous use on alternating current. A centrifuga, switch is usually incorporated in the machine to open the capacitor circuitl and this operates when the motor reaches operating speed. (2) Another starting method is to provide the machine with a commutator for repulsion-motor start. (The repulsion motor is discussed in Sec. 8-9.) A centrifugal switch will raise the brushes from the commutator, after start.

8-7. Three-phase to d-q Transformation. To show the broad applicability of most of the previous work of this chapter, it is important to show that a polyphase machine can be reduced to an equivalent two-phase machine or, more precisely, that the polyphase machine coordinates can be written in terms of d-q coordinates. Only when this has been done can it be asserted that the primitive machine that has been used to represent the various d-c and two-phase a-c machines which have been studied in detail can also represent the more general polyphase a-c machines. The demonstration required is most easily effected by showing that a transformation can be found which permits the polyphase system to be written in terms of the d-q system of coordinates. The procedure to be followed is essentially an extension of that of Sec. 8-2, and examines the phase fluxes of the machine.

For an appropriately excited balanced three-phase winding, the individual phase fluxes combine to produce the over-all flux of constant magnitude which rotates with respect to the three-phase winding at the time frequency of the phase fluxes. To show this, it is first noted that the phase fluxes relative to the phase axes are given by

$$\phi_a = \phi_m \cos{(\omega t + \varphi_0)}$$
$$\phi_b = \phi_m \cos\left(\omega t + \varphi_0 - \frac{2\pi}{3}\right) \tag{8-77}$$
$$\phi_c = \phi_m \cos\left(\omega t + \varphi_0 - \frac{4\pi}{3}\right)$$

where φ_0 is the time-reference phase angle of the flux variations. The resultant flux at any instantaneous space phase angle φ relative to the d axis, which is chosen as a reference, is obtained by writing

$$\phi = \phi_a e^{j\varphi} + \phi_b e^{j(\varphi - 2\pi/3)} + \phi_c e^{j(\varphi - 4\pi/3)} \tag{8-78}$$

which is
$$\phi = e^{j\varphi}(\phi_a + \phi_b e^{-j2\pi/3} + \phi_c e^{-j4\pi/3}) \tag{8-79}$$

By direct expansion, or by an examination of Fig. 8-28, it is seen that this is

$$\phi = \tfrac{3}{2}\phi_m \qquad (8\text{-}80)$$

which is a constant and equal to $\tfrac{3}{2}$ times the unit of flux for the phase fluxes.

Now we wish to express the resultant flux relative to the d-q reference frame. The direct-axis flux is made up of contributions from the three

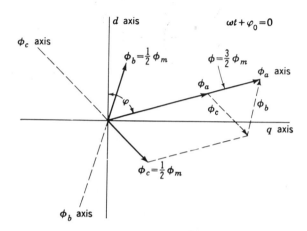

FIG. 8-28. Flux vector relations for the three-phase system.

phase fluxes. For any angle φ, the flux along ϕ_d is

$$\phi_d = \frac{2}{3}\left[\phi_a \cos \varphi + \phi_b \cos\left(\varphi - \frac{2\pi}{3}\right) + \phi_c \cos\left(\varphi - \frac{4\pi}{3}\right)\right] \quad (8\text{-}81)$$

Similarly, the quadrature-axis flux ϕ_q is

$$\phi_q = \frac{2}{3}\left[-\phi_a \sin \varphi - \phi_b \sin\left(\phi - \frac{2\pi}{3}\right) - \phi_c \sin\left(\varphi - \frac{4\pi}{3}\right)\right] \quad (8\text{-}82)$$

To express the phase fluxes in terms of the derived d-q fluxes, it is convenient to refer to Fig. 8-29, which shows the flux vector relations. It follows directly from this figure that the flux in phase a is given by

$$\left.\begin{aligned}
\phi_a &= \phi_d \cos \varphi - \phi_q \sin \varphi \\
\phi_b &= \phi_d \cos\left(\varphi - \frac{2\pi}{3}\right) - \phi_q \sin\left(\varphi - \frac{2\pi}{3}\right) \\
\phi_c &= \phi_d \cos\left(\varphi - \frac{4\pi}{3}\right) - \phi_q \sin\left(\varphi - \frac{4\pi}{3}\right)
\end{aligned}\right\} \quad (8\text{-}83)$$

Similarly,

These relations may be written in matrix form for both the direct and the inverse transformations.   These are

$$\begin{bmatrix} \phi_d \\ \phi_q \end{bmatrix} = \frac{2}{3} \begin{bmatrix} \cos\varphi & \cos\left(\varphi - \dfrac{2\pi}{3}\right) & \cos\left(\varphi - \dfrac{4\pi}{3}\right) \\ -\sin\varphi & -\sin\left(\varphi - \dfrac{2\pi}{3}\right) & -\sin\left(\varphi - \dfrac{4\pi}{3}\right) \end{bmatrix} \begin{bmatrix} \phi_a \\ \phi_b \\ \phi_c \end{bmatrix} \quad (8\text{-}84)$$

and
$$\begin{bmatrix} \phi_a \\ \phi_b \\ \phi_c \end{bmatrix} = \begin{bmatrix} \cos\varphi & -\sin\varphi \\ \cos\left(\varphi - \dfrac{2\pi}{3}\right) & -\sin\left(\varphi - \dfrac{2\pi}{3}\right) \\ \cos\left(\varphi - \dfrac{4\pi}{3}\right) & -\sin\left(\varphi - \dfrac{4\pi}{3}\right) \end{bmatrix} \begin{bmatrix} \phi_d \\ \phi_q \end{bmatrix} \quad (8\text{-}85)$$

With these transformations, the demonstration is completed.

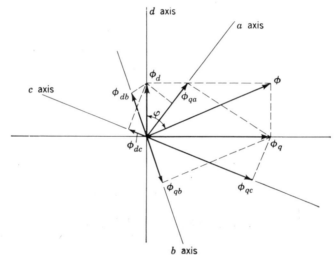

Fig. 8-29. The decomposition of the d-q flux diagram.

8-8. Other Transformations.   It is well to review the work of the previous few sections, since it is important to understand the mathematical procedures that have been employed in these studies.   Our work may be summarized as follows:

1. Our study of the performance characteristics of rotating electrical machinery assumes at the outset the two-axis generalized machine of Fig. 8-1.   This machine is provided with time- and space-invariant axes, which have been called the d-q axes.   Although the sketch shows two stator and two rotor windings, more or fewer windings may be used, depending on the complexity of the machine under study.   The generalized machine is described by a set of as many electrical equations as there are terminal pairs, plus one mechanical equation.   In matrix

notation these equations are

$$V_{dq} = [R + Lp + G\omega][I_{dq}] = [Z_{dq}I_{dq}]$$
$$T_e = [I_t GI]$$
(8-86)

2. For machines with d-c excitation in both stator and rotor windings, the machine a-b axes are stationary, and the stationary d-q axis model is directly applicable to a description of such d-c machinery. It is necessary in this case to associate corresponding parts of the general machine with those of the actual machine.

3. In the case of a-c machinery, a rotational transformation has been introduced to refer the actual machine a-b system to the stationary-axis d-q system. This was accomplished by considering the general d-q equations given by Eq. (8-3) and then introducing in them the two-phase rotational transformation equations given by Eq. (8-17). This leads to the following sequence of steps: Begin with the general equations given in Eq. (8-17), and write the representative transformation as

$$[V_{ab}] = [A_{dq,ab}V_{dq}]$$

where
$$[A_{dq,ab}] = \begin{bmatrix} \cos\varphi & -\sin\varphi \\ \sin\varphi & \cos\varphi \end{bmatrix}$$
(8-87)

If both the stator and rotor variables must be transformed, the results become

$$\begin{bmatrix} A^s V_{dq}^s \\ A^r V_{dq}^r \end{bmatrix} = [Z_{dq}] \begin{bmatrix} A^s I_{dq}^s \\ A^r I_{dq}^r \end{bmatrix}$$

or
$$[A V_{dq}] = [Z_{dq}][A I_{dq}]$$
(8-88)

Actually, at this point, two possible procedures exist. In one, and this was the procedure followed in Secs. 8-3 through 8-6, the operations dictated in Eqs. (8-88) were carried out. Specifically, we wrote

$$[V_{ab}] = [A V_{dq}] = [Z_{dq}][A I_{dq}] = [Z_{dq}I_{ab}]$$
(8-89)

Hence the machine was studied in terms of the transformed $[V]$ and $[I]$ variables, but with $[Z_{dq}]$ being that appropriate to the d-q variables. In the analysis the typical variables were of the form

$$[A^r V_{dq}^r] = \begin{bmatrix} \cos\varphi & -\sin\varphi \\ \sin\varphi & \cos\varphi \end{bmatrix} \begin{bmatrix} v_d^r \\ v_q^r \end{bmatrix} = \begin{bmatrix} v_d^r \cos\varphi - v_q^r \sin\varphi \\ v_d^r \sin\varphi + v_q^r \cos\varphi \end{bmatrix}$$
$$= \begin{bmatrix} \text{Re } (v_d^r + jv_q^r)e^{j\varphi} \\ \text{Im } (v_d^r + jv_q^r)e^{j\varphi} \end{bmatrix} = \begin{bmatrix} \text{Re } (V^r)e^{j\varphi} \\ \text{Im } (V^r)e^{j\varphi} \end{bmatrix}$$
(8-90)

The resulting expressions involving relations among the V^r, I^r, V^s, I^s were then used as the basis for subsequent discussion of the machine characteristics.

The second procedure, and this is equally valid and would have led to the same results as those by use of the first procedure, also begins with Eqs. (8-88), which we rewrite here for convenience:

$$[AV_{dq}] = [Z_{dq}AI_{dq}]$$

Now premultiply both sides of this equation by A^{-1}. This leads to

$$[A^{-1}A][V_{dq}] = [A^{-1}Z_{dq}A][I_{dq}] \qquad (8\text{-}91)$$

which may be written simply as

$$\left. \begin{array}{l} [V_{dq}] = [Z_{ab}I_{dq}] \\ [Z_{ab}] = [A^{-1}Z_{dq}A] \end{array} \right\} \qquad (8\text{-}92)$$

where

In this expression Z is transformed from the d-q reference frame to the

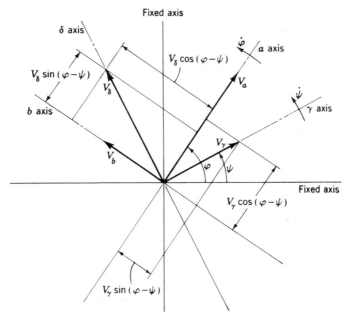

Fig. 8-30. Geometrical interpretation of the γ-δ transformation.

a-b machine variables, and the study appears in terms of the transformed $[Z_{ab}]$ for the system.

As can readily be imagined, the simple, uniformly rotating frame a-b might not necessarily satisfy the constraints imposed by all possible machines. An example of a machine that would not meet the conditions of simple uniform rotation is one provided with one or more sets of brushes, with provision for driving the brush carriage mechanically by some external drive. Another example is that in which asymmetry is introduced by a brush set which is oriented at an angle with respect to the d-q frame.   To examine the manner of approach, we consider this latter case in some detail.

We consider the γ-δ transformation [4],[1] which is a rotating real transformation.   It is a generalization of the a-b, d-q transformation already discussed.   The equations of motion with the rotor variables in the γ-δ system, and with a-b variables on the stator, are suitable to a discussion of the repulsion motor.   In the present case both the a-b and the γ-δ sets are free to rotate relative to a fixed set of reference axes.   The geometry of the situation is that illustrated in Fig. 8-30. The transformation is such that

$$[V_{ab}] = [A_{\gamma\delta} V_{\gamma\delta}] \tag{8-93}$$

where
$$[A_{\gamma\delta}] = \begin{bmatrix} \cos(\varphi - \Psi) & \sin(\varphi - \Psi) \\ -\sin(\varphi - \Psi) & \cos(\varphi - \Psi) \end{bmatrix}$$

The corresponding inverse transformation is

$$[A_{\gamma\delta}^{-1}] = \begin{bmatrix} \cos(\varphi - \Psi) & -\sin(\varphi - \Psi) \\ \sin(\varphi - \Psi) & \cos(\varphi - \Psi) \end{bmatrix} \tag{8-94}$$

Observe that these transformations are precisely of the form of the single rotating system given by Eqs. (8-16) and (8-17) and reduce to this former set when $\Psi = 0$.

We now proceed in the manner of Eqs. (8-92) to find transformed equations for the electrical and the mechanical terminals of the generalized machine.   We consider the equations for a system with the stator variables in the d-q coordinates and the rotor variables in the γ-δ system.   We thus examine

$$\begin{bmatrix} v_d{}^s \\ v_q{}^s \\ v_\gamma{}^r \\ v_\delta{}^r \end{bmatrix} = \begin{bmatrix} u^{-1} & 0 \\ \hline 0 & A^{-1} \end{bmatrix} \begin{bmatrix} R_d{}^s + L_d{}^s p & 0 & M_d p & 0 \\ 0 & R_q{}^s + L_q{}^s p & 0 & M_q p \\ M_d p & -M_q \omega & R_d{}^r + L_d{}^r p & -L_q{}^r \omega \\ M_d \omega & M_q p & L_d{}^r \omega & R_q{}^r + L_q{}^r p \end{bmatrix}$$

$$\times \begin{bmatrix} u & 0 \\ \hline 0 & A \end{bmatrix} \begin{bmatrix} i_d{}^s \\ i_q{}^s \\ i_\gamma{}^r \\ i_\delta{}^r \end{bmatrix} \tag{8-95}$$

where $[u]$ is the unit matrix and $[A]$ is the γ-δ transformation matrix. Also, the expression for the torque is written

$$T_e = [I_t G I] = [AI]_t[G][AI]$$

[1] Numbers enclosed in brackets correspond to numbers of the References at the end of the chapter.

which may be written as

$$T_e = [I_t][A_tGA][I] \tag{8-96}$$

so that

$$T_e = [i_{d^s} \quad i_{q^s} \quad i_{\gamma^r} \quad i_{\delta^r}][A_t]\begin{bmatrix} 0 & 0 & 0 & 0 \\ 0 & 0 & 0 & 0 \\ 0 & -M_q & 0 & -L_{q^r} \\ M_d & 0 & L_{d^r} & 0 \end{bmatrix}[A]\begin{bmatrix} i_{d^s} \\ i_{q^s} \\ i_{\gamma^r} \\ i_{\delta^r} \end{bmatrix} \tag{8-97}$$

By carrying out the designated expansions for the smooth-air-gap machine, the foregoing electrical equations become

$$\begin{bmatrix} v_{d^s} \\ v_{q^s} \\ v_{\gamma^r} \\ v_{\delta} \end{bmatrix}$$

$$= \begin{bmatrix} R^s + L^s p & 0 & M[(\cos\Psi)p & M[(-\sin\Psi)p \\ & & -(\sin\Psi)\dot{\Psi}] & -(\cos\Psi)\dot{\Psi}] \\ 0 & R^s + L^s p & M[(\sin\Psi)p & M[(\cos\Psi)p \\ & & -(\cos\Psi)\dot{\Psi}] & -(\sin\Psi)\dot{\Psi}] \\ M[(\cos\Psi)p & -M[(\sin\Psi)p & M[(\sin\Psi)p & M[(\cos\Psi)p \\ -(\sin\Psi)\varphi] & +(\cos\Psi)\varphi] & -(\cos\Psi)\dot{\Psi}] & -(\sin\Psi)\dot{\Psi}] \\ -M[(-\sin\Psi)p & M[(\cos\Psi)p & R^r + L^r p & -L^r(\varphi-\dot{\Psi}) \\ -(\cos\Psi)\varphi] & -(\sin\Psi)\varphi] & L^r(\varphi-\dot{\Psi}) & R^r + L^r p \end{bmatrix}\begin{bmatrix} i_{d^s} \\ i_{q^s} \\ i_{\gamma^r} \\ i_{\delta^r} \end{bmatrix} \tag{8-98}$$

Also the torque equation becomes

$$T_e = -M[(i_{q^s}i_{\gamma^r} - i_{d^s}i_{\delta^r})\cos\Psi - (i_{q^s}i_{\delta^r} + i_{d^s}i_{\gamma^r})\sin\Psi] \tag{8-99}$$

Note that these expressions reduce to Eqs. (8-3) and (8-5) for $\Psi = \dot{\Psi} = 0$. Further for an n-pole-pair machine, a multiplier n must be included on the right-hand side of this equation.

A somewhat more formal and more involved discussion of the general equations of the rotating machine and their transformation is given in Chap. 11, when the general n-m-phase machine is studied in some detail. It is there discussed that a variety of transformations are possible, the ultimate selection of any transformation being dictated by the require-ment that the transformed equations are amenable to solution. In so far as rotating machinery is concerned, different transforma-tions prove effective for different types of machines, and the selection of the appropriate transformation in a given case often requires considerable insight into the character of the constraints that exist in the machine.

8-9. The Repulsion Motor. The repulsion motor is a single-phase a-c-operated machine, the rotor of which is provided with a com-mutator. The brushes are short-circuited together, and the brush position is at some

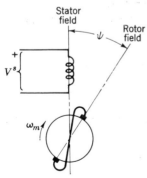

Fig. 8-31. The repulsion motor.

arbitrary angle Ψ with respect to the axis specified by the stator field. A schematic diagram of the machine is given in Fig. 8-31. Owing to the brush orientation, the field due to the rotor currents is differently aligned from that due to the stator currents. The interaction of the two fields results in the production of a torque.

An analysis of the operation of this machine proceeds from the general equations of Eqs. (8-98) and (8-99), appropriately modified. Clearly only two electrical equations exist, one for the stator and the second for the rotor. Also for fixed Ψ, $\dot{\Psi} = 0$. Thus the appropriate equations for the repulsion motor are

$$\begin{bmatrix} v_d{}^s \\ v_\gamma{}^r \end{bmatrix} = \begin{bmatrix} R^s + L^s p & M(\cos \Psi)p \\ M[(\cos \Psi)p - (\sin \Psi)]\dot{\varphi} & R^r + L^r p \end{bmatrix} \begin{bmatrix} i_d{}^s \\ i_\gamma{}^r \end{bmatrix} \quad (8\text{-}100)$$
$$T_e = -M i_d{}^s i^r \sin \Psi$$

with the equations to be subjected to the following constraints:

$$v^r = 0$$
$$\dot{\varphi} = \omega_m = \text{const}$$
$$v_d{}^s = v^s = V^s \cos \omega t$$

Upon expanding the electrical equations of the machine, as specified in Eqs. (8-100), and subject to the machine constraints, we get

$$V^s \cos \omega t = (R^s + L^s p)i^s + M \cos \Psi p i_\gamma{}^r$$
$$0 = M[(\cos \Psi)p - (\sin \Psi)\omega_m]i^s + (R^r + L^r p)i_\gamma{}^r \quad (8\text{-}101)$$

Observe that these are linear differential equations with constant coefficients, and the solution is readily obtained.

The steady-state response of the machine is obtained by assuming sinusoidal potentials and currents. Thus by writing in Eqs. (8-101) the currents of the form

$$i^s = I^s \cos (\omega t + \theta^s)$$
$$i_\gamma{}^r = I^r \cos (\omega t + \theta^r) \quad (8\text{-}102)$$

then the controlling equations become

$$\mathbf{V}^s = (R^s + j\omega L^s)\mathbf{I}^s + j\omega M \cos \Psi \mathbf{I}^r$$
$$0 = (j\omega M \cos \Psi - \omega_m M \sin \Psi)\mathbf{I}^s + (R^r + j\omega L^r)\mathbf{I}^r \quad (8\text{-}103)$$

These equations may be solved for the currents. The results are

$$\mathbf{I}^s = \frac{(R^r + j\omega L^r)\mathbf{V}^s}{(R^s + j\omega L^s)(R^r + j\omega L^r) + \omega^2 M^2 \cos^2 \Psi + j\omega\omega_m M^2 \sin \Psi \cos \Psi} \Bigg\}$$

and

$$\mathbf{I}^r = \frac{(-j\omega M \cos \Psi + \omega_m M \sin \Psi)\mathbf{V}^s}{(R^s + j\omega L^s)(R^r + j\omega L^r) + \omega^2 M^2 \cos^2 \Psi + j\omega\omega_m M^2 \sin \Psi \cos \Psi} \Bigg\}$$
$$(8\text{-}104)$$

These currents may be written as

$$\mathbf{I}^s = I^s e^{j\theta^s} \qquad \mathbf{I}^r = I^r e^{j\theta^r}$$

where

$$I^s = \frac{V^s \sqrt{(R^r)^2 + (\omega L^r)^2}}{\sqrt{\begin{array}{l}[R^s R^r - \omega^2(L^s L^r - M^2 \cos^2 \Psi)]^2 \\ \qquad + [\omega(L^r R^s + L^s R^r + \omega_m M^2 \sin \Psi \cos \Psi]^2\end{array}}}$$

$$\theta^s = \tan^{-1} \frac{\omega L^r}{R^r} - \tan^{-1} \frac{\omega(L^r R^s + L^s R^r + \omega_m M^2 \sin \Psi \cos \Psi)}{R^s R^r - \omega^2(L^s L^r - M^2 \cos^2 \Psi)}$$

and where

$$I^r = \frac{V^s \sqrt{(\omega_m M \sin \Psi)^2 + (\omega M \cos \Psi)^2}}{\sqrt{\begin{array}{l}[R^s R^r - \omega^2(L^s L^r - M^2 \cos^2 \Psi)]^2 \\ \qquad + [\omega(L^r R^s + L^s R^r + \omega_m M^2 \sin \Psi \sin \Psi)]^2\end{array}}}$$

$$\theta^r = -\tan^{-1} \frac{\omega \cos \Psi}{\omega_m \sin \Psi} - \tan^{-1} \frac{\omega(L^r R^s + L^s R^r + \omega_m M^2 \sin \Psi \cos \Psi)}{R^s R^r - \omega^2(L^s L^r - M^2 \cos^2 \Psi)}$$

$$(8\text{-}105)$$

To find an expression for the torque, Eqs. (8-102) are combined with

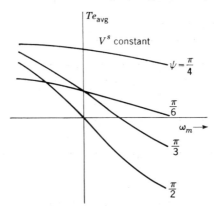

FIG. 8-32. Torque-speed curves of the repulsion motor.

Eq. (8-91).   The result is

$$T_e = -MI^s I_\gamma^r \sin \Psi[\cos (\omega t + \theta^s) \cos (\omega t + \theta^r)]$$

By using the trigonometric identity for the product of two cosines, this becomes

$$T_e = -\tfrac{1}{2}MI^s I_\gamma^r \sin \Psi[\cos (\theta^s - \theta^r) + \cos (2\omega t + \theta^s + \theta^r)] \quad (8\text{-}106)$$

The time-average torque, which is obtained by averaging T_e over a period, is

$$T_e\Big|_{av} = -\tfrac{1}{2}MI^s I_\gamma^r \sin \Psi \cos (\theta^s - \theta^r) \qquad (8\text{-}107)$$

which is, by Eqs. (8-105),

$$T_e\bigg|_{av} = \cfrac{\tfrac{1}{2}M^2 \sin \Psi(\omega^2 L^r \cos \Psi - \omega_m R^r \sin \Psi)V^{s2}}{[R^s R^r - \omega^2(L^s L^r - M^2 \cos^2 \Psi)]^2}$$
$$+ [\omega(L^r R^s + L^s R^r + \omega_m M^2 \sin \Psi \cos \Psi)]^2$$

$$(8-108)$$

Observe from this equation that the torque falls almost linearly with speed ω_m. Figure 8-32 shows typical torque-speed curves of the repulsion motor. Note that for the n-pole-pair machine we must write $n\omega_m$ for ω_m; and a factor n appears as a factor on the right.

REFERENCES

1. Kron, G.: "Equivalent Circuits of Electrical Machinery," John Wiley & Sons, Inc., New York, 1951.
2. Gibbs, W. J.: "Tensors in Electric Machine Theory," Chapman & Hall, Ltd., London, 1952.
3. Adkins, B.: "The General Theory of Electric Machines," Chapman & Hall, Ltd., London, 1957.
4. White, D., and H. H. Woodson: "Electromechanical Energy Conversion," John Wiley & Sons, Inc., New York, 1959.
5. Takeuchi, T. J.: "Matrix Theory of Electrical Machinery," The Ohm-sha, Ltd. Tokyo, 1958.
6. Lynn, J. W.: The Tensor Equations of Electric Machines, *Proc. IEE*, **C102**: 149 (1955).
7. Messerle, H. K.: Dynamic Circuit Theory, *Trans. AIEE*, **59**: 567 (April, 1960).

PROBLEMS

8-1. A simplified reluctance motor is illustrated in the accompanying diagram.

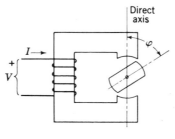

FIG. P8-1

Designate

L_d = maximum inductance when movable iron slug is in direct axis, when $\theta = 0$ and π

L_q = minimum inductance when movable iron slug is in quadrature axis, when $\theta = \pi/2$ and $3\pi/2$

(a) Write the network equation for the electrical circuit. Discuss the terms in this equation.

(b) Find an expression for the torque on the rotating element.

(c) If the movable slug is rotated at constant speed ω, and if the current is of the form $i = I_0 \cos \omega t$, is a nonzero time-average torque possible?

(d) If the rotor speed is $\omega_m \neq \omega$, is a nonzero time-average torque possible?

8-2. A perturbation equation may be deduced for the basic machine for small disturbances about its steady-state operation.

(a) Show that dT_e may be written in the form $dT_e = I_t(G + G_t) \, dI$.

(b) From considerations of the electrical and mechanical equations for variations of the mechanical torque and potential with variations in current and speed, write the matrix giving dV and dT_e. Show that this may be written in the form $\Delta V_0 = Z_0 \, \Delta I_0$, where Z_0 is the motional-impedance matrix for small oscillations, and where ΔV_0 and ΔI_0 allow for the mechanical variables.

8-3. For some analyses of the synchronous machine it is convenient, as shown in Fig. 8-8, to express the inductances as

$$L_d{}^r = M_d + (L_d{}^r - M_d) \qquad L_d{}^s = M_d + (L_d{}^s - M_d)$$

which are in terms of mutual and leakage inductances, and to define the quantities

$$X_{md} = \omega M_d \qquad X^r_{sd} = \omega(L_d{}^r - M_d) \qquad X^s_{sd} = \omega(L_d{}^s - M_d)$$

$X_d{}^r = X_{md} + X^r_{sd}$ direct-axis synchronous reactance

$X_d{}^{r\prime} = X^s_{sd} + \dfrac{X_{md} + X^s_{sd}}{X_{md} X^s_{sd}}$ direct-axis transient reactance

$T'_{d0} = \dfrac{1}{\omega R_d{}^s} X_d{}^r$ direct-axis open-circuit transient time constant

$T'_d = \dfrac{1}{\omega R_d{}^s} X_d{}^{r\prime}$ direct-axis short-circuit transient time constant

Show that Eq. (8-18) can be written in the form

$$X_d{}^{r\prime}(p) = \frac{1 + T'_d p}{1 + T'_{d0} p} X_d{}^r$$

8-4. Show that for the nonsalient-pole synchronous machine the reactive power as a function of angle is given by the expression

$$Q = -\frac{V_0 V_{q0}}{X_q} \cos \delta + \frac{V_0{}^2}{X_q}$$

Sketch the form of this variation with δ.

8-5. Consider a two-pole two-phase 60-cps nonsalient-pole synchronous machine. The windings are distributed sinusoidally in space around the periphery of the air gap. The machine has the following parameters:

$$L_a{}^r = L_b{}^r = 0.21 \text{ henry} \qquad M^{sr} = 0.20 \text{ henry}$$
$$R_a{}^r = R_b{}^r = 1 \text{ ohm} \qquad I_f = 3.6 \text{ amp}$$

Deduce the following:

(a) The rotor phase potentials on open circuit

(b) The rotor phase currents when each phase has a connected 50-ohm resistive load

(c) The average power converted from mechanical to electrical form

8-6. A 440-volt three-phase 60-cps Y-connected synchronous motor has a rated armature current of 26.3 amp. The armature resistance is negligible, $X_d = 5.02$ ohms per phase, and $X_q = 3.34$ ohms per phase. Assuming an input of 15 kw, determine:

(*a*) The power angle δ for excitation voltage 200, 250, 300, 400 volts
(*b*) The power factor and line current for an excitation of 300 volts

8-7. A 3,000-kva 60-cps 13,200-volt three-phase salient-pole alternator has the following per-unit parameters: $R^r = 0.005$, $X_d = 1.12$, $X_q = 0.85$. Calculate the regulation at 0.8 pf, current lagging and leading.

8-8. A 300-kva three-phase 60-cps synchronous machine is used as a generator to supply a 440-volt 200-kw 0.8-power-factor lagging load. The open-circuit characteristics of the alternator follow:

Field amperes........	5	10	15	20	25	30	35	40	45	50
Terminal volts.......	120	240	345	432	497	537	566	582	608	625

The effective resistance per phase is 0.61 ohm, $X_d = 0.825$ ohm, and $X_q = 0.555$ ohm.
(*a*) What is the field excitation for this load?
(*b*) What will be the per cent voltage rise if the load is disconnected? Assume no change in speed.
(*c*) What will be the change in phase angle of the terminal voltage when the load is disconnected?

8-9. The direct-axis reactance X_d of a synchronous machine can be obtained by carrying out short-circuit tests. In these tests the phase windings are short-circuited,

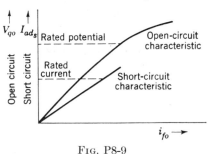

FIG. P8-9

and the short-circuit phase currents are measured as a function of the applied field current, under conditions of constant synchronous speed. A plot of short-circuit current I_{ad_s} versus i_{f0} is very nearly linear, as sketched. Also sketched is the open-circuit saturation curve. Show from Eqs. (8-25) that $X_d = V_{q0}/I_{ad_s}$.

8-10. From the phase diagram of the overexcited synchronous motor (Fig. 8-15) show that

$$\tan \delta = \frac{I_0^r X_q \cos \theta + I_0^r R^r \sin \theta}{V_0 + I_0^r X_q \sin \theta - I_0^r R^r \cos \theta}$$

$$X_q = \frac{V_0 \sin \delta - I_0^r R^r \sin (\theta + \delta)}{I_0^r \cos (\theta + \delta)}$$

8-11. A salient-pole synchronous motor has the following per-unit parameters: $X_d = 1.25$, $X_q = 1.00$. Find $\mathbf{V}_{q0}$ when the motor takes rated current (leading) at rated voltage, delivering 0.5 p.u. mechanical power.

8-12. A 50-cps synchronous alternator is driven by a four-cycle diesel engine. Owing to a misfire of one cylinder, a torque pulsation is produced every two revolutions of the machine. The pertinent data follow:

Alternator: 6,600 volts, 1,500 kva, 0.8 pf, 28 poles, 214 rpm; angle δ at full load $= 25°$
Mechanical system: Weight 16,000 kg; radius of gyration 0.95 m

(a) Show that the effective spring constant for small changes relative to any steady conditions (this is known as the synchronizing torque coefficient) is $dP/d\delta$.

(b) Deduce the equation of motion which specifies the incremental variation about the steady motion. Denote by J the polar moment of inertia of the rotor, including its connected load; by D the braking torque coefficient due to the reaction of the current induced in the damping winding upon the main field; by P_0 the synchronizing torque coefficient; by T_L the externally applied torque.

(c) Calculate the natural frequency of the mechanical system.

(d) Would any serious resonance response effects of the system be expected? Explain.

8-13. A synchronous machine is usually equipped with damper windings. The most common form of damper winding consists of squirrel-cage bars in the pole faces, which are connected together at the ends by copper rings. Consider the special case of one damper bar on the direct axis and one on the quadrature axis.

(a) Set up the equations for a two-phase synchronous machine with damper windings.

(b) Establish the direct-axis and the quadrature-axis equivalent circuits of the machine.

8-14. The constants of a synchronous machine are the following:

$$R_d{}^s = 0.15 \text{ ohm} \qquad R_d{}^r = 0.02 \text{ ohm}$$
$$L_d{}^s = 0.20 \text{ henry} \qquad L_d{}^r = 0.006 \text{ henry} \qquad M_d = 0.0087 \text{ henry}$$

Balanced potentials of 125 volts rms are applied to the terminals of the machine. The excitation frequency is 60 cps.

(a) Start with Eq. (8-16), and write the equations in Laplace transformed form.

(b) Suppose that the machine terminals are short-circuited. If $v_d{}^r = 125 \sqrt{2} \sin \omega t$ at the time of the short circuit, determine the transient current in the d phase.

8-15. A six-pole 15-hp 600-volt 60-cps three-phase Y-connected wound-rotor induction motor has the following parameters relative to the stator:

$$R^r = 0.76 \text{ ohm} \qquad\qquad R^s = 0.90 \text{ ohm} \qquad X_m = \omega^s M = 47.6 \text{ ohms}$$
$$X_1 = \omega^s(L^s - M) = 2.1 \text{ ohms} \qquad X_2 = \omega^s(L^r - M) = 2.0 \text{ ohms}$$

The no-load rotational losses at rated voltage and frequency $= 504$ watts; stray load loss $= 100$ watts. Determine the following, when the slip is 2 per cent: rotor and stator currents; power factor; output; efficiency; torque.

8-16. For the motor of Prob. 8-15, calculate the starting torque and maximum torque. At what slip will maximum torque occur? What will be the power factor and output when the machine develops maximum torque? How much resistance should be inserted into the rotor circuit in order that maximum torque may occur at standstill? How much resistance should be inserted in the rotor circuit so that the speed is reduced to 100 rpm at full-load torque?

8-17. The rotor of Prob. 8-15 is operated as a brake at a slip of 1.5 per cent. Determine: speed of the machine; primary power input; total copper loss in the rotor; braking effort at the pulley, in newton-meters.

8-18. A series of tests were conducted on a 5-hp six-pole three-phase 60-cps Y-connected-stator squirrel-cage induction motor. The results obtained were the following:

No load: $V = 220$, $I = 5.25$ amp, $P = 460$ watts
Blocked: $I = 16$ amp, $P = 1,100$ watts, 0.4 pf
Friction and windage: 108 watts
Effective stator resistance per phase: 0.62 ohm

Draw the equivalent circuit of the motor for a slip of 3 per cent, assuming that the effective rotor reactance is equal to that of the primary.

8-19. A 15-hp 440-volt three-phase Y-connected 60-cps squirrel-cage induction motor, when operating full load, has an efficiency of 89 per cent and a power factor of 0.90. The starting current is 7 times full load and is to be reduced to 2.5 times full load by means of a starting compensator. What should be the percentage voltage tap of an autotransformer to achieve this result? Neglect saturation and no-load admittance.

8-20. It is sometimes convenient to simplify the form of the torque equation [Eq. (8-50)]. If the stator resistance R^s is neglected and the approximate equivalent circuit is used, the torque equation can be written in the following form:

$$T = T_{max} \frac{2}{s_{max}/s + s/s_{max}}$$

(a) Derive this equation.

(b) Show from this equation, neglecting the load torques, that the accelerating time from standstill to slip s is given by the expression

$$t = \frac{J\omega^s}{T_{max}} \left(\frac{1 - s^2}{4s_{max}} + \frac{s_{max}}{2} \log \frac{1}{s} \right)$$

8-21. The speed of an induction motor can be changed by changing the frequency of the excitation source. When this is done, the air-gap flux is usually maintained at its normal value by varying the magnitude of the impressed voltage in the same ratio as the frequency, V/f being thus kept constant.

(a) Upon writing $\alpha = f/f_n$, where f is the operating frequency and f_n is the normal frequency, and noting that the synchronous speed becomes $\alpha\omega^s$, the impressed voltage is αV_n, and all reactances become αX, show that Eq. (8-50) evaluated from the approximate equivalent circuit may be written as

$$T_e = \frac{n(R^r/\alpha s)(V^s)^2}{\omega^s[(R^s/\alpha + R^r/\alpha s)^2 + (X^r + X^s)^2]}$$

where X^r and X^s are the leakage reactances.

(b) Sketch speed-torque curves for $\alpha = 1$, 0.5, 0.2, using a normalized scale.

(c) What can be said about the effect of the reduced frequency on the slip at pull-out, and the effect of reduced frequency on the magnitude of the pull-out and starting torques?

8-22. A 60-cps induction motor for which $X^s = X^r = 0.08$ ohm and $R^s = R^r = 0.02$ ohm is to be operated at half speed from a 30-cps supply. The motor voltage is also reduced to half its rated value.

(a) What will be the pull-out torque at this reduced speed compared with its normal value?

(b) What will be the starting torque at this reduced frequency and voltage compared with its normal value?

8-23. A 3-hp four-pole 60-cps 220-volt three-phase induction motor has the following parameters per phase: $R^s = 0.84$; $R^r = 0.60$; $X_1 = X_2 = 1.06$; $X_m = 38.4$ ohms.

It develops its full load at 3.6 per cent slip. If the frequency is changed to 50 cps, but with an applied 220 volts, at what slip will the motor operate to develop the original rated torque? What is the output? If both the frequency and the applied voltage are reduced to five-sixths the rated value, find the new speed of the motor to develop the original rated torque.

8-24. An induction motor has the following constants:

$$R^s = 1.5 \text{ ohms} \qquad R^r = 8.64 \text{ ohms}$$
$$L^s = 0.0053 \text{ henry} \qquad L^r = 0.0064 \text{ henry} \qquad M = 0.0318 \text{ henry}$$

The motor is being driven at 95 per cent synchronous speed when balanced stator voltages of 110 volts rms, 60 cps, are suddenly applied.

(a) The complete equations of the induction motor are given by Eqs. (8-46) and (8-47). Laplace-transform these equations.

(b) Find the stator transient and the rotor transient currents.

8-25. (a) Starting with Eq. (8-50) for the torque of the polyphase induction motor, and assuming that the load and friction torques are negligible, deduce an expression for the total energy dissipated in the rotor circuit for a change in slip from s_1 to s_2.

(b) Does the power loss in the rotor circuit depend on the rotor circuit resistance?

(c) Consider a 10-hp three-phase squirrel-cage induction motor that is rated at 220 volts, 28 amp, 0.85 pf, 1,150 rpm. The drive has a total inertia of 0.04 kg-m². Calculate the number of starts per minute that this drive can make under no-load conditions without exceeding the total power dissipated in the motor under normal full-load running conditions. How many starts per minute could be made if the motor speed were 1,750 rpm, all other conditions remaining the same?

8-26. It is noted in the text that a normal three-phase induction motor will continue to run even though one of the supply lines is opened, provided, of course, that the load torque is less than the pull-out torque of the machine. That is, the machine will continue to run with single-phase excitation. However, a two-phase motor of the type discussed in Sec. 8-5 will stop if the voltage on one phase is reduced to zero. Account for the difference in behavior of these two machines.

8-27. Consider a two-phase servomotor that is being driven from an external source of mechanical energy, with one phase winding being excited at rated potential and frequency. Under certain conditions the potential developed across the unexcited terminals is proportional to speed. Deduce the voltage-speed relationship, and specify the conditions for the rotor parameters which will yield linear output relationship.

8-28. One winding of a two-phase servomotor is excited by a source $v_a = V(t) \cos \omega^s t$, the second winding being excited by $v_b = V_b \sin \omega^s t$. Observe that $V(t)$ is a function of time, whereas V_b is a constant. In an important application the frequency of $V(t)$ is small compared with ω^s, so that $V(t)$ can be treated as a constant. Deduce the equation of motion of such a device which relates the speed of the machine to the excitation function $V(t)$.

8-29. A single-phase induction motor has the following parameters when referred to the stator,

$$R^s = 0.40 \text{ ohm} \qquad\qquad R^r = 0.30 \text{ ohm} \qquad B = \frac{2}{\omega^s M} = 0.134 \text{ mho}$$
$$X_1 = \omega^s(L^s - M) = 1.00 \text{ ohm} \qquad X_2 = 1.00 \text{ ohm} \qquad G = 0.015 \text{ mho}$$

where G is the conductance in parallel with B to account for the iron losses. Friction and windage = 75 watts.

(a) Find the equivalent impedance of the motor at a slip of 0.015.

(b) Determine the various currents, when the applied voltage is 115 volts; input power; power factor; efficiency.

8-30. Tests on a four-pole 60-cps 230-volt single-phase induction motor yield the following:

	V, volts	I, amp	P, watts
No load.................	230	11.1	365
Blocked rotor............	50	31.6	1,540

The effective value of $R^r = 1.30$ ohms; friction and windage $= 120$ watts. Find the parameters of the motor.

8-31. A wound-rotor inductor motor has a three-phase stator winding, but the rotor is wound for two-phase operation, but for the same number of poles as the stator. Under balanced stator excitation, will the machine operate? Explain.

8-32. A 25-cps four-pole repulsion motor is operated with its brushes shifted 45° (electrical) from the direct axis. Tests made on the machine yield the following data:

Blocked rotor: $V = 53.3$ volts, $I = 60$ amp, $P = 865$ watts.

The mutual impedance when the brushes are shifted to the direct axis is found to be $0.083 + j0.595$ ohms at 25 cps.

Find the current, power factor, speed, and average torque when the applied voltage is its rated 115 volts.

8-33. The primitive machine is to be operated as a so-called d-c induction machine. In this case the brush carriage of the machine is being driven at a constant speed ω_b by an external mechanical drive. The a-b γ-δ transformed equations apply in this case. The electrical constraints are

$$v_a{}^s = -R_1 i_a{}^s \qquad i_a{}^r = I^r = \text{const} \qquad \dot\varphi = \omega_m$$
$$v_b{}^s = -R_1 i_b{}^s \qquad i_b{}^r = 0$$

Deduce an expression for the electromagnetic torque as a function of the brush carriage speed. Sketch the variation of torque as a function of brush carriage speed, and show the influence of R_1.

9

Air-gap Fields in Rotating Machines

The previous two chapters have studied the rotary power converter employing the Kron primitive machine. It had previously been noted that the White and Woodson machine was also to be introduced as the basis for continued study of the rotating machine. A study of this model will contribute to a better understanding of the operation of rotating electrical machines. It is the purpose of the present chapter to provide the background for this study. This will be done by examining the **E** and **H** fields and, through these, the field energies and power flow in the air gap of the White and Woodson idealized machine. These fields will later be related to the operational characteristics of this machine. To develop the fields for the general machine, we shall consider a sequence of progressively more complicated cases.

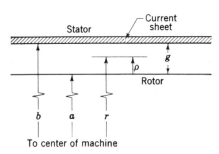

FIG. 9-1. The general features of a linear current along the stator surface.

9-1. The Air-gap Fields—D-C Stator Excitation. As a first case, we consider the cylindrical machine to be provided with a single winding on the stator surface. As was discussed in Sec. 7-2, where distributed windings were viewed as current sheets which produced mmf waves, the equivalent sheet current density, the mmf, and the flux density could be related to each other. Such interrelations were illustrated in Fig. 7-6 for the uniform current sheet and in Fig. 7-7 for the sinusoidal current sheet. It is desired to continue the discussion of these matters. Initially we suppose that a constant linear current-density distribution exists along the stator surface, as illustrated in Fig. 9-1. As noted in Sec. 7-2, the constant current density along the stator surface is

$$J = \frac{Ni}{\pi b} \qquad \text{amp/m} \qquad (9\text{-}1)$$

Equation (7-2), which relates the magnetic-flux density to the mmf for the constant current distribution, is repeated here for convenience,

$$B = \frac{\mu_0 F}{g} \tag{9-2}$$

We suppose now that the current-density distribution is of the form

$$J_z = J_M \cos \varphi \tag{9-3}$$

By choosing a path as shown in Fig. 7-6, the mmf amplitude is one-half of that resulting from encircling the total current in one band. This is

$$F_M = \int \mathbf{H} \cdot d\mathbf{l} = \pi b \left(\frac{1}{2\pi} \int_{-\pi/2}^{\pi/2} J_M \cos \varphi \, d\varphi \right) = J_M b \tag{9-4}$$

and the mmf acting across the air gap at any point is

$$F_r = F_M \sin \varphi = b J_M \sin \varphi \tag{9-5}$$

Now by Eq. (9-2), which shows that the flux-density wave is proportional to the mmf wave, we then have that

$$B_r = \frac{\mu_0 b J_M}{g} \sin \varphi$$

which permits us to write

$$\mathbf{H} = -\mathbf{a}_r \frac{b J_M}{g} \sin \varphi \tag{9-6}$$

The negative sign results from the chosen reference coordinate system.

In the general case, the wave of current density may not be sinusoidal, although it will be periodic along the periphery of the machine. In general, therefore, the analysis would continue by representing the current-density wave by a Fourier-series expansion. We consider, for example, the square wave of Fig. 7-5, which may be represented by the series

$$J_z = \frac{iN}{\pi b} \frac{4}{\pi} \left(\cos \varphi + \frac{1}{3} \cos 3\varphi + \frac{1}{5} \cos 5\varphi + \cdots \right)$$

which is $J_z = i \left(\frac{4N}{\pi^2 b} \cos \varphi + \frac{4N}{3\pi^2 b} \cos 3\varphi + \frac{4N}{5\pi^2 b} \cos 5\varphi + \cdots \right)$

$$\tag{9-7}$$

The terms in the parentheses may be interpreted as the equivalent conductor densities of fictitious sinusoidally distributed coils. It is convenient in the general case to denote by Z_n the maximum value of the nth conductor density. Equation (9-7) thus has the form

$$J_z = i(Z_1 \cos \varphi + Z_3 \cos 3\varphi + Z_5 \cos 5\varphi + \cdots) \tag{9-8}$$

and each harmonic current sheet density is of the form

$$J_n = iZ_n \cos n\varphi \qquad (9\text{-}9)$$

In this expression n may be interpreted as the number of space cycles of current density in 2π radians of the mechanical angle φ. The flux-density wave is obtained in the same way that Eq. (9-6) results from Eq. (9-2) through Eq. (9-5). The result, which is just an extension of Eq. (9-6), is given by the expression

$$B_r = \frac{\mu_0 b}{g} \sum_n \frac{iZ_n \sin n\varphi}{n}$$

from which it follows directly that

$$\mathbf{H} = -\mathbf{a}_r \sum \frac{b i Z_n}{ng} \sin n\varphi \qquad (9\text{-}10)$$

Attention is called to a second component of magnetic-field intensity that exists in the air gap. To find an expression for this component of field, reference is again made to Fig. 7-6, except that now the path $DEFG$ is taken somewhat differently from before. Now DE and FG are to be infinitesimal lengths, with DE just within the air gap and GF just within the iron. This is the equivalent of the surface boundary condition $\mathbf{J} = \mathbf{n} \times \mathbf{H}$. It follows now that at the boundary $r = b$, which is the stator surface,

$$H_\varphi \Big|_{r=b} = -J_z \qquad (9\text{-}11)$$

At the surface of the rotor, which is here assumed to be infinitely permeable, the field must vanish. Thus

$$H_\varphi \Big|_{r=a} = 0 \qquad (9\text{-}12)$$

Hence the H_φ field will be of the form

$$H_\varphi = -F(r)iZ_n \cos n\varphi \qquad \begin{cases} F(r) = 1 \text{ when } r = b \\ F(r) = 0 \text{ when } r = a \end{cases}$$

It will be assumed that $F(r)$ varies linearly between the surfaces a and b and is written

$$F(r) = \frac{\rho}{g}$$

where ρ is measured from the rotor surface. More elaborate calculations show this to be a valid approximation. The present component of field for each conductor density is

$$\mathbf{H} = -\mathbf{a}_\varphi \frac{\rho i Z_n}{g} \cos n\varphi \qquad (9\text{-}13)$$

Finally, it is desired to deduce the electric field in the air gap.   Clearly, since a current density exists at the surface of the rotor, this implies the existence of an axial electric field.   At the stator surface the axial field must satisfy the condition

$$E_z \Big|_{r=b} = \frac{J_z}{\gamma} \tag{9-14}$$

where γ is the surface conductivity of the winding material of the infinitely thin sheet in which the surface current of density J flows.   Also, the electric field in the Z direction at the rotor surface must vanish, since otherwise there would be a surface current.   Hence

$$E_z \Big|_{r=a} = 0 \tag{9-15}$$

A field configuration that satisfies the boundary conditions is the following:

$$E_z = G(r) \frac{iZ_n}{\gamma} \cos n\varphi \qquad \begin{cases} G(r) = 1 \text{ when } r = b \\ G(r) = 0 \text{ when } r = a \end{cases}$$

Here $G(r)$ varies from zero at the rotor surface to unity at the stator surface.   It will be assumed that $G(r)$ varies linearly between the rotor and stator surface, and is chosen of the form

$$G(r) = \frac{\rho}{g}$$

More elaborate calculations justify this approximation.   Hence we write finally

$$\mathbf{E} = \mathbf{a}_z \frac{\rho i Z_n}{g} \cos n\varphi \qquad (9\text{-}16)$$

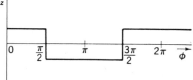

FIG. 9-2. The space distribution of E_z for the single-excitation-winding d-c excitation case.

It is possible to deduce an expression for the applied potential to the terminals of the winding.   The space distribution of the electric field is chosen to be the constant form resulting from a constant current-density distribution, as illustrated in Fig. 9-2.   The applied potential V of the N-turn coil, the effect of the end turns being neglected, is the sum of the potentials along the wires and is

$$V = \int \mathbf{E} \cdot d\mathbf{l} = \int_{-\pi/2}^{\pi/2} \int_0^L \frac{i}{\gamma} \frac{4N}{\pi^2 b} \left(\cos\varphi + \frac{1}{3}\cos 3\varphi + \cdots \right) b \, d\varphi \, dz$$
$$- \int_{-\pi/2}^{\pi/2} \int_0^L \frac{i}{\gamma} \frac{4N}{\pi^2 b} \left(\cos\varphi + \frac{1}{3}\cos 3\varphi + \cdots \right) b \, d\varphi \, dz \tag{9-17}$$

where L is the axial length of the conductor.   Upon performing the

indicated integrations, the result is

$$V = \frac{2NLi}{\gamma} \qquad (9\text{-}18)$$

This is a result that could have been written down by inspection.

In summary, we have found that the fields within the air gap for the d-c excitation conditions in a distributed winding on the stator surface for each equivalent set of coils are the following:

$$
\begin{aligned}
\mathbf{H} &= -\mathbf{a}_r \frac{ibZ_n}{ng} \sin n\varphi - \mathbf{a}_\varphi \frac{piZ_n}{g} \cos n\varphi \\
\mathbf{E} &= \mathbf{a}_z \frac{piZ_n}{\gamma g} \cos n_\varphi
\end{aligned}
\qquad (9\text{-}19)
$$

These fields have the orientation shown in Fig. 9-3. They may be con-

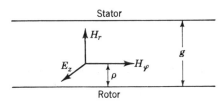

Stator

H_r

E_z — H_φ

ρ

g

Rotor

FIG. 9-3. The fields in the singly excited machine.

sidered as the first-order fields, as higher-order effects that arise from the approximations must be considered in deducing the complete field configuration.[1]

With the **E** and **H** fields known, the Poynting theorem may be employed to study the power flow in the air gap of the machine. Recall that in the volume enclosed by the surface over which the Poynting radiation is evaluated the total energy balance must account for

Instantaneous power converted to mechanical form
  + instantaneous power absorbed in volume due to flow of currents
  + instantaneous rate of change of stored electric and magnetic energy

In a formal way, it is required that we evaluate the expressions

$$\oint \mathbf{S} \cdot \mathbf{n}\, dA = \int_{\substack{\text{stator and} \\ \text{rotor} \\ \text{surfaces}}} \mathbf{S} \cdot \mathbf{n}\, dA + \int_{\substack{\text{axial} \\ \text{air-gap} \\ \text{rings}}} \mathbf{S} \cdot \mathbf{n}\, dA + \int_{\substack{\text{radial} \\ \text{air-gap} \\ \text{surfaces}}} \mathbf{S} \cdot \mathbf{n}\, dA$$

$$(9\text{-}20)$$

More specifically, this is

$$
\begin{aligned}
\oint \mathbf{S} \cdot \mathbf{n}\, dS = {}& \int S_r \Big|_{\rho=0} (a\, d\varphi\, dz) - \int S_r \Big|_{\rho=g} (b\, d\varphi\, dz) \\
& + \int S_z \Big|_{z=0} (r\, d\varphi\, dr) - \int S_z \Big|_{z=L} (r\, d\varphi\, dr) + \int S_\varphi \Big|_{\varphi=0} (dr\, dz) \\
& \qquad\qquad\qquad\qquad\qquad\qquad\qquad - \int S_\varphi \Big|_{\varphi=2\pi} (dr\, dz) \quad (9\text{-}21)
\end{aligned}
$$

[1] For a more extensive discussion, see D. C. White and H. H. Woodson, "Electromechanical Energy Conversion," chap. 3, John Wiley & Sons, Inc., New York, 1959.

The first two integrals on the right specify the power flow into and out of the radial surfaces at the rotor and stator. The third and fourth integrals specify the power flow into and out of the axial surfaces an each end of the rotor. The fifth and sixth integrals specify the power flow along the air gap in the transverse direction.

To evaluate these integrals, it is first noted that

$$S_r = (\mathbf{E} \times \mathbf{H})_r = E_\varphi H_z - E_z H_\varphi = -E_z H_\varphi$$
$$S_\varphi = (\mathbf{E} \times \mathbf{H})_\varphi = E_z H_r - E_r H_z = E_z H_r \qquad (9\text{-}22)$$
$$S_z = (\mathbf{E} \times \mathbf{H})_z = E_r H_\varphi - E_\varphi H_r = 0$$

It is noted also that at the rotor surface $S_r \big|_{\rho=0} = 0$; so the first integral vanishes. The third and fourth integrals vanish because $S_z = 0$. The fifth and sixth integrals must cancel each other, since continuity of the fields dictates that $S_\varphi(0) = S_\varphi(2\pi)$. In addition, $S_\varphi = 0$ at each limit. Hence Eq. (9-21) reduces to the single integral

$$\oint \mathbf{S} \cdot \mathbf{n} \, dA = -\int S_r \big|_{\rho=g} (b \, d\varphi \, dz)$$

which becomes $\displaystyle \oint \mathbf{S} \cdot \mathbf{n} \, dA = -\int_0^L \int_0^{2\pi} \frac{1}{\gamma} (iZ_n)^2 \cos^2 n\varphi \, (b \, dz \, d\varphi) \qquad (9\text{-}23)$

The integral reduces to

$$\oint \mathbf{S} \cdot \mathbf{n} \, dA = -\frac{\pi L}{\gamma b} (bZ_n)^2 i^2 \qquad (9\text{-}24)$$

In this expression the term $(bZ_n)^2$ has the dimensions of turns squared, and γ is the conductivity (mhos). Thus the term $(\pi L/\gamma b)(bZ_n)^2$ has the dimensions of resistance. Equation (9-24) may now be written as

$$\oint \mathbf{S} \cdot \mathbf{n} \, dA = -Ri^2 \qquad (9\text{-}25)$$

where

$$R = \frac{\pi L}{\gamma b} (bZ_n)^2$$

This expression shows that the average power flow is from the air gap into the stator conductors, where it is dissipated in joule heat. This result is consistent, of course, with the physical analysis of the system. The result means that no change occurs in the stored energy in the field, which is consistent with the d-c excitation. Moreover, no energy conversion occurs. This latter would hardly be expected, since no rotor winding or rotor current exists to provide the possibility for such energy conversion.

9-2. A-C-excited Distributed Winding. We continue with the discussion of a machine provided with a single stator winding only. In the discussion in the foregoing section, certain assumptions were implicit. Not only was it explicitly assumed that all the reluctance of the magnetic path was contained in the air gap, but also implied was the assumption that the results were independent of the motion of the rotor. This latter means that effects due to polarization or magnetization of the material mediums of the system were being neglected. In the present section we continue with these assumptions and add the additional assumption that all secondary effects in the iron or dielectrics of the machine due to the application of a time-varying excitation are negligible.

For clarity, it will be assumed that the excitation winding is the stator winding and that the stator terminal current is i^s, where

$$i^s = I^s \sin (\omega^s t + \theta^s) \tag{9-26}$$

We continue with the assumption that there is no rotor current, either because of the absence of a winding or because the rotor winding is open-circuited, if it exists. In this expression θ^s is the phase relative to some specified time reference. The resultant linear current density given by Eq. (9-9) is

$$\mathbf{J}^s = \mathbf{a}_z i^s Z_n{}^s \cos n\varphi^s$$

which is
$$\mathbf{J}^s = \mathbf{a}_z I^s Z_n{}^s \sin (\omega^s t + \theta^s) \cos n\varphi^s \tag{9-27}$$

We wish to find the air-gap fields for this time-varying sheet current density.

In so far as the magnetic-field-strength components are concerned, a careful review leading to Eqs. (9-10) and (9-13) will show that these expressions will not be affected by a time-dependent current. Thus we have, from the first of Eqs. (9-19),

$$\mathbf{H}^s = -\mathbf{a}_r \frac{bI^s Z_n{}^s}{ng} \sin (\omega^s t + \theta^s) \sin n\varphi^s - \mathbf{a}_\varphi \frac{\rho I^s Z_n{}^s}{g} \sin (\omega^s t + \theta^s) \cos n\varphi^s \tag{9-28}$$

However, the electric field will be affected by the time-varying current.

To find the electric field, use is made of the fundamental field relations that

$$\operatorname{curl} \mathbf{E}^s = -\mu_0 \frac{\partial \mathbf{H}^s}{\partial t} \tag{9-29}$$

$$\operatorname{div} \mathbf{E}^s = 0$$

In cylindrical coordinates (φ, r, z) these equations have the form

$$\mathbf{a}_r \left(\frac{1}{r} \frac{\partial E_z{}^s}{\partial \varphi} - \frac{\partial E_\varphi{}^s}{\partial z} \right) + \mathbf{a}_\varphi \left(\frac{\partial E_r{}^s}{\partial z} - \frac{\partial E_z{}^s}{\partial r} \right) + \mathbf{a}_z \left(\frac{\partial E_\varphi{}^s}{\partial r} - \frac{1}{r} \frac{\partial E_r{}^s}{\partial \varphi} \right)$$

$$= -\mu_0 \frac{\partial \mathbf{H}^s}{\partial t} \tag{9-30}$$

$$\frac{1}{r} \frac{\partial (rE_r{}^s)}{\partial r} + \frac{1}{r} \frac{\partial E_\varphi{}^s}{\partial \varphi} + \frac{\partial E_z{}^s}{\partial z} = 0$$

We now write from Eq. (9-28) and the first of Eqs. (9-30)

$$\frac{\partial E_\varphi{}^s}{\partial z} - \frac{1}{r}\frac{\partial E_z{}^s}{\partial \varphi} = \omega^s \mu_0 \frac{bZ_n{}^sI^s}{ng} \cos(\omega^s t + \theta^s)\sin n\varphi^s$$

$$\frac{\partial E_z{}^s}{\partial r} - \frac{\partial E_r{}^s}{\partial z} = \omega^s \mu_0 \frac{pZ_n{}^sI^s}{g} \cos(\omega^s t + \theta^s)\cos n\varphi^s \qquad (9\text{-}31)$$

$$\frac{1}{r}\frac{\partial E_r{}^s}{\partial \varphi} - \frac{\partial E_\varphi{}^s}{\partial r} = 0$$

From the second of Eqs. (9-30) we may write

$$\frac{\partial(rE_r{}^s)}{\partial r} + \frac{\partial E_\varphi{}^s}{\partial \varphi} = 0 \qquad (9\text{-}32)$$

if it is specified that $E_z{}^s$ is to be independent of z. Field components which satisfy Eqs. (9-31) and Eq. (9-32) and the air-gap boundary conditions will satisfy the needs of the problem.

To deduce the form of the $\mathbf{E}^s$ field, we choose $E_z{}^s$ to be of the form suggested by Eqs. (9-19), namely,

$$E_z{}^s = \frac{pZ_n{}^sI^s}{\gamma g} \sin(\omega^s t + \theta^s)\cos n\varphi^s \qquad (9\text{-}33)$$

We now proceed as follows: This expression is combined with the first two of Eqs. (9-31) to deduce expressions for $\partial E_\varphi{}^s/\partial z$ and $\partial E_r{}^s/\partial z$. These equations may be integrated to yield expressions for E_φ and E_r. The resulting functions of integration are chosen as zero. Also, in the resulting expressions, write $r \doteq b$. The results are the equations for the $\mathbf{E}^s$ field components within the air gap. These are

$$E_r{}^s = z\frac{Z_n{}^sI^s}{\gamma g}\sin(\omega^s t + \theta^s)\cos n\varphi^s - z\frac{pZ_n{}^sI^s}{g}\mu_0\omega^s \cos(\omega^s t + \theta^s)\cos n\varphi^s$$

$$E_\varphi{}^s = -nz\frac{pZ_n{}^sI^s}{\gamma g b}\sin(\omega^s t + \theta^s)\sin n\varphi^s$$

$$\qquad\qquad + z\frac{bZ_n{}^sI^s}{ng}\mu_0\omega^s \cos(\omega^s t + \theta^s)\sin n\varphi^s \qquad (9\text{-}34)$$

$$E_z{}^s = \frac{pZ_n{}^sI^s}{\gamma g}\sin(\omega^s t + \theta^s)\cos n\varphi^s$$

The validity of these field expressions is verified by showing that they do approximately satisfy Eqs. (9-31) and (9-32).

We now wish to examine the radiation flow. This is done, as in Sec. 9-1, by employing the Poynting theorem. This requires that we again evaluate Eq. (9-21), but now the $\mathbf{E}$ and $\mathbf{H}$ fields given by Eqs. (9-28) and (9-34) must be used. Actually, as before, the fifth and sixth integrals of Eq. (9-21) vanish, since these must be equal and opposite. The first integral vanishes because the integrand is zero. The third integral vanishes since $E_r{}^s\big|_{z=0} = 0$ and $E_\varphi{}^s\big|_{z=0} = 0$, and hence the integrand is zero. Thus only the second and fourth integrals must be evaluated. The second integral is written explicitly as

$$\int_0^L \int_0^{2\pi} S_r \bigg|_{\rho=g} (b\,d\varphi\,dz) = -\int_0^L \int_0^{2\pi} \frac{1}{\gamma} (Z_n{}^s I^s)^2 \sin^2 (\omega^s t + \theta^s)$$
$$\cos^2 n\varphi^s (b\,d\varphi\,dz) \quad (9\text{-}35)$$

The result of this integration leads to the expression

$$\int_0^L \int_0^{2\pi} S_r \bigg|_{\rho=g} (b\,d\varphi\,dz) = -\frac{\pi L}{\gamma b} (bZ_n{}^s)^2 (I^s)^2 \sin^2 (\omega^s t + \theta^s)$$

which is

$$\left.\begin{array}{c} \displaystyle\int_0^L \int_0^{2\pi} S_r \bigg|_{\rho=g} (b\,d\varphi\,dz) = -Ri^2 \\[3mm] \text{where} \qquad\qquad R = \dfrac{\pi L}{\gamma b} (bZ_n{}^s)^2 \end{array}\right\} \qquad (9\text{-}36)$$

It is observed that this expression is precisely that given in Eqs. (9-25) for the d-c case, except that now the current i denotes the instantaneous value. If this expression is integrated in time over a period to give the average power dissipated in joule heat in the volume, then the result becomes RI^2, where I is the rms value of the current.

The fourth term of Eq. (9-21) is given by the following complicated expression:

$$-\int S_z \bigg|_{z=L} (r\,d\varphi\,dr) = \int_a^b \int_0^{2\pi} \left\{ \frac{\rho I^s Z_n{}^s}{g} \sin (\omega^s t + \theta^s) \cos n\varphi \left[\frac{LI^s Z_n{}^s}{\gamma g} \right.\right.$$
$$\sin (\omega^s t + \theta^s) \cos n\varphi^s - \frac{L\rho I^s Z_n{}^s}{g} \mu_0 \omega^s \cos (\omega^s t + \theta^s) \cos n\varphi^s \bigg]$$
$$+ \frac{bI^s Z_n{}^s}{ng} \sin (\omega^s t + \theta^s) \sin n\varphi^s \left[\frac{nL\rho I^s Z_n{}^s}{\gamma bg} \sin (\omega^s t + \theta^s) \sin n\varphi^s \right.$$
$$\left.\left. - \frac{LbI^s Z_n{}^s}{ng} \mu_0 \omega^s \cos (\omega^s t + \theta^s) \sin n\varphi^s \right] \right\} (r\,d\varphi\,dr) \quad (9\text{-}37)$$

Integrating in φ yields approximately

$$-\int S_z \bigg|_{z=L} (r\,d\varphi\,dr) = -\int_a^b \pi\mu_0 \omega^s L \left[\left(\frac{b}{ng}\right)^2 + \left(\frac{\rho}{g}\right)^2 \right] (I^s Z_n{}^s)^2$$
$$\sin (\omega^s t + \theta^s) \cos (\omega^s t + \theta^s) r\,dr \quad (9\text{-}38)$$

Also, to the order b/g, this expression integrates to

$$-\int S_z \bigg|_{z=L} (r\,d\varphi\,dr) = -\pi\mu_0 \omega^s L \left(\frac{b}{ng}\right)^2 (I^s Z_n{}^s)^2 \frac{b^2 - a^2}{2} \sin (\omega^t t + \theta^s)$$
$$\cos (\omega^s t + \theta^s)$$

which may be written as

$$-\int S_z \Big|_{z=L} (r\,d\varphi\,dr) = -\omega^s \left[\frac{L\pi}{n^2} \mu_0 \frac{b^3}{g} (Z_n{}^s)^2 \right] (I_s)^2 \sin(\omega^s t + \theta^s)$$
$$\cos(\omega^s t + \theta^s) \quad (9\text{-}39)$$

It is of interest to evaluate the magnetic energy stored in the volume enclosed by the surface of integration. This is given by the expression

$$W_m{}^s = \int_\tau \tfrac{1}{2}\mu_0 (H^s)^2\,d\tau \qquad (9\text{-}40)$$

This expression becomes, by including the explicit form for $\mathbf{H}^s$,

$$W_m{}^s = \int_a^b \int_0^{2\pi} \int_0^L \tfrac{1}{2}\mu_0 \left\{ \left[\frac{b}{ng} I^s Z_n{}^s \sin(\omega^s t + \theta^s) \sin n\varphi^s \right]^2 \right.$$
$$\left. + \left[\frac{\rho}{g} I^s Z_n{}^s \sin(\omega^s t + \theta^s) \cos n\varphi^s \right]^2 \right\} r\,dr\,d\varphi\,dz$$

The evaluation of this integral in φ and z leads to the following expression:

$$W_m{}^s = \tfrac{1}{2}\mu_0\pi L \int_a^b \left[\left(\frac{b}{ng}\right)^2 + \left(\frac{\rho}{g}\right)^2 \right] [I^s Z_n{}^s \sin(\omega^s t + \theta^s)]^2 r\,dr \quad (9\text{-}41)$$

This is the instantaneous stored energy in the magnetic field. Note that the quantity

$$\frac{\partial W_m{}^s}{\partial t} = \int_a^b \pi\mu_0\omega^s L \left[\left(\frac{b}{ng}\right)^2 + \left(\frac{\rho}{g}\right)^2 \right] [I^s Z_n{}^s \sin(\omega^s t + \theta^s)]$$
$$[I^s Z_n{}^s \cos(\omega^s t + \theta^s)] r\,dr \quad (9\text{-}42)$$

is exactly the negative of that given by the fourth term of Eq. (9-21), as given by Eq. (9-38). It follows, therefore, that the power out of the air gap is

$$\oint \mathbf{S} \cdot \mathbf{n}\,dA = -Ri^2 - \frac{\partial W_m{}^s}{\partial t} \qquad (9\text{-}43)$$

This expression shows that the Poynting vector, when integrated over a surface enclosing the air gap, gives the power lost in the copper and the power flow making up the increase of magnetic energy stored in the volume.

No effort is made to evaluate the stored electric energy per unit volume since the ratio of electric to magnetic energy per unit volume proves to be inversely proportional to c^2, where c is the velocity of propagation of light. That this is so follows directly from the ratio

$$\frac{W_e}{W_m} = \frac{\tfrac{1}{2}\epsilon_0 E^2}{\tfrac{1}{2}\mu_0 H^2} = \frac{\epsilon_0 E^2}{\mu_0 H^2}$$

But by Eqs. (2-26) and (2-19) this may be written

$$\frac{W_e}{W_m} = \frac{\epsilon_0}{\mu_0} (\mu_0 v)^2 = \left(\frac{v}{c}\right)^2$$

where v denotes the velocity of propagation of the fields in the machine. Since $v \ll c$, this ratio is negligible for any practical machine.

It is interesting to express the magnetic energy in terms of the inductance of the stator winding. This is accomplished by recalling that

$$W_m{}^s = \tfrac{1}{2}L^s(i^s)^2 = \int_\tau \tfrac{1}{2}\mu_0(H^s)^2 \, d\tau \tag{9-44}$$

But it follows, from Eq. (9-41) to the order b/g, that

$$L^s = \left[L \frac{\pi}{n^2} \mu_0 \frac{b^3}{g} (Z^s)^2 \right] \tag{9-45}$$

Thus, Eq. (9-43) may now be written in the form

$$\oint \mathbf{S} \cdot \mathbf{n} \, dA = -R^s(i^s)^2 - L^s \frac{\partial i^s}{\partial t} i^s \tag{9-46}$$

which may be written simply as

$$\oint \mathbf{S} \cdot \mathbf{n} \, dA = -v^s i^s \tag{9-47}$$

This may be interpreted to show that the power flowing into the stator winding through its terminals is the negative of the power flowing out over the surface enclosing the stator winding. This establishes a clear connection between the field concept and the circuit concept.

9-3. The A-C-excited Two-winding System.[1] We now consider the machine to be provided with two windings, one on the stator and one on the rotor. It is possible to analyze the two-winding rotating machine in a manner that almost parallels that followed in Secs. 9-1 and 9-2. The problem becomes somewhat more complex because now both the stator and rotor windings carry currents, and so both currents contribute to the air-gap fields. It is supposed that the stator and rotor currents are of the form

$$\begin{aligned}
i^s &= I^s \sin (\omega^s t + \theta^s) \\
i^r &= I^r \sin (\omega^r t + \theta^r)
\end{aligned} \tag{9-48}$$

so that linear current densities exist on the surfaces of the stator and rotor, which are given by

$$\begin{aligned}
\mathbf{J}^s &= \mathbf{a}_z I^s Z_n{}^s \sin (\omega^s t + \theta^s) \cos n\varphi^s \\
\mathbf{J}^r &= \mathbf{a}_z I^r Z_n{}^r \sin (\omega^r t + \theta^r) \cos n\varphi^r
\end{aligned} \tag{9-49}$$

[1] The present development provides a starting point for the electromagnetic-field analysis of the transformer (see Introduction to Chap. 3).

The boundary conditions for the fields due to each linear current density must be appropriate to the geometry of the machine.

Instead of carrying out the solution in all its details, an approximate solution will be undertaken. The approximation to be made is in the expression for the magnetic-field components.

In the general case, the magnetic-field intensity produced by the stator current acting alone is specified by Eq. (9-28) and is here written for convenience:

$$\mathbf{H}^s = -\mathbf{a}_r \frac{bI^sZ_n{}^s}{ng} \sin (\omega^s t + \theta^s) \sin n\varphi^s$$
$$- \mathbf{a}_\varphi \frac{\rho I^sZ_n{}^s}{g} \sin (\omega^s t + \theta^s) \cos n\varphi^s \quad (9\text{-}50)$$

Correspondingly, the magnetic-field intensity produced by the rotor current acting alone will have a similar form, although modified slightly to take account of the different geometry. The result in this case is

$$\mathbf{H}^r = -\mathbf{a}_r \frac{aI^rZ_n{}^r}{ng} \sin (\omega^r t + \theta^r) \sin n\varphi^r$$
$$- \mathbf{a}_\varphi \frac{\rho - g}{g} I^rZ_n{}^r \sin (\omega^r t + \theta^r) \cos n\varphi^r \quad (9\text{-}51)$$

But the air-gap width is small compared with the dimensions b and a in most electric machines, and we make the following approximations:

$$\text{Since } r - a = \rho \qquad \text{then } r\, dr \doteq b\, d\rho \left.\begin{array}{c} \\ \\ \end{array}\right\} \quad 0 \le \rho \le g \quad (9\text{-}52)$$
$$b - a = g \qquad \qquad b \doteq a \gg g$$

Now, upon neglecting all terms in ρ/b or g/b of order higher than the first, the field equations become approximately, in the absence of rotation,

$$\mathbf{H}^s = -\mathbf{a}_r \frac{bI^rZ_n{}^s}{ng} \sin (\omega^s t + \theta^s) \sin n\varphi^s - \mathbf{a}_\varphi \frac{\rho I^sZ_n{}^s}{g} \sin (\omega^s t + \theta^s) \cos n\varphi^s$$
$$\mathbf{H}^r = -\mathbf{a}_r \frac{(b - g)I^rZ_n{}^r}{ng} \sin (\omega^r t + \theta^r) \sin n\varphi^r \quad (9\text{-}53)$$
$$- \mathbf{a}_\varphi \frac{(\rho - g)I^rZ_n{}^r}{g} \sin (\omega^r t + \theta^r) \cos n\varphi^r$$

With these expressions, we may evaluate many of the important factors of the two-winding system.

In our further considerations, which will be concerned with the energy stored in the air gap and with considerations of torque between the two windings, these quantities will be evaluated to the first order in ρ/b and g/b. In these cases we shall have to integrate the energy density $\frac{1}{2}\mu_0 H^2$ over the volume of the air gap. Now, because terms of the first order in the field equations become second-order or higher-order when the fields are squared and integrated over the volume, we may further simplify the form of the field expressions. Thus, for finding stored energy, and so equivalent circuit parameters, Eqs. (9-53) may be simplified to the form

$$
\begin{aligned}
\mathbf{H}^s &= -\mathbf{a}_r \frac{bI^sZ_n{}^s}{ng} \sin (\omega^s t + \theta^s) \sin n\varphi^s \\
\mathbf{H}^r &= -\mathbf{a}_r \frac{bI^rZ_n{}^r}{ng} \sin (\omega^r t + \theta^r) \sin n\varphi^r
\end{aligned}
\tag{9-54}
$$

which are written as

$$
\begin{aligned}
\mathbf{H}^s &= -\mathbf{a}_r H_{r0}^s \sin (\omega^s t + \theta^s) \sin n\varphi^s \\
\mathbf{H}^r &= -\mathbf{a}_r H_{r0}^r \sin (\omega^r t + \theta^r) \sin n\varphi^r
\end{aligned}
\tag{9-55}
$$

Observe that to the approximation given the fields are radial only. It is noted that it is precisely this fact which justified the method of presentation in this chapter, which began from considerations of the air-gap mmf.

Two specific cases will be examined: (1) the two coils are stationary with respect to each other, and (2) the rotor is moving with respect to the stator.

Stationary Rotor. In the present case, when the rotor is stationary, this condition is specified by the requirement that $\omega^s = \omega^r$. There may be a space angle between the space phases φ^s and φ^r. For convenience, we write

$$
\varphi^s = \varphi^r + \varphi
\tag{9-56}
$$

The stored energy in the air gap that results from the radial fields is of particular interest, since this energy can change for a virtual displacement of the rotor, thereby showing the presence of torque generation.

The total stored energy due to the radial fields is

$$
W_m = \tfrac{1}{2}\mu_0 \int (\mathbf{H}^s + \mathbf{H}^r)^2 Lgb \, d\varphi
$$

which may be expanded to

$$
W_m = \tfrac{1}{2}\mu_0 \int [(\mathbf{H}^s)^2 + (\mathbf{H}^r)^2 + 2\mathbf{H}^s \cdot \mathbf{H}^r] Lgb \, d\varphi
\tag{9-57}
$$

It is convenient to write this expression in terms of the self- and mutual inductances of the windings. This is done by writing

$$
\begin{aligned}
\tfrac{1}{2}\mu_0 \int (\mathbf{H}^s)^2 Lgb \, d\varphi &= \tfrac{1}{2}L^s(i^s)^2 \\
\tfrac{1}{2}\mu_0 \int (\mathbf{H}^r)^2 Lgb \, d\varphi &= \tfrac{1}{2}L^r(i^r)^2 \\
\mu_0 \int (\mathbf{H}^s \cdot \mathbf{H}^r) Lgb \, d\varphi &= M^{sr} i^s i^r
\end{aligned}
\tag{9-58}
$$

The first of these expressions leads, by Eqs. (9-54), to the integral

$$
\tfrac{1}{2}\mu_0 \left(\frac{b}{ng}\right)^2 (Z_n{}^s)^2 (i^s)^2 Lgb \int_0^{2\pi} \sin^2 n\varphi^s \, d\varphi = \tfrac{1}{2}L^s(i^s)^2
$$

It follows from this expression that

$$L^s = \mu_0 L \frac{\pi b^3}{n^2 g} (Z_n{}^s)^2 \tag{9-59}$$

This is precisely the expression previously found in Eq. (9-45). In an entirely similar way, it may be shown that

$$L^r = \mu_0 L \frac{\pi b^3}{n^2 g} (Z_n{}^r)^2 \tag{9-60}$$

The expression for M^{sr} becomes, from the integral,

$$\mu_0 L g b \left(\frac{b}{ng}\right)^2 (Z_n{}^s Z_n{}^r)(i^s i^r) \int_0^{2\pi} \sin n\varphi^r \sin n(\varphi^r + \varphi) \, d\varphi^r = M^{sr} i^s i^r$$

from which, upon integration,

$$M^{sr} = \mu_0 L \frac{\pi b^3}{n^2 g} (Z_n{}^s Z_n{}^r) \cos n\varphi \tag{9-61}$$

It is now noted that each winding acting alone contributes constant average energy to the field and so each separately will not be able to produce torque. The product term is a function of φ and does produce torque. The time-average value of the interaction quantity $\bar{W}_m$ is

$$\bar{W}_m = \tfrac{1}{2}\mu_0 L g b \int_0^{2\pi} H_{r0}^s H_{r0}^r \sin n\varphi^r \sin n(\varphi^r + \varphi) \, d\varphi^r$$

where the factor $\tfrac{1}{2}$ arises from the time-averaging process. The torque produced by the system is then given by

$$\bar{T}_\varphi = \frac{\partial \bar{W}_m}{\partial \varphi} = \tfrac{1}{2}\mu_0 L g b n H_{r0}^s H_{r0}^r \int_0^{2\pi} \sin n\varphi^r \cos n(\varphi^r + \varphi) \, d\varphi^r$$

This expression integrates to the form

$$\bar{T}_\varphi = \tfrac{1}{2}\mu_0 \pi L g b n H_{r0}^s H_{r0}^r \sin n\varphi \tag{9-62}$$

Observe therefore that there is a torque which is proportional to the product of the stator and rotor currents and the sine of the angle between the stator and rotor magnetic-field axes.

Rotating System. In this case, when there is a relative motion between the stator and rotor, the motional effects must be included. Suppose that the rotor is moving with a velocity $\mathbf{v}_m$ relative to the stator in the reference direction; then

$$\mathbf{v}_m = \mathbf{a}_\varphi b \dot{\varphi}$$

The magnetic-field vector due to the rotor excitation, when referred to the fixed stator frame of reference, is given by the electrodynamic equation

$$(\mathbf{H}^r)^s = \mathbf{H}^r - \mathbf{v}_m \times \epsilon_0 \mathbf{E}^r \tag{9-63}$$

Attention is called to the fact that this equation is valid only for $v/c \ll 1$, a condition that is met in rotating machinery. Further, from the known form of $E_z{}^r$, which would be given by properly adapting Eq. (9-32), it follows that $\mathbf{v}_m \times \epsilon_0 \mathbf{E}^r \ll \mathbf{H}^r$ within the limits of approximation which have here been made in the fields. Thus the transformation for the magnetic field from the rotor to the stator reference system is

$$(\mathbf{H}^r)^s = \mathbf{H}^r \qquad (9\text{-}64)$$

The resulting air-gap field is

$$(\mathbf{H})^s = \mathbf{H}^s + (\mathbf{H}^r)^s \qquad (9\text{-}65)$$

Hence the stored magnetic energy in the air gap is again given by Eq. (9-57).

For the case of the moving rotor system, $\omega^s \neq \omega^r$. Suppose we write

$$\omega = \omega^s \pm \omega^r$$

It is now desired to take a time average over the period $2\pi/\omega$, which includes many cycles of both ω^s and ω^r. In this case we note that we may write

$$n\varphi = \omega t \qquad (9\text{-}66)$$

The interaction energy is given by

$$W_m = \mu_0 Lgb \int [H_{r0}^s \sin(\omega^s t + \theta^s)\sin n\varphi^s][H_{r0}^r \sin(\omega^r t + \theta^r)\sin n\varphi^r]\, d\varphi^r \qquad (9\text{-}67)$$

This expression is now rewritten in the form

$$W_m = \tfrac{1}{2}\mu_0 Lgb \int H_r^{s0} H_{r0}^r \{\cos[(\omega^s - \omega^r)t + (\theta^s - \theta^r)] \\ - \cos[(\omega^s + \omega^r)t + (\theta^s + \theta^r)]\}\sin n\varphi^s \sin n\varphi^r\, d\varphi$$

It is desired to carry out the integration in the space angle φ^r and then to deduce the time-average value of $\bar{W}_m$. The first of these integrations leads to

$$W_m = \tfrac{1}{2}\mu_0 Lgb\pi H_{r0}^s H_{r0}^r \{\cos[(\omega^s - \omega^r)t + (\theta^s - \theta^r)] \\ - \cos[(\omega^s + \omega^r)t + (\theta^s + \theta^r)]\}\cos n\varphi \qquad (9\text{-}68)$$

The second of the integrations must be taken in two steps. The results are

$$\bar{W}_m\Big|_{\omega=\omega^s-\omega^r} = \tfrac{1}{4}\pi\mu_0 Lgbn H_{r0}^s H_{r0}^r \cos(\theta^s - \theta^r)$$

$$\bar{W}_m\Big|_{\omega=\omega^s+\omega^r} = -\tfrac{1}{4}\pi\mu_0 Lgbn H_{r0}^s H_{r0}^r \cos(\theta^s + \theta^r) \qquad (9\text{-}69)$$

It follows from these expressions that

$$\bar{T}\Big|_{\omega=\omega^s-\omega^r} = \tfrac{1}{4}\pi\mu_0 Lgbn H_{r0}^s H_{r0}^r \sin(\theta^s - \theta^r)$$

$$\bar{T}\Big|_{\omega=\omega^s+\omega^r} = -\tfrac{1}{4}\pi\mu_0 Lgbn H_{r0}^s H_{r0}^r \sin(\theta^s + \theta^r) \qquad (9\text{-}70)$$

These latter equations are identical except for the angle $\theta^s - \theta^r$ or $\theta^s + \theta^r$. The angle $\theta^s - \theta^r$ is the space angle between stator and rotor fields when the rotor is rotating with an angular speed $\omega = \omega^s - \omega^r$. A similar meaning exists for the angle $\theta^s + \theta^r$. If both space angles $\theta^s - \theta^r$ and $\theta^s + \theta^r$ are denoted by the angle δ, then it follows that Eqs. (9-70) are both of the form

$$\bar{T} = kH^s_{r0}H^r_{r0} \sin \delta \tag{9-71}$$

Such a relation for the torque applies in any rotating machine, as already seen.

Because of the simple relation between the mechanical power developed by the machine and the torque, the power converted from electrical form to mechanical form is directly

$$P_{\text{mech}} = f_e v_m = \tfrac{1}{4} v_m \pi \mu_0 Lgn H^s_{r0} H^r_{r0} \sin \delta \tag{9-72}$$

It is of some interest to calculate the energy flow through the stator windings and into the rotor windings. To do this requires expressions for $E_z{}^s$ and $E_z{}^r$, since with these fields the appropriate Poynting vectors can be found and these can then be integrated over the appropriate surfaces. The required fields are deduced most conveniently by applying basic electrodynamic considerations relating the generation of an electric field by a moving magnetic field. Thus, from the fact that

$$\mathbf{E} = \mathbf{B} \times \mathbf{v}$$

we may write directly that

$$\left. \begin{aligned} E_z{}^s &= -\mu_0 H_r{}^r v_m \\ E_z{}^r &= \mu_0 H_r{}^s v_m \end{aligned} \right\} \tag{9-73}$$

and

These fields are valid to the order ρ/b when the expressions for $\mathbf{H}$ given by Eqs. (9-53) are used.

The power flowing out of the stator windings into the air gap is given by the expression

$$P^s = \oint \mathbf{S} \cdot \mathbf{n}\, dA = \int_0^L \int_0^{2\pi} S_r \Big|_{\rho = g} b\, d\varphi\, dz \tag{9-74}$$

which by Eqs. (9-73) and the known form for S_r is

$$P^s = \oint \mathbf{S} \cdot \mathbf{n}\, dA = + \int_0^L \int_0^{2\pi} \mu_0(H_r{}^r H_\varphi{}^s) \Big|_{\rho = g} v_m b\, d\varphi\, dz \tag{9-75}$$

The integral becomes

$$P^s = \int_0^L \int_0^{2\pi} v_m \mu_0 [H^r_{r0} \sin(\omega^r t + \theta^r) \sin n\varphi^r]$$

$$\left[H^s_{r0} \frac{n}{b} \sin(\omega^s t + \theta^s) \cos n\varphi_s \right] b\, d\varphi\, dz \tag{9-76}$$

This expression is similar to that given in Eq. (9-67), and the same procedure in integration may be used. The result of this integration is the expression

$$\bar{P}^s = \tfrac{1}{4} v_m \mu_0 \pi L g n H^s_{r0} H^r_{r0} \sin \delta \qquad (9\text{-}77)$$

In a similar way, the power transferred by the fields to the rotor winding is given by the expression

$$P^r = \oint \mathbf{S} \cdot \mathbf{n} \, dS = \int S_r \Big|_{\rho=0} b \, d\varphi \, dz = - \int\!\!\int \mu_0 (H_r{}^s H_\varphi{}^r) \Big|_{\rho=0} v_m b \, d\varphi \, dz$$

The resulting integral is the following:

$$P^r = \int_0^L \int_0^{2\pi} v_m \mu_0 [H^s_{r0} \sin (\omega^s t + \theta^s) \sin n\varphi^s]$$

$$\left[H^r_{r0} \frac{n}{b} \sin (\omega^r t + \theta^r) \cos n\varphi^r \right] b \, d\varphi \, dz \qquad (9\text{-}78)$$

Observe that this expression is identical with that for P^s. The conclusion is simply that the power supplied through the stator windings into the air gap is, in turn, supplied to the rotor windings. Moreover, the expression for P^r obtained from considerations of the Poynting theorem agrees with that obtained for P_{mech} obtained from considerations of the magnetic energy stored in the air gap, in accordance with Eq. (9-72).

9-4. The Two-winding Stator. The discussion in Sec. 9-3 centered about the nonsalient-pole machine with a single current sheet on the stator and a single current sheet on the rotor surface. Such a geometry exists in the single-phase induction machine. The resulting fields in the air-gap space were obtained by the superposition of the fields due to each current sheet.

We now wish to extend our considerations to multiple windings on each surface. We shall again employ superposition to find the resulting fields. Initially, we shall examine the case of two stator windings which are so disposed on the stator that they produce two current sheets which are located $2\pi/4$ electrical radians apart. These are sometimes called semi-four-phase windings but more often are called two-phase windings. Also, it will be supposed that the windings are excited by a balanced two-phase set of currents which are of equal amplitude but which are 90° apart in time phase. This is the same situation discussed in Sec. 8-2 and illustrated in Figs. 8-3 and 8-4.

The approximate air-gap field intensity produced by the two current sheets, for a two-pole configuration ($n = 1$), is, from Eqs. (9-55),

$$\mathbf{H}_r{}^s = \mathbf{H}^s_{ar} + \mathbf{H}^s_{br} = -\mathbf{a}_r \left[H^s_{r0} \sin \omega^s t \sin \varphi^s \right.$$

$$\left. + H^s_{r0} \sin \left(\omega^s t - \frac{\pi}{2} \right) \sin \left(\varphi^s - \frac{\pi}{2} \right) \right] \qquad (9\text{-}79)$$

This expression may be written as

$$H_r{}^s = -H_{r0}^s(\sin \omega^s t \sin \varphi^s + \cos \omega^s t \cos \varphi^s) \qquad (9\text{-}80)$$

which is the form

$$H_r{}^s = -H_{r0}^s \cos (\omega^s t - \varphi^s) \qquad (9\text{-}81)$$

This result is of fundamental importance in polyphase electrical machines, and as already shown, the field is easily interpreted as a traveling wave which is constant in amplitude, which is distributed sinusoidally in space, and which revolves in the φ^s direction (the peripheral direction) at a speed $d\varphi^s/dt = \omega^s$, in electrical space radians per second, equal to the exciting frequency.

In addition to the radial components of field, there exists a transverse component of magnetic-field intensity. This resultant field component is obtained precisely in the same manner as that employed in finding the resultant radial field. Now, however, we begin with the second term in Eqs. (9-53). The resulting field component is

$$H_\varphi{}^s = -\frac{\rho}{b} H_{r0}^s \sin (\omega^s t - \varphi^s) \qquad (9\text{-}82)$$

The electric field, which is in the axial direction, results from the electrodynamic effects of the moving magnetic field, as given by Eqs. (9-73). This field has the form

$$E_z{}^s = \mu_0 H_r{}^s v_\varphi{}^s = \mu_0 v_\varphi{}^s H_{r0}^s \cos (\omega^s t - \varphi^s) \qquad (9\text{-}83)$$

Hence for the two-phase winding appropriately excited the fields are

$$\begin{aligned}
H_r{}^s &= -H_{r0}^s \cos (\omega^s t - \varphi^s) \\
H_\varphi{}^s &= -\frac{\rho H_{r0}^s}{b} \sin (\omega^s t - \varphi^s) \\
E_z{}^s &= -\mu_0 v_\varphi{}^s H_{r0}^s \cos (\omega^s t - \varphi^s)
\end{aligned} \qquad (9\text{-}84)$$

There are several features of such fields that are particularly interesting. We first examine the total magnetic energy stored in the air gap. The expression for the volume density of magnetic energy, to the order ρ/b, is simply

$$w_m = \tfrac{1}{2}\mu_0(H_r{}^s)^2 = \tfrac{1}{2}\mu_0[H_{r0}^s \cos (\omega^s t - \varphi^s)]^2 \qquad (9\text{-}85)$$

The total magnetic energy stored in the air gap is then

$$W_m = \int_0^L \int_0^g \int_0^{2\pi} \tfrac{1}{2}\mu_0(H_{r0}^s)^2 \cos^2 (\omega^s t - \varphi^s)b \, dr \, d\varphi \, dz \qquad (9\text{-}86)$$

The integration is carried out directly and yields

$$W_m = \frac{\pi}{2} \mu_0 Lbg(H_{r0}^s)^2 \qquad (9\text{-}87)$$

This expression may also be written in the following form, by including the known expression for H_{r0}^s,

$$W_m = \frac{\pi}{2}\mu_0 \frac{Lb^3}{n^2g}(Z_n{}^s)^2(i_a{}^s)^2 + \frac{\pi}{2}\mu_0 \frac{Lb^3}{n^2g}(Z_n{}^s)^2(i_b{}^s)^2 \qquad (9\text{-}88)$$

which, by Eq. (9-60), is

$$W_m = \tfrac{1}{2}L_a{}^s(i_a{}^s)^2 + \tfrac{1}{2}L_b{}^s(i_b{}^s)^2 \qquad (9\text{-}89)$$

This expression is in the form expected, although it is noted that no energy is stored in the mutual inductance that exists between the two stator windings.

Consider now the Poynting vector. Two components exist, $S_\varphi{}^s$ and $S_r{}^s$. These terms have the form

$$\begin{aligned} S_\varphi{}^s &= E_z{}^s H_r{}^s = \mu_0 v_\varphi{}^s (H_{r0}^s)^2 \cos^2(\omega^s t - \varphi^s) \\ S_r{}^s &= -E_z{}^s H_\varphi{}^s = -\mu_0 v_\varphi{}^s \frac{\rho}{b}(H_{r0}^s)^2 \sin(\omega^s t - \varphi^s)\cos(\omega^s t - \varphi^s) \end{aligned} \qquad (9\text{-}90)$$

Now we examine the expression[1]

$$\frac{\rho}{b}\frac{\partial S_\varphi{}^s}{\partial \varphi^s} + S_r{}^s = \frac{\rho}{b}\mu_0 v_\varphi{}^s (H_{r0}^s)^2 \sin(\omega^s t - \varphi^s)\cos(\omega^s t - \varphi^s)$$

Observe also that

$$\rho\frac{\partial W_m}{\partial t} = -\mu_0 \rho \omega^s (H_{r0}^s)^2 \cos(\omega^s t - \varphi)\sin(\omega^s t - \varphi^s)$$

It follows from these expressions that

$$-\frac{\rho}{b}\frac{\partial S_\varphi{}^s}{\partial \varphi^s} = \rho\frac{\partial W_m}{\partial t} + S_r{}^s \qquad (9\text{-}91)$$

This expression shows that the Poynting radiation in the peripheral direction consists of two equal parts, one of which serves to build up the space magnetic energy, the other part being transmitted in the radial direction into the stator. It is of interest to examine the power represented by these terms.

The energy flow from the air gap into one of the stator windings is given by the integrated value of that part of the quantity $S_r{}^s$ which is due to the component of H_φ belonging to the current in that phase. We thus examine the expression

$$P_{ra}^s = \int_0^L \int_0^\pi S_{ra}^s \Big|_{\rho=g} b\,d\varphi\,dz = \int_0^L \int_0^\pi (E_z{}^s H_{\varphi a}^s)\Big|_{\rho=g} b\,d\varphi\,dz \qquad (9\text{-}92)$$

---

[1] F. Dahlgren, Some Remarks on the Energy Flow in Rotating Electric Machines, *Trans. Roy. Inst. Technol.*, Stockholm, no. 38, 1950.

This may be written

$$P_{ra}^s = \int_0^L \int_0^\pi \left(\frac{g}{b} H_{r0}^s \sin \omega^s t \sin \varphi^s \right) [\mu_0 v_\varphi{}^s H_{r0}^s \cos (\omega^s t - \varphi^s)] b \, d\varphi \, dz$$

This integrates to the form

$$P_{ra}^s = \frac{\pi g}{2b} \mu_0 L v_\varphi{}^s (H_{r0}^s)^2 \sin \omega^s t \cos \omega^s t$$

which, by Eq. (9-60), is

$$P_{ra}^s = \tfrac{1}{2}\omega^s \left[\pi\mu_0 \frac{Lb^3}{n^2 g} (Z_n{}^s)^2 \right] (I^s)^2 \sin 2\omega^s t \qquad (9\text{-}93)$$

This expression may be written in the form of a reactive power,

$$P_{ra}^s = \tfrac{1}{2}(X_a{}^s)(I^s)^2 \sin 2\omega^s t \qquad (9\text{-}94)$$

Based on these results, the procedure of the flow of energy in the air gap of a symmetrical smooth polyphase machine at no load has a direct explanation. The magnetic-field energy is transported along the periphery of the machine as Poynting radiation. The field energy corresponds at each moment to an amount of energy in each winding phase which is entirely reactive, in the present case. This energy flows from phase to phase through the external source and corresponds to the reactive power in the transmission conductors. The transportation of energy also accounts for the flow of the field energy itself.

9-5. The Effect of Saliency. In all the foregoing considerations it has been assumed that the air gap was of uniform width. This not only

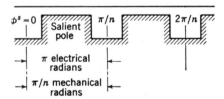

FIG. 9-4. The assumed form of the salient-pole machine.

assumed a nonsalient structure, but it also neglected any variations in the air-gap width which might be produced by the slots in which the windings of the magnetic structure are placed. It is now desired to discuss the changes in the analysis in order to take account of the salient-pole structure.

In the salient-pole machine, it is assumed that one side of the air gap is smooth. The other side of the air gap will have magnetic variations of the general form illustrated in Fig. 9-4. Observe that the magnetic variations must exhibit symmetry about π electrical space radians, or π/n mechanical radians for an n-pole-pair machine.

Now one may proceed by assuming a uniform air-gap length g, which is equal to the average gap length of the salient structure, with the effect of the nonuniform air gap being replaced by a space-dependent permeability. A reasonable approximation would be of the form

$$\mu_{radial} = \mu - \mu_2 \cos 2n\varphi^s \tag{9-95}$$

although a series expansion with a greater number of terms could be assumed. The effect of such a space-dependent permeability will appear in the expression for the magnetic energy stored in the air gap and will result in additional inductance terms in the final expression for the energy. The general features of any subsequent calculations are substantially those with the constant permeability, although the resultant expressions will contain terms that arise from the existence of the space-dependent permeability.

PROBLEMS

9-1. As an extension of the discussion in Sec. 9-3, consider a two-winding salient-pole machine with a space-dependent permeability given by Eq. (9-25).

(a) Find an expression for the magnetic energy stored in the air-gap magnetic field.

(b) Deduce expressions for the various self- and mutual-inductance terms which may be defined.

9-2. Consider a smooth rotor machine with sinusoidally distributed windings. Suppose that the numbers of rotor and stator turns are equal and that $L^s = L^r$ for the four windings.

(a) If the stator circuits are excited by balanced two-phase currents

$$i_a{}^s = I^s \cos \omega^s t \qquad i_b{}^s = I^s \sin \omega^s t$$

and the rotor windings are open, specify the amplitude of the resulting constant-amplitude rotating air-gap flux wave.

(b) Now suppose that the stator windings are open, and assume that the rotor, which is being driven at an angular speed $\dot\varphi = \omega_m$, is excited by a balanced two-phase set of currents of such magnitude that the air-gap flux wave is the same as that in (a). Specify the rotor excitation currents.

10

The Generalized Machine: Alternative Formulation

The discussion in the foregoing chapter showed how to deduce the **E** and **H** fields in the air gap of a rotary machine with idealized geometry that result from the currents on the surfaces of the stator and the rotor. With this as a starting point, it is possible to develop the fields in the air gap of a two-phase machine. But we have already found in Chap. 8, and will again show this in Chap. 11, that the theory of the two-phase machine can be adapted to describe the characteristics of a wide variety of rotating machines. Thus the material to follow is, in fact, a presentation of generalized machine theory. Now, however, the formulation proceeds from considerations of the fields in the air gap.

10-1. The Smooth-rotor Two-phase Doubly Excited Machine. The machine now under survey is essentially the two-phase machine, which consists of two windings in space quadrature (electrically) on the stator surface and two windings in space quadrature (electrically) on the rotor surface. These windings are excited by balanced sets of two-phase currents in time quadrature. The machine geometry is essentially that considered in Sec. 9-4. A schematic representation of the machine under survey is given in Fig. 10-1. We wish to deduce the electrical and mechanical equations for this machine and to deduce some of the essential characteristics of its motion. These equations will later be employed in the description of special machine types.

We first seek the air-gap fields which arise from the four windings for the case where the current-density distribution is sinusoidal over each phase belt, when Z_n becomes Z. As already discussed in Sec. 9-4, the air-gap fields, when referred to a frame of reference that is fixed in space relative to the stator structure, will consist of the fields due to the stator windings and the fields due to the moving rotor windings. These latter fields may be found by first expressing them in rotor coordinates and then transforming them to the fixed coordinate system.

The fields due to the stator excitation alone, referred to the fixed stator frame of reference, are precisely those given by Eqs. (9-84). These are rewritten here for convenience,

$$H_r{}^s = -H_{r0}^s \cos (\omega^s t - \varphi^s)$$

$$H_\varphi{}^s = -\frac{\rho}{b} H_{r0}^s \sin (\omega^s t - \varphi^s)$$

$$E_z{}^s = -\mu_0 v_\varphi{}^s H_{r0}^s \cos (\omega^s t - \varphi^s)$$

where $\qquad v_\varphi{}^s = b\omega^s$

(10-1)

Correspondingly, the fields due to the excited rotor windings, when the rotor is stationary, are specified by the expressions

$$H_r{}^r = -H_{r0}^r \cos (\omega^r t - \varphi^r)$$

$$H_\varphi{}^r = -\frac{\rho - g}{g} \sin (\omega^r t - \varphi^r)$$

$$E_z{}^r = -\mu_0 v_\varphi{}^r H_{r0}^r \cos (\omega^r t - \varphi^r)$$

(10-2)

Now suppose that the rotor is moving in the direction of the moving stator field, with a velocity

$$\mathbf{v}_m = \mathbf{a}_\varphi b\dot{\varphi}$$

where $\qquad \varphi^s - \varphi^r = \varphi$

(10-3)

The respective fields due to the rotor excitation when referred to the fixed stator frame of reference are given by the electrodynamic trans-

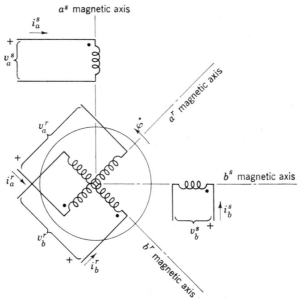

Fig. 10-1. Schematic representation of a two-axis two-pole machine.

formations

$$(\mathbf{E}^r)^s = \mathbf{E}^r - \mathbf{v}_m \times \mu_0 \mathbf{H}^r$$
$$(\mathbf{H}^r)^s = \mathbf{H}^r - \mathbf{v}_m \times \epsilon_0 \mathbf{E}^r \tag{10-4}$$

since the velocity of the rotor as seen from the fixed stator reference is in the reference direction. Attention is called to the fact that these equations are valid only for $v/c \ll 1$, a condition that is met in rotating machinery. Further, from the known form of $E_z{}^r$, it follows that $\mathbf{v}_m \times \epsilon_0 \mathbf{E}^r \ll \mathbf{H}^r$ within the limits of the approximations which have here been made in the fields. Thus the transformation for the magnetic field from the rotor to the stator reference system is

$$(\mathbf{H}^r)^s = \mathbf{H}^r \tag{10-5}$$

For the electric field, to the order ρ/b,

$$(\mathbf{E}^r)^s = \mathbf{E}^r - \mathbf{a}_\varphi b \dot{\varphi} \times (-\mathbf{a}_r \mu_0 H_r{}^r)$$
$$= \mathbf{E}^r - \mathbf{a}_z b \dot{\varphi} \mu_0 H_r{}^r \tag{10-6}$$

The resulting air-gap fields are now, for the $\mathbf{H}$ field,

$$(\mathbf{H})^s = \mathbf{H}^s + (\mathbf{H}^r)^s$$
$$= \mathbf{H}^s + \mathbf{H}^r$$

which, by Eqs. (10-1) and (10-2), are

$$(H)^s = -[H_{r0}^s \cos(\omega^s t - \varphi^s) + H_{r0}^r \cos(\omega^r t - \varphi^r)] \tag{10-7}$$

For the electric field

$$(\mathbf{E})^s = \mathbf{E}^s + (\mathbf{E}^r)^s = \mathbf{E}^s + \mathbf{E}^r - \mathbf{a}_z \mu_0 v_m H_r{}^r$$

By Eqs. (10-1) and (10-2) this is

$$(\mathbf{E})^s = -\mathbf{a}_z[\mu_0 v_\varphi{}^s H_{r0}^s \cos(\omega^s t - \varphi^s) + \mu_0(v_\varphi{}^r - v_m)H_{r0}^r \cos(\omega^r t - \varphi^r)] \tag{10-8}$$

With the air-gap fields established, we may now evaluate the parameters of the machine under survey. This is most easily done by finding the stored magnetic energy from field considerations and then expressing the results in terms of circuit parameters, as was done in Sec. 9-4. In the present case we must evaluate the following expression:

$$W_m = \int_{\substack{\text{air-gap} \\ \text{volume}}} \tfrac{1}{2}\mathbf{H} \cdot \mathbf{B} \, d\tau = \tfrac{1}{2}\mu_0 \int_{\substack{\text{air-gap} \\ \text{volume}}} H^2 \, d\tau \tag{10-9}$$

To the first order in ρ/b this is, by Eq. (9-80),

$$W_m = \int_0^L \int_0^g \int_0^{2\pi} \tfrac{1}{2}\mu_0(-H_{r0}^{sa} \sin \omega^s t \sin \varphi^s - H_{r0}^{sb} \cos \omega^s t \cos \varphi^s$$
$$- H_{r0}^{ra} \sin \omega^r t \sin \varphi^r - H_{r0}^{rb} \cos \omega^r t \cos \varphi^r)b \, dr \, d\varphi^s \, dz \tag{10-10}$$

This expression is integrated in the manner of Eq. (9-86). The result becomes, upon collecting terms and employing the known forms for H_{r0}^{sa}, etc.,

$$
\begin{aligned}
W_m = \ & \frac{1}{2}(i_a{}^s)^2 \left[(Z_a{}^s)^2 \frac{L\pi}{n^2}\mu_0 \frac{b^3}{g}\right] + \frac{1}{2}(i_b{}^s)^2 \left[(Z_b{}^s)^2 \frac{L\pi}{n^2}\mu_0 \frac{b^3}{g}\right] + (i_a{}^s)(i_b{}^s)[0] \\
& + \frac{1}{2}(i_a{}^r)^2 \left[(Z_a{}^r)^2 \frac{L\pi}{n^2}\mu_0 \frac{b^3}{g}\right] + \frac{1}{2}(i_b{}^r)^2 \left[(Z_b{}^r)^2 \frac{L\pi}{n^2}\mu_0 \frac{b^3}{g}\right] + (i_a{}^r)(i_b{}^r)[0] \\
& + (i_a{}^s)(i_a{}^r) \left[(Z_a{}^s)(Z_a{}^r) \frac{L\pi}{n^2}\mu_0 \frac{b^3}{g}\cos\varphi\right] \\
& - (i_a{}^s)(i_b{}^r) \left[(Z_a{}^s)(Z_b{}^r) \frac{L\pi}{n^2}\mu_0 \frac{b^3}{g}\sin\varphi\right] \\
& + (i_b{}^s)(i_a{}^r) \left[(Z_b{}^s)(Z_a{}^r) \frac{L\pi}{n^2}\mu_0 \frac{b^3}{g}\sin\varphi\right] \\
& + (i_b{}^s)(i_b{}^r) \left[(Z_b{}^s)(Z_b{}^r) \frac{L\pi}{n^2}\mu_0 \frac{b^3}{g}\cos\varphi\right] \quad (10\text{-}11)
\end{aligned}
$$

But for the balanced machine

$$
\begin{aligned}
Z_a{}^s &= Z_b{}^s = Z^s \\
Z_a{}^r &= Z_b{}^r = Z^r
\end{aligned}
$$

Now write the quantities, as before,

$$
\begin{aligned}
L_a{}^s = L_b{}^s = L^s &= (Z^s)^2 \frac{L\pi}{n^2}\mu_0 \frac{b^3}{g} \\
L_a{}^r = L_b{}^r = L^r &= (Z^r)^2 \frac{L\pi}{n^2}\mu_0 \frac{b^3}{g} \quad (10\text{-}12) \\
M^{sr} = M^{rs} &= (Z^s)(Z^r) \frac{L\pi}{n^2}\mu_0 \frac{b^3}{g}
\end{aligned}
$$

Then the expression for W_m becomes

$$
\begin{aligned}
W_m = \ & \tfrac{1}{2}(i_a{}^s)^2 L^s + \tfrac{1}{2}(i_b{}^s)^2 L^s + (i_a{}^s)(i_b{}^s)(0) + \tfrac{1}{2}(i_a{}^r)^2 L^r + \tfrac{1}{2}(i_b{}^r)^2 L^r \\
& + (i_a{}^r)(i_b{}^r)(0) + (i_a{}^s)(i_a{}^r)M^{sr}\cos\varphi - (i_a{}^s)(i_b{}^r)M^{sr}\sin\varphi \\
& + (i_b{}^s)(i_a{}^r)M^{sr}\sin\varphi + (i_b{}^s)(i_b{}^r)M^{sr}\cos\varphi \quad (10\text{-}13)
\end{aligned}
$$

This expression may be written in the general form

$$
W_m = \tfrac{1}{2} \sum_{i=1}^{2} \sum_{j=1}^{2} L_{ij} i_i i_j \quad (10\text{-}14)
$$

which, in matrix form, is

$$
W_m = \tfrac{1}{2}[I]_t[L][I]
$$

where

$$[L] = \begin{bmatrix} L_a{}^s & 0 & M^{sr}\cos\varphi & -M^{sr}\sin\varphi \\ 0 & L_b{}^s & M^{sr}\sin\varphi & M^{sr}\cos\varphi \\ M^{sr}\cos\varphi & M^{sr}\sin\varphi & L_a{}^r & 0 \\ -M^{sr}\sin\varphi & M^{sr}\cos\varphi & 0 & L_b{}^r \end{bmatrix}$$

(10-15)

$$[I] = \begin{bmatrix} i_a{}^s \\ i_b{}^s \\ i_a{}^r \\ i_b{}^r \end{bmatrix}$$

It is reasonable to expect, of course, that a resistance matrix may also be written which specifies the resistances of the respective phases.   Such a matrix would have the diagonal form shown, since there are no mutual resistance effects,

$$R = \begin{bmatrix} R_a{}^s & 0 & 0 & 0 \\ 0 & R_b{}^s & 0 & 0 \\ 0 & 0 & R_a{}^r & 0 \\ 0 & 0 & 0 & R_b{}^r \end{bmatrix}$$

(10-16)

We can now write, using Kirchhoff's potential law and the induction law of Faraday, a loop equation relative to each electrical terminal pair. There results the set of equations

$$\begin{aligned}
v_a{}^s &= R_a{}^s(i_a{}^s) + p[L_a{}^s(i_a{}^s) + M^{sr}\cos\varphi(i_a{}^r) - M^{sr}\sin\varphi(i_b{}^r)] \\
v_b{}^s &= R_b{}^s(i_b{}^s) + p[L_b{}^s(i_b{}^s) + M^{sr}\sin\varphi(i_a{}^r) + M^{sr}\cos\varphi(i_b{}^r)] \\
v_a{}^r &= R_a{}^r(i_a{}^r) + p[M^{sr}\cos\varphi(i_a{}^s) + M^{sr}\sin\varphi(i_b{}^s) + L_a{}^r(i_a{}^r)] \\
v_b{}^r &= R_b{}^r(i_b{}^r) + p[-M^{sr}\sin\varphi(i_a{}^s) + M^{sr}\cos\varphi(i_b{}^s) + L_b{}^r(i_b{}^r)]
\end{aligned}$$

(10-17)

This set of equations is conveniently written in matrix form,

$$[V] = [R][I] + p[\psi]$$

(10-18)

where $[\psi]$ is the flux-linkage matrix

$$[\psi] = [L][I]$$

and where

$$[V] = \begin{bmatrix} v_a{}^s \\ v_b{}^s \\ v_a{}^r \\ v_b{}^r \end{bmatrix}$$

The mechanical equation of the system has been discussed in Chap. 7 and is here written down, since the situation is precisely what it was before except that no commutator exists to impose its constraints.   The mechanical equation is

$$T = J\ddot{\varphi} + D\dot{\varphi} + k\varphi - T_e$$

where the electrical torque generated is

$$T_e = \frac{1}{2}[I]_t \left[\frac{\partial L}{\partial \varphi}\right][I]$$

(10-19)

The machine under survey is thus completely characterized by the five equations:

1. Four electrical equations, in accordance with Eq. (10-18),

$$[V] = [R][I] + p\{[L][I]\}$$

which is written conveniently as

$$[V] - [I]\left[\frac{\partial L}{\partial \varphi}\right]\dot{\varphi} = [R][I] + [L]p[I]$$

(10-20)

2. Mechanical equation

$$T = J\ddot{\varphi} + D\dot{\varphi} + k\varphi - T_e$$

where

$$T_e = \frac{1}{2}[I]_t\left[\frac{\partial L}{\partial \varphi}\right][I]$$

(10-21)

In the expanded form these equations are the following:

Electrical equations:

$$v_a{}^s + \dot{\varphi}[M^{sr}\sin\varphi(i_a{}^r) + M^{sr}\cos\varphi(i_b{}^r)]$$
$$= (R_a{}^s + L_a{}^s p)i_a{}^s + M^{sr}\cos\varphi(pi_a{}^r) - M^{sr}\sin\varphi(pi_b{}^r)$$
$$v_b{}^s - \dot{\varphi}[M^{sr}\cos\varphi(i_a{}^r) - M^{sr}\sin\varphi(i_b{}^r)]$$
$$= (R_b{}^s + L_b{}^s p)i_b{}^s + M^{sr}\sin\varphi(pi_a{}^r) + M^{sr}\cos\varphi(pi_b{}^r)$$
$$v_a{}^r + \dot{\varphi}[M^{sr}\sin\varphi(i_a{}^s) - M^{sr}\cos\varphi(i_b{}^s)]$$
$$= (R_a{}^r + L_a{}^r p)i_a{}^r + M^{sr}\cos\varphi(pi_a{}^s) + M^{sr}\sin\varphi(pi_b{}^s)$$
$$v_b{}^r + \dot{\varphi}[M^{sr}\cos\varphi(i_a{}^s) + M^{sr}\sin\varphi(i_b{}^s)]$$
$$= (R_b{}^r + L_b{}^r p)i_b{}^r - M^{sr}\sin\varphi(pi_a{}^s) + M^{sr}\cos\varphi(pi_b{}^s)$$

(10-22)

Mechanical equation:

$$T_e = M^{sr}[(i_a{}^r i_b{}^s - i_b{}^r i_a{}^s)\cos\varphi - (i_b{}^r i_b{}^s - i_a{}^r i_a{}^s)\sin\varphi]$$ (10-23)

These five equations of motion form a complex set of nonlinear differential equations, the solution of which cannot be found in closed form for arbitrary sets of conditions. They can be handled for particular sets of constraints. However, some useful information is possible from an inspection of these general equations.

We examine the expression for the instantaneous electromagnetic torque for general features of energy conversion. Assume that the machine is in steady-state operation, when

$$\dot{\varphi} = \omega_m = \text{const}$$

from which
$$\varphi = \omega_m t + \alpha$$

Thus, for constant-speed operation, Eq. (10-23) becomes

$$T_e = M^{rs}[(i_a{}^r i_a{}^s - i_b{}^r i_b{}^s) \cos (\omega_m t + \alpha) - (i_b{}^r i_b{}^s + i_a{}^r i_a{}^s) \sin (\omega_m t + \alpha)]$$
$$(10\text{-}24)$$

It is observed that each of the four terms in this expression is a triple product, involving a stator current, a rotor current, and a trigonometric function (sine or cosine) of $\omega_m t + \alpha$. Now, from the orthogonal properties of trigonometric functions, an average torque is possible only if the product of the stator current and rotor current is itself a sine or cosine function of $\omega_m t$. That is, a necessary condition for the generation of an average torque is that

$$i^r i^s = A \cos \omega_m t + B \sin \omega_m t \qquad (10\text{-}25)$$

Since, however, i^s involves ω^s and i^r involves ω^r, then Eq. (10-25) requires that ω_m must be of the form $\omega^s + \omega^r$ or $\omega^s - \omega^r$. In general, therefore, an average torque is possible if

$$\omega^r = \pm \omega^s \pm \omega_m \qquad (10\text{-}26)$$

To examine some of the possibilities, suppose that i^s is constrained to be of the form

$$i^s = I^s \sin \omega_m t$$

Two possibilities exist which permit the development of an average torque. These are:

1. $i^r = I^r \sin 2\omega_m t$.
2. $i^r = I^r = \text{const}$.

Both these possibilities are important, and machines of each type exist. The first corresponds to the synchronous-induction machine, and the second corresponds to the synchronous machine. Observe that in both cases fixed-frequency currents exist in both the stator and rotor windings, which thus specifies that the machine will run only at "synchronous" speed.

Another operable constraint is possible for a nonzero average torque, this being specified by

$$i^s = I^s \sin \omega t$$

with a rotor current of the form

$$i^r = I^r \sin (\pm \omega \pm \omega_m)t$$

In this case the machine will be of the induction type or of the synchronous-induction type, depending upon how the rotor excitation is realized. In fact, for an average torque to exist over a range of speeds, the current on one member must have a varying frequency that follows the speed variation. Such varying frequency currents are possible in different ways:

1. If the currents are induced electromagnetically in one member from the other member (as in induction machines)
2. If the currents are obtained from sources having a controlled adjustable frequency output
3. If the currents are obtained by physical constraints (for example, a commutator) so that the frequency difference is introduced mechanically

There is some interest in finding the energy flow from the air gap into one of the stator windings. This is given by the integrated value of that part of the quantity S_r which is due to the component H_φ belonging to the current in that phase. Thus, we examine the expression

$$P^s_{ar} = \int_0^L \int_0^\pi S^s_{ar}\Big|_{\rho=g} b \, d\varphi \, dz = \int_0^L \int_0^\pi E_z{}^s H^s_{\varphi a}\Big|_{\rho=g} b \, d\varphi \, dz \quad (10\text{-}27)$$

This may be written, by Eqs. (10-1), (10-2), and (10-8),

$$P^s_{ar} = \int_0^L \int_0^\pi [-\mu_0 v_\varphi{}^s H^s_{r0} \cos(\omega^s t - \varphi^s) - \mu_0(v_\varphi{}^r - v_m) H^r_{r0} \cos(\omega^r t - \varphi^r)]$$
$$\left(-\frac{g}{b} H^s_{r0} \sin \omega^s t \sin \varphi^s\right) b \, d\varphi^s \, dz \quad (10\text{-}28)$$

This integrates to

$$P^s_{ar} = \tfrac{1}{2}\mu_0 L\pi \frac{g}{b} v_\varphi{}^s (H^s_{r0})^2 \sin \omega^s t \cos \omega^s t$$
$$- \tfrac{1}{2}\mu_0 L\pi \frac{g}{b} (v_\varphi{}^r - v_m) H^s_{r0} H^r_{r0} \cos \omega^s t \sin(\omega^r t + \varphi) \quad (10\text{-}29)$$

Observe that the first term in this expression is exactly that given by Eq. (9-93) and denotes the reactive component of the power that flows from phase to phase through the external power source. The second term may be written as

$$\frac{1}{4}\left[\mu_0 \frac{L\pi b^3}{n^2 g}(Z^s Z^r)\right](v_\varphi{}^r - v_m)\{\sin[(\omega^s + \omega^r)t + \varphi] - \sin[(\omega^s - \omega^r)t - \varphi]\}$$

But, in the manner of deriving Eqs. (9-69), it is found that these terms are, since $n\varphi = \omega t$,

$$P^s_{ar}\Big|_{\omega=\omega^s+\omega^r} = \frac{1}{4}\left[\mu_0 \frac{L\pi b^3}{n^2 g}(Z^s Z^r)\right](v_\varphi{}^r - v_m)\sin\varphi$$

$$P^s_{ar}\Big|_{\omega=\omega^s-\omega^r} = \frac{1}{4}\left[\mu_0 \frac{L\pi b^3}{n^2 g}(Z^s Z^r)\right](v_\varphi{}^r - v_m)\sin\varphi$$

$$(10\text{-}30)$$

These expressions specify the power which passes through the stator windings and which will ultimately reach the rotor. They show, as mentioned above, that where one current possesses a varying frequency that follows the speed variation an average torque will exist over a range of speeds.

10-2. The Smooth-air-gap Two-phase Synchronous Machine. As a first example of the adaptation of the general equations of the two-phase machine [Eq. (10-20)] to a particular set of constraints, we consider the two-phase two-pole synchronous machine. In this case the constraints are the following:

$$i_u{}^s = i^s$$
$$i_b{}^s \text{ and } v_b{}^s \text{ do not exist, since the } b \text{ winding is absent}$$
$$v_a{}^s = -V^s = \text{const} \tag{10-31}$$
$$\dot{\varphi} = \omega_m$$
$$\varphi = \omega_m t + \delta$$

Here, as in Sec. 8-3, it is assumed that the d-c field is stationary in space and that the a-c windings rotate with respect to this stationary field structure. This is, as already noted, just the reverse of the situation that actually exists in the machine. From an analytic point of view, the relative motion is of importance. Also, the choice of $-V^s$ for $v_a{}^s$ is to obtain the conventional representation for the machine.

The electrical equations are written in the form given by the second of Eqs. (10-20) subject to Eqs. (10-31). There result

$$\begin{aligned}
-V^s + \dot{\varphi}[M^{sr} \sin \varphi(i_a{}^r) &+ M^{sr} \cos \varphi(i_b{}^r)] \\
&= (R^s + L^s p)i^s + M^{sr} \cos \varphi(pi_a{}^r) - M^{sr} \sin \varphi(pi_b{}^r) \\
v_a{}^r + \dot{\varphi}M^{sr} \sin \varphi(i^s) &= (R^r + L^r p)i_a{}^r + M^{sr} \cos \varphi(pi^s) \\
v_b{}^r + \dot{\varphi}M^{sr} \cos \varphi(i^s) &= (R^r + L^r p)i_b{}^r - M^{sr} \sin \varphi(pi^s)
\end{aligned} \tag{10-32}$$

The torque equation becomes

$$T_e = -M^{rs}i^s(i_b{}^r \cos \varphi + i_a{}^r \sin \varphi) \tag{10-33}$$

For the case of a balanced load under steady-state conditions, we may write

$$\begin{aligned}
v_a{}^r &= V^r \sin \omega^r t \\
v_b{}^r &= V^r \cos \omega^r t
\end{aligned} \tag{10-34}$$

and correspondingly

$$\begin{aligned}
i_a{}^r &= I^r \sin (\omega^r t - \theta^r) \\
i_b{}^r &= I^r \cos (\omega^r t - \theta^r)
\end{aligned} \tag{10-35}$$

Subject to these conditions, it is noted that since $\dot{\varphi} = \omega^r$

$$\dot{\varphi}M^{sr}(i_a{}^r \sin \varphi + i_b{}^r \cos \varphi) = M^{sr}[\cos \varphi(pi_a{}^r) - \sin \varphi(pi_b{}^r)] \tag{10-36}$$

and the field-circuit equation reduces to

$$-V^s = (R^s + L^s p)i^s \qquad (10\text{-}37)$$

Equation (10-36) shows that, for a balanced load on the rotor and steady-state conditions, the speed potential (motional emf) due to the rotation of the a-phase rotor current $i_a{}^r$ is canceled by the transformer potential induced by the time-changing b phase current $i_b{}^r$. Similarly the motional emf due to $i_b{}^r$ is canceled by the transformer potential due to $i_a{}^r$. Thus, under the conditions noted, the field circuit is independent of the load circuit.

Also, under the balanced load conditions specified by Eqs. (10-34) and (10-36), the electromagnetic-torque equation may be simplified. Equation (10-33) now becomes

$$
\begin{aligned}
T_e &= -M^{rs}i^s I^r[\cos \varphi \cos (\omega^r t - \theta^r) + \sin \varphi \sin (\omega^r t - \theta^r)] \\
&= -M^{rs}i^s I^r \cos [(\omega^r t - \theta^r) - (\omega_m t + \delta)] \\
&= -M^{rs}i^s I^r \cos (\theta^r + \delta) \qquad (10\text{-}38)
\end{aligned}
$$

The second and third equations of Eqs. (10-32) together with Eqs. (10-34) and (10-35) may be used to deduce an expression for I^r which may be combined with Eq. (10-38) to yield a working expression for T_e. Let us consider the second of Eqs. (10-32). Writing, for convenience,

$$-V_g = \dot{\varphi}M^{sr}i^s = \frac{-\omega^r M^{sr} V^s}{R^s} \qquad (10\text{-}39)$$

then in phasor notation we have

$$\mathbf{V}^r - \mathbf{V}_g e^{j\delta} = (R^r + jX^r)\mathbf{I}^r e^{-j\theta^r} = Z^r\mathbf{I}^r e^{-j(\theta^r - \eta)} \qquad (10\text{-}40)$$

Solve this expression to get

$$\mathbf{I}^r e^{-j\theta^r} = \frac{\mathbf{V}^r - \mathbf{V}_g e^{j\delta}}{Z^r e^{j\eta}} \qquad (10\text{-}41)$$

A phasor diagram is given in Fig. 10-2. It is seen from this figure that

$$I^r = \frac{\sqrt{(V^r)^2 + (V_g)^2 - 2V^r V_g \cos \delta}}{Z^r} \qquad (10\text{-}42)$$

Also

$$I^r = \frac{V_g \cos \delta - V^r}{Z^r \sin (\theta^r - \eta - \pi/2)} = \frac{V^r - V_g \cos \delta}{Z^r \cos (\theta^r - \eta)} \qquad (10\text{-}43)$$

and

$$I^r = \frac{V_g \sin \delta}{Z^r \cos (\theta^r - \eta - \pi/2)} = \frac{V_g \sin \delta}{Z^r \sin (\theta^r - \eta)} \qquad (10\text{-}44)$$

We are now in a position to express the torque, given by Eq. (10-38), in a form that is more informative than that above, by eliminating I^r and θ^r. To do this, write

$$\cos (\theta^r + \delta) = \cos [(\theta^r - \eta) + (\delta + \eta)]$$

and expand to obtain

$$T_e = -M^{rs}i^sI^r[\cos{(\theta^r - \eta)} \cos{(\delta + \eta)} - \sin{(\theta^r - \eta)} \sin{(\delta + \eta)}]$$
$$(10\text{-}45)$$

Combine this expression with Eqs. (10-43) and (10-44) to get

$$T_e = \frac{V_g}{\omega_m}\left[\frac{(V^r - V_g \cos{\delta}) \cos{(\delta + \eta)}}{Z^r} - \frac{V_g \sin{\delta} \sin{(\delta + \eta)}}{Z^r}\right] \quad (10\text{-}46)$$

This expression is now expanded and rearranged.   Also use is made of the relations $R^r = Z^r \cos{\eta}$ and $X^r = Z^r \sin{\eta}$.   The result is

$$T_e = \frac{-V_g}{\omega_m(Z^r)^2}(V_g R^r - V^r R^r \cos{\delta} + V^r X^r \sin{\delta}) \quad (10\text{-}47)$$

It is noted that for most conventional synchronous machines the rotor resistance R^r is small compared with the synchronous reactance

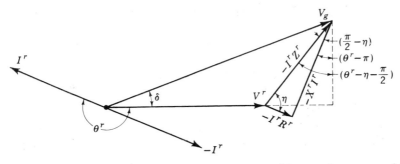

FIG. 10-2. The sinor diagram of the smooth-air-gap two-phase synchronous machine.

$X^r = \omega^r L^r$.   Also, the generated potential V_g is nearly of the same magnitude as V^r.   Under these conditions, $Z^r \doteq X^r$, and Eq. (10-47) becomes

$$T_e \doteq \frac{V_g V^r}{\omega_m X^r} \sin{\delta} \qquad (10\text{-}48)$$

From this

$$P_e = \omega_m T_e \doteq -\frac{V_g V^r}{X^r} \sin{\delta} \qquad (10\text{-}49)$$

This expression is the same as Eq. (8-34), which was obtained from the analysis of the Kron primitive machine.   The "power-angle char-acteristic" is illustrated in Fig. 8-14.

Attention is called to the fact that the present discussion of the synchronous machine has been limited to smooth-air-gap machines.   For synchronous machines with saliency, the analysis in Sec. 8-3 is preferred over that by an extension of the above analysis.

Example 10-2.1. A synchronous motor has a synchronous reactance of 0.60 p.u. If the power factor $\cos \theta = 0.80$ current leading and $\delta = -20°$, find the current I^r, the power, and the motional emf V_g.

Solution. With $V = 1$ p.u., and by choosing $Z = X$ (then $\eta = 90°$), then

$$Z = X = 0.60 \text{ p.u.}$$

By Eq. (10-43) $V^r = V_g \cos \delta + Z^r I^r \cos (\theta^r - \eta)$

By Eq. (10-44) $0 = V_g \sin \delta - Z^r I^r \sin (\theta^r - \eta)$

Upon eliminating V_g, there results

$$V^r Z^r I^r \cos (\theta^r - \eta) = Z^r I^r \frac{\sin (\theta^r - \eta) \cos \delta}{\sin \delta}$$

or $Z^r I^r [\cos (\theta^r - \eta) + \sin (\theta^r - \eta) \cot \delta] = V^r$

or $$I^r = \frac{V^r \tan \delta}{Z^r [\cos (\theta^r - \eta) \tan \delta + \sin (\theta^r - \eta)]}$$

For the assumed relation that $Z^r \doteq X$, $\eta = \pi/2$, the expression for I^r is

$$I^r = \frac{V^r \tan \delta}{X(\sin \theta^r \tan \delta - \cos \theta^r)}$$

$$= \frac{1 \times 0.363}{0.60(-0.60 \times 0.363 + 0.80)} = \frac{0.363}{0.60 \times 0.582} = -1.04 \text{ p.u.}$$

The power is

$$P = V^r I^r \cos \theta^r = 1 \times 1.04 \times 0.80 = 0.832 \text{ p.u.}$$

The motional emf is

$$V_g \doteq \frac{X^r I^r \cos \theta^r}{\sin \delta} = \frac{0.60 \times 1.04 \times 0.80}{0.342} = 1.46 \text{ p.u.}$$

10-3. The Two-phase Induction Machine. A second adaptation of the general equations of the two-phase machine is to the two-phase two-pole induction machine. In this case the constraints are the following:

$$v_a{}^r = v_b{}^r = 0$$
$$\dot{\varphi} = \omega_m \qquad\qquad (10\text{-}50)$$
$$\varphi = \omega_m t + \alpha$$

A word of explanation is required on these constraints. As was discussed in Sec. 8-4, the wound-rotor induction machine is often provided with a starting resistor which is connected in series with each rotor phase, as a means of improving the starting-torque characteristics of the machine. This resistance is reduced to zero after start so as to achieve the desirable operating characteristics of the low resistance of the rotor circuit. If a complete analysis were desired, then the first of Eqs. (10-50) would be replaced by

$$v_a{}^r = -i_a{}^r Z^r \qquad v_b{}^r = -i_b{}^r Z^r \qquad (10\text{-}51)$$

Clearly, of course, by an appropriate modification of the R^r and L^r of the rotor circuit the effects of starting impedance can be included in the analysis under the conditions of analysis specified by Eqs. (10-50).

Note also that the second of Eqs. (10-50), and in consequence the third of this set, specifies that the speed of the machine will remain constant. Actually this is not exactly true, since the induction motor is not a constant-speed machine. However, for most practical induction machines the mechanical speed of response is much slower than the electrical speed of response, and the volt-ampere equations with constant speed will closely describe the electrical performance, even under conditions of dynamic operation.

Subject to the above-specified constraints, the electrical equations for the present machine, which result from Eqs. (10-22), are the following:

$$
\begin{aligned}
v_a{}^s &+ \omega_m M^{sr} \sin (\omega_m t + \alpha) i_a{}^r + \omega_m M^{sr} \cos (\omega_m t + \alpha) i_b{}^r \\
&= (R^s + L^s p) i_a{}^s + M^{sr} \cos (\omega_m t + \alpha) p i_a{}^r - M^{sr} \sin (\omega_m t + \alpha) p i_b{}^r \\
v_b{}^s &- \omega_m M^{sr} \cos (\omega_m t + \alpha) i_a{}^r + \omega_m M^{sr} \sin (\omega_m t + \alpha) i_b{}^r \\
&= (R^s + L^s p) i_b{}^s + M^{sr} \sin (\omega_m t + \alpha) p i_a{}^r + M^{sr} \cos (\omega_m t + \alpha) p i_b{}^r \\
v_a{}^r &+ \omega_m M^{sr} \sin (\omega_m t + \alpha) i_a{}^s - \omega_m M^{sr} \cos (\omega_m t + \alpha) i_b{}^s \\
&= (R^r + L^r p) i_a{}^r + M^{sr} \cos (\omega_m t + \alpha) p i_a{}^s + M^{sr} \sin (\omega_m t + \alpha) p i_b{}^s \\
v_b{}^r &+ \omega_m M^{sr} \cos (\omega_m t + \alpha) i_a{}^s + \omega_m M^{sr} \sin (\omega_m t + \alpha) i_b{}^s \\
&= (R^r + L^r p) i_b{}^r - M^{sr} \sin (\omega_m t + \alpha) p i_a{}^s + M^{sr} \cos (\omega_m t + \alpha) p i_b{}^s
\end{aligned} \tag{10-52}
$$

For the potentials we make use of the constraint condition that

$$
v_a{}^r = v_b{}^r = 0 \tag{10-53a}
$$

and we choose the applied potentials to be balanced, and of the form

$$
\begin{aligned}
v_a{}^s &= V^s \cos \omega^s t \\
v_b{}^s &= V^s \sin \omega^s t
\end{aligned} \tag{10-53b}
$$

The corresponding currents are written

$$
\begin{aligned}
i_a{}^s &= I^s \cos (\omega^s t - \theta^s) \\
i_b{}^s &= I^s \sin (\omega^s t - \theta^s) \\
i_a{}^r &= I^r \cos (\omega^r t - \theta^r) \\
i_b{}^r &= I^r \sin (\omega^r t - \theta^r)
\end{aligned} \tag{10-54}
$$

Subject to Eqs. (10-53) and (10-54), Eqs. (10-52) may be reduced. Consider the first of the set, which now becomes

$$
\begin{aligned}
V^s \cos \omega^s t &+ \omega_m M^{sr} I^r [\sin (\omega_m t + \alpha) \cos (\omega^r t - \theta^r) \\
&+ \cos (\omega_m t + \alpha) \sin (\omega^r t - \theta^r)] = (R^s + L^s p) i_a{}^s \\
+ \omega^r M^{sr} I^r [&- \cos (\omega_m t + \alpha) \sin (\omega^r t - \theta^r) - \sin (\omega_m t + \alpha) \cos (\omega^r t - \theta^r)]
\end{aligned}
$$

This is

$$
\begin{aligned}
V^s \cos \omega^s t &+ \omega_m M^{sr} I^r [\sin (\omega_m t + \alpha + \omega^r t - \theta^r)] \\
&= (R^s + L^s p) i_a{}^s - \omega^r M^{sr} I^r [\sin (\omega_m t + \alpha + \omega^r t - \theta^r)]
\end{aligned}
$$

or

$$
V^s \cos \omega^s t + (\omega_m + \omega^r) M^{sr} I^r [\sin (\omega_m + \omega^r) t + \alpha - \theta^r] = (R^s + L^s p) i_a{}^s
$$

which is the expression

$$V^s \cos \omega^s t + \omega^s M^{sr} I^r \sin (\omega^s t + \alpha - \theta^r) = (R^s + L^s p) i_a{}^s \quad (10\text{-}55)$$

The same method of reduction leads to similar forms for the other three of Eqs. (10-52).   The complete set of equations that results is the following:

Stator:
$$
\left.
\begin{aligned}
V^s \cos \omega^s t + \omega^s M^{sr} I^r \sin (\omega^s t + \alpha - \theta^r) &= (R^s + L^s p) i_a{}^s \\
V^s \sin \omega^s t - \omega^s M^{sr} I^r \cos (\omega^s t + \alpha - \theta^r) &= (R^s + L^s p) i_b{}^s \\
\omega^r M^{sr} I^s \sin (\omega^r t - \theta^s - \alpha) &= (R^r + L^r p) i_a{}^r \\
-\omega^r M^{sr} I^s \cos (\omega^r t - \theta^s - \alpha) &= (R^r + L^r p) i_b{}^r
\end{aligned}
\right\} \quad (10\text{-}56)
$$
Rotor:

It is noted from the two rotor equations of this set that the stator currents I^s induce potentials in the rotor, which, in turn, produce rotor currents. Moreover, the frequency of these rotor currents is $\omega^r = \omega^s - \omega_m$.   But this is precisely one of the conditions for the development of an average torque, as discussed in Sec. 10-1.   The induction machine can thus develop an average torque at any speed.

It is convenient to write Eqs. (10-56) in sinor form.   The stator set is, by taking the first equation plus j times the second,

$$V^s e^{j\omega^s t} - j\omega^s M^{sr} I^r e^{j(\omega^s t + \alpha - \theta^r)} = (R^s + L^s p) i^s$$
$$= (R^s + L^s p) I^s e^{j(\omega^s t - \theta^s)}$$

or simply $$\mathbf{V}^s - j\omega^s M^{sr} \mathbf{I}^r = (R^s + j\omega^s L^s) \mathbf{I}^s \quad (10\text{-}57)$$
where
$$\mathbf{V}^s = V^s e^{j0}$$
$$\mathbf{I}^r = I^r e^{j(\alpha - \theta^r)}$$
$$\mathbf{I}^s = I^s e^{-j\theta^s}$$

The rotor set leads to the equation

$$-j\omega^r M^{sr} I^s e^{j(\omega^r t - \theta^s - \alpha)} = (R^r + j\omega^r L^r) I^r e^{j(\omega^r t - \theta^r)}$$

or equivalently

$$-j\omega^r M^{sr} \mathbf{I}^s = (R^r + j\omega^r L^r) \mathbf{I}^r \quad (10\text{-}58)$$

This expression may also be written as

$$-j\omega^s M^{sr} \mathbf{I}^s = \left(\frac{R^r}{s} + j\omega^s L^r\right) \mathbf{I}^r \quad (10\text{-}59)$$

Taken together, the stator and rotor equations are

$$\mathbf{V}^s - j\omega^s M^{sr} \mathbf{I}^r = (R^s + j\omega^s L^s) \mathbf{I}^s$$
$$-j\omega^s M^{sr} \mathbf{I}^s = \left(\frac{R^r}{s} + j\omega^s L^r\right) \mathbf{I}^r \quad (10\text{-}60)$$

An equivalent circuit appropriate to these two equations is drawn in Fig. 10-3a.   An equivalent, mutually coupled network is shown in

Fig. 10-3b. These figures show that in the equivalent circuit the rotor is short-circuited through a resistance $R^r(1 - s)/s$ which is the equivalent power sink which accounts for the energy converted between the electrical and the mechanical systems. Attention is called to the fact that these equivalent circuits are precisely those given in Fig. 8-19, which

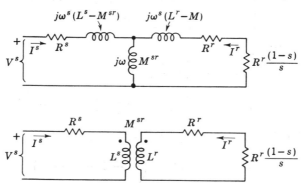

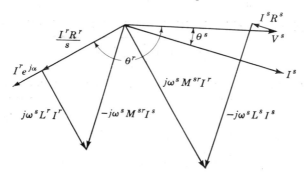

Fig. 10-3. Equivalent circuits of the two-phase induction machine.

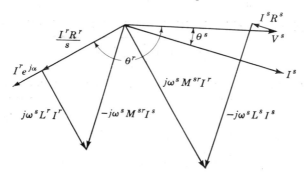

Fig. 10-4. The sinor diagram of the two-phase induction machine.

were previously deduced from considerations of the Kron primitive machine. The phasor diagram appropriate to these equations is given in Fig. 10-4.

An expression for the electromagnetic torque is readily deduced from Eq. (10-23) and Eqs. (10-54). The expression is

$$T_e = M^{sr}\{[I^r \cos(\omega^r t - \theta^r)I^s \sin(\omega^s t - \theta^s)$$
$$- I^r \sin(\omega^r t - \theta^r)I^s \cos(\omega^s t - \theta^s)] \cos(\omega_m t + \alpha)$$
$$- [I^r \sin(\omega^r t - \theta^r)I^s \sin(\omega^s t - \theta^s)$$
$$+ I^r \cos(\omega^r t - \theta^r)I^s \cos(\omega^s t - \theta^s)] \sin(\omega_m t + \alpha)\}$$

This is

$$T_e = M^{sr}I^rI^s[\sin(\omega^s t - \theta^s - \omega^r t + \theta^r) \cos(\omega_m t + \alpha)$$
$$- \cos(\omega^s t - \theta^s - \omega^r t + \theta^r) \sin(\omega_m t + \alpha)]$$

which reduces to

$$T_e = M^{sr}I^sI^r[\sin\{(\omega^s - \omega^r)t - \theta^s + \theta^r - \omega_m t - \alpha]\}$$

or finally
$$T_e = M^{sr}I^sI^r \sin(\theta^r - \theta^s - \alpha) \qquad (10\text{-}61)$$

This expression is rewritten by multiplying by the factor

$$\frac{\omega^s}{\omega^s} = \frac{1-s}{\omega_m}\omega^s$$

since, by definition,

$$1 - s = 1 - \frac{\omega^r}{\omega^s} = \frac{\omega_m}{\omega^s}$$

Then
$$T_e = \frac{1-s}{\omega_m}I^r[\omega^s M^{sr}I^s \sin(\theta^r - \theta^s - \alpha)] \qquad (10\text{-}62)$$

But from the phasor diagram (Fig. 10-3) we may write

$$I^r\frac{R^r}{s} = \omega^s M^{sr}I^s \cos\left(\theta^r - \theta^s - \alpha - \frac{\pi}{2}\right)$$

or
$$I^r\frac{R^r}{s} = \omega^s M^{sr}I^s \sin(\theta^r - \theta^s - \alpha) \qquad (10\text{-}63)$$

This expression is combined with Eq. (10-62) to get for the machine

$$T_e = \frac{|I^r|^2}{\omega_m}\frac{1-s}{s}R^r \qquad (10\text{-}64)$$

Note that in this expression I^r is the peak value of the current. This equation is identical with Eq. (8-50), as it must be. If this expression is combined with I^r deduced from Eqs. (10-60), the result is that given by Eqs. (8-51). The subsequent steps again lead to the torque-speed curve illustrated in Fig. 8-20.

An informative second form for the converted power $\omega_m T_e$ is also possible. Refer to the sinor diagram to see that

$$V^s \cos\theta^s - I^sR^s = \omega^s M^{sr}I^r \cos\left(\theta^r - \frac{\pi}{2} - \theta^s - \alpha\right)$$

$$= \omega^s M^{sr}I^r \sin(\theta^r - \alpha - \theta^s) \qquad (10\text{-}65)$$

This expression is combined with Eq. (10-62) to write

$$T_e = \frac{1-s}{\omega_m}[V^sI^s \cos\theta^s - (I^s)^2R^s] \qquad (10\text{-}66)$$

This expression shows that the converted power is

$$T_e\omega_m = (1-s)(\text{input power} - \text{stator losses}) \qquad (10\text{-}67)$$

We may write, by consideration of conservation of energy, that

Power into stator = power converted + stator loss + rotor loss

This permits us to identify the terms

Power converted: $(1 - s)[V^sI^s \cos \theta^s - (I^s)^2R^s]$

Stator loss: $(I^s)^2R^s$ (10-68)

Rotor loss: $(I^r)^2R^r = s[V^sI^s \cos \theta^s(I^s)^2R^s]$

Clearly, of course, for the balanced two-phase machine here being studied, the respective powers per phase will be one-half the foregoing, which gives the total machine powers. The variables V^s, I^s, I^r are peak values, and if rms values are used, the factor $\frac{1}{2}$ in the above equations will disappear. Thus the foregoing yield the results per phase.

Attention is again directed to the fact that the characteristics that have been derived above are for steady-state conditions. For many problems the equivalent circuits that have been developed may be used for dynamic-problem study. However, more general considerations than in the foregoing must be employed to establish the allowable limits of such an extension. The work in the next chapter will examine this matter in considerable detail.

PROBLEMS

10-1. A six-pole two-phase nonsalient-pole synchronous motor is operating under steady-state load from a 60-cps 440-volt two-phase supply. The synchronous reactance of the machine is $\omega^sL^s = 6.21$ ohms, and the mutual reactance is $\omega^sM^{sr} = 5.90$ ohms. If the machine draws 15 kw from the lines when $I_f = 2.8$ amp d-c, calculate the following:

(a) Speed of the machine
(b) Peak value of V_g
(c) Phase angle between V_g and V^r
(d) Line currents
(e) The limits of the power-factor angle when the excitation current I_f is changed ±20 per cent

10-2. A two-phase a-c generator is rated to deliver 3,500 kw at 10,000 volts. The armature has an effective resistance of 0.64 ohm per phase and a synchronous reactance of 13.7 ohms per phase.

(a) What is the regulation of this alternator on a noninductive load taking the rated kva?

(b) What is the regulation on an inductive load taking rated kva at zero power factor?

(c) What is the regulation on a capacitive load taking rated kva at zero power factor?

10-3. A 1,000-hp four-pole 60-cps 4,200-volt Y-connected nonsalient-pole rotor synchronous machine has an effective armature resistance of 0.17 ohm per phase and a synchronous reactance of 1.3 ohms per phase. Neglecting the effects of saturation, calculate the excitation voltage for:

(a) Full output at unity power factor, assuming an efficiency of 91 per cent.

(b) Ten per cent overload at 0.9 power factor leading, assuming an efficiency of 89.5 per cent.

(c) Construct the phasor diagrams for each case, and determine the power angles.

10-4. A three-phase Y-connected synchronous motor is to be operated from a 3,300-volt source. The excitation is adjusted for 3,500 volts on open circuit. The synchronous reactance is 4.00 ohms per phase, and the effective resistance is 0.25 ohm per phase. Determine the current and power factor for an output of 750 kw.

10-5. A six-pole 60-cps three-phase wound-rotor induction motor has both the rotor and stator windings connected in Y. The maximum torque is 250 per cent, and this occurs at a slip of 18 per cent. For a rotor resistance of 1.00 ohm per phase, and assuming constant reluctance, determine:

(a) The minimum voltage to be impressed so that the motor can still supply its rated torque

(b) The resistance to be inserted into the rotor circuit so that the motor will develop full-load starting torque at the reduced voltage

10-6. Tests on a 5-hp six-pole 220-volt squirrel-cage induction motor yield the following data:

	V, volts	I, amp	P, watts
No load..............	220	9.8	540
Blocked rotor...........	60	20.2	1,080

The effective resistance of the stator winding is 1.60 ohms per phase. Draw the equivalent circuit of the motor for a slip of 2.5 per cent, assuming that the primary and secondary leakage reactances are equal. Compute stator current, power factor, output power, and efficiency at this value of slip.

10-7. The parameters of a three-phase four-pole 60-cps Y-connected induction motor, relative to the stator, are

$$R^s = 0.118 \text{ ohm} \qquad\qquad R^r = 0.102 \text{ ohm}$$
$$X_1 = \omega^s(L^s - M) = 0.208 \text{ ohm} \qquad X_2 = \omega^s(L^r - M) = 0.208 \text{ ohm}$$

Core loss: 407 watts
Friction and windage: 400 watts
No-load current: 11.9 amp at 0.2 pf

The motor is operated as a brake by driving the motor at 200 rpm against the field.
(a) How are the stator iron losses supplied?
(b) What is the braking effort, in watts?
(c) What is the braking torque?

10-8. A 50-hp 440-volt 60-cps four-pole three-phase squirrel-cage induction motor has a starting torque of 160 per cent and a maximum torque of 280 per cent of full-load torque. Neglect the stator resistance, assume that the rotor resistance is constant independent of the rotor frequency, and neglect rotational losses. Find:

(a) The slip at full load
(b) The slip at maximum torque
(c) Rotor starting current, in per unit of full-load current
(d) Rotor copper loss at full load, in watts
(e) Full-load torque, in newton-meters

10-9. A 220-volt four-pole 60-cps three-phase squirrel-cage induction motor develops a maximum torque of 260 per cent at a slip of 18 per cent. What is the

maximum torque if the machine is connected to a 200-volt 50-cps source of power?
Neglect stator resistance.   At what speed will the maximum torque be developed?

10-10. A 2,300-volt 32-pole 50-cps 2,400-kva three-phase nonsalient-pole synchronous motor has a synchronous reactance of 0.464 p.u.   The rotational inertia of
the machine is 110,000 kg-m². The excitation is 1.4 p.u.   Find:

(*a*) The maximum stiffness coefficient.

(*b*) The highest natural period of hunting.

(*c*) Suppose that the motor is running at no load with a negligible displacement
angle and a load of 1,500 kw is suddenly applied.   Neglect damping, and determine the
final displacement angle after oscillations have died out.   What peak displacement is
reached during the oscillation?

10-11. A selsyn is a device that consists essentially of three stator windings which
are 120° apart in space phase and connected in Y.   Suppose that these windings are

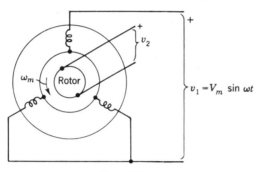

v_2

$+$

$v_1 = V_m \sin \omega t$

ω_m Rotor

FIG. P10-11

excited by the potential $v_1 = V_m \sin \omega t$, as illustrated.   Suppose that the rotor winding
is represented as a single concentrated coil of N turns.

(*a*) If the rotor is driven mechanically at r rps, what is the output potential at the
rotor terminals?

(*b*) If $\omega_m = 2\pi r$ is small compared with ω, what is the form of the output?

(*c*) Suppose that the output is passed through a low-pass filter with a cutoff
frequency ω_m.   What is the form of the output potential?

10-12. An induction frequency changer is essentially a polyphase wound-rotor
machine.   Either the stator or the rotor is excited from a source of polyphase power,
the unexcited winding being the output winding of the machine.   Rotor and stator
are wound for the same number of poles.   The rotor is driven at an appropriately
chosen speed by an external mechanical system.

Suppose that a two-pole machine has its stator excited from a polyphase source of
supply.   Assume that the flux distribution in the air gap is sinusoidally distributed.
It is required to find the potential in one winding of the rotor when the rotor is driven
at the constant speed ω_m.

11

The *n-m* Symmetrical Machine

Our discussion in Chap. 8 showed that the two-phase machine provides sufficient generality in analysis to describe the performance of the three-phase machine in particular, and the n-phase machine in general, under conditions of balanced excitation. In this chapter procedures will be established for handling the general machine with an n-phase stator and an m-phase rotor under unbalanced excitation.

The machine to be discussed, which is a generalization of that discussed in Chap. 10, assumes geometric symmetry. As before, it neglects the effects of the slots. Saliency is restricted to either the stator or the rotor, and moreover, as discussed in Sec. 9-5, saliency is assumed to introduce only a second space harmonic in the air-gap permeance.

The analysis of the n-m-winding machine involves two important steps: (1) Deduce the equations of motion of the machine (one for each electrical port, and one for the mechanical port) in terms of a set of variables. (2) Eliminate as many of the variables as possible without losing any of the essential information. To accomplish objective 1 involves a procedure quite like that discussed in Chap. 10. To accomplish objective 2 involves the introduction of mathematical transformations. It will be found necessary to employ two different known transformations in order to accomplish our goal, but even so some restrictions still remain. The symmetrical component transformation of Fortescue will replace the unbalanced excitation by a balanced equivalent set and will also reduce the complexity of the system equations to a form which is interpreted as that of an equivalent two-phase machine. The Ku transformation will serve to reduce these equations, which possess variable coefficients, to equations with constant coefficients for the electrical set when the speed is constant. If the stator or rotor parameters are not symmetrical, the transformations will not achieve the desired results.

11-1. The *n-m*-winding Symmetrical Machine. The machine to be studied consists of a stator which has n identical coils per pair of poles located around its periphery which are spaced $2\pi/n$ electrical degrees apart. Likewise, the rotor will have m identical coils per pair of poles on its periphery spaced $2\pi/m$ electrical degrees apart. Also, the machine is assumed to be of the nonsalient-pole type with a uniform air gap. Hence, this machine is essentially a more generalized form of that which has been considered in some detail in Sec. 10-1.

The resistance-parameter matrices may be written directly. Since each coil of the stator is physically identical with each other and similarly the coils on the rotor are physically identical, then, in accordance with Eq. (10-16), we may write the stator and rotor resistance matrices as

$$[R_n{}^s] = \begin{bmatrix} R_a{}^s & 0 & 0 & \cdots & 0 \\ 0 & R_b{}^s & 0 & \cdots & 0 \\ 0 & 0 & R_c{}^s & \cdots & 0 \\ 0 & 0 & \cdots & \cdots & 0 \\ 0 & 0 & \cdots & \cdots & R_n{}^s \end{bmatrix}$$

$$[R_m{}^r] = \begin{bmatrix} R_a{}^r & 0 & 0 & \cdots & 0 \\ 0 & R_b{}^r & 0 & \cdots & 0 \\ 0 & \cdots & \cdots & \cdots & 0 \\ 0 & \cdots & \cdots & \cdots & 0 \\ 0 & \cdots & \cdots & \cdots & R_m{}^r \end{bmatrix} \tag{11-1}$$

But since, for identical coils,

$$\left.\begin{aligned} R_a{}^s = R_b{}^s = R_c{}^s = \cdots = R_n{}^s = R^s \\ R_a{}^r = R_b{}^r = R_c{}^r = \cdots = R_m{}^r = R^r \end{aligned}\right\} \tag{11-2}$$

and

then the resistance-parameter matrices may be written in the forms

$$\begin{aligned} [R_n{}^s] = R^s[U]_n \\ [R_m{}^r] = R^r[U]_m \end{aligned} \tag{11-3}$$

where $[U]_n$ and $[U]_m$ are unit matrices.

The inductance-parameter matrices, which will specify the self- and the mutual inductances of the stator coils and the rotor coils, cannot be easily calculated. However, the expressions will have the general forms shown in Eqs. (10-15) for the uniformly distributed windings. Owing to the complexity of the general matrix, we consider the submatrices which are the elements of the partitioned form of the total inductance matrix. That is, we write first the inductance matrix in terms of the elements for each separate winding. These are of the form

$$[L_n{}^s] = \begin{bmatrix} L_{aa}^s & L_{ab}^s & L_{ac}^s & \cdots & L_{an}^s \\ L_{ba}^s & L_{bb}^s & L_{bc}^s & \cdots & L_{bn}^s \\ \cdots & \cdots & \cdots & \cdots & \cdots \\ L_{na}^s & L_{nb}^s & \cdots & \cdots & L_{nn}^s \end{bmatrix}$$

$$[L_m{}^r] = \begin{bmatrix} L_{aa}^r & L_{ab}^r & L_{ac}^r & \cdots & L_{am}^r \\ \cdots & \cdots & \cdots & \cdots & \cdots \\ L_{ma}^r & L_{mb}^r & \cdots & \cdots & L_{mm}^r \end{bmatrix} \tag{11-4}$$

In these expressions the diagonal terms denote the self-inductances of the separate windings; the other terms are mutual inductances between the pairs of windings specified by the subscripts. Moreover, owing to the equality of the mutual inductances between pairs of windings when viewed from either winding, these inductance matrices must be symmetrical around both diagonals. This symmetry is specified by writing

$$[L_n{}^s] = [L_n{}^s]_t$$
$$[L_m{}^r] = [L_m{}^r]_t \tag{11-5}$$

where, as usual, the symbol t denotes that the transpose of the matrix is being specified.

Owing to the physical symmetry that exists in the machine winding distribution, certain additional symmetries exist in the elements of the parameter matrices. It is clear that the following apply:

$$L_{aa}^s = L_{bb}^s = L_{cc}^s = \cdots = L_{nn}^s$$
$$L_{ab}^s = L_{ba}^s, \text{ etc.}$$

Also, the physical arrangement of the a and b coils is identical with the physical arrangement of the a and n coils; similarly for the a and c and the a and $n-1$ coils, etc. Thus we have that

$$L_{ab}^s = L_{an}^s, \text{ etc.}$$
$$L_{ac}^s = L_{a(n-1)}^s$$

or, in general,

$$L_{j(j+k)}^s = L_{j(j-k)}^s$$

As a result of these symmetries, the inductance matrix $[L_n{}^s]$ becomes

$$[L_n{}^s] = \begin{bmatrix} L_{aa}^s & L_{ab}^s & L_{ac}^s & L_{ad}^s & \cdots & L_{ac}^s & L_{ab}^s \\ L_{ab}^s & L_{aa}^s & L_{ab}^s & \cdots & \cdots & \cdots & L_{ac}^s \\ L_{ac}^s & L_{ab}^s & L_{aa}^s & L_{ab} & \cdots & \cdots & L_{ad}^s \\ \cdots & \cdots & \cdots & \cdots & \cdots & \cdots & \cdots \\ L_{ab}^s & \cdots & \cdots & \cdots & \cdots & \cdots & L_{aa}^s \end{bmatrix} \tag{11-6}$$

In a similar way the inductance-parameter matrix of the rotor winding will have the form

$$[L_m{}^r] = \begin{bmatrix} L_{aa}^r & L_{ab}^r & L_{ac}^r & \cdots & L_{ac}^r & L_{ab}^r \\ L_{ab}^r & L_{aa}^r & L_{ab}^r & \cdots & \cdots & L_{ac}^r \\ L_{ac}^r & L_{ab}^r & L_{aa}^r & L_{ab}^r & \cdots & \cdots \\ \cdots & \cdots & \cdots & \cdots & \cdots & \cdots \\ L_{ab}^r & L_{ac}^r & \cdots & \cdots & \cdots & L_{aa}^r \end{bmatrix} \tag{11-7}$$

Matrices of the type in Eqs. (11-6) and (11-7) are said to possess cylindrical symmetry.

The mutual inductances between the stator and rotor coils are difficult to calculate, as already seen in Sec. 10-1. However, based on our prior work, the expected matrices will be of the form

$$[L^{sr}_{nm}] = \begin{bmatrix} L^{sr}_{aa} & L^{sr}_{ab} & L^{sr}_{ac} & \cdots & L^{sr}_{am} \\ L^{sr}_{ba} & \cdots & \cdots & \cdots & \cdots \\ \cdots & \cdots & \cdots & \cdots & \cdots \\ L^{sr}_{na} & L^{sr}_{nb} & \cdots & \cdots & L^{sr}_{nm} \end{bmatrix}$$

$$[L^{rs}_{mn}] = \begin{bmatrix} L^{rs}_{aa} & L^{rs}_{ab} & L^{rs}_{ac} & \cdots & L^{rs}_{an} \\ \cdots & \cdots & \cdots & \cdots & \cdots \\ L^{rs}_{ma} & L^{rs}_{mb} & \cdots & \cdots & L^{rs}_{mn} \end{bmatrix} \qquad (11\text{-}8)$$

The explicit form for each element of the matrix will be the amplitude factor M^{sr} and an appropriate trigonometric factor that takes account of the space-phase displacement among the various windings or coils. The angles involved are those contained in the following tabulation, where the stator windings are specified by the angles $\varphi^s - n\theta^s$, and where the rotor windings are specified by the angles $\varphi^r - m\theta^r$, with $\theta^s = 2\pi/n$, $\theta^r = 2\pi/m$. More specifically the angles are:

Stator winding	$n\theta^s$	Rotor winding	$m\theta^r$
a	0	a	0
b	θ^s	b	θ^r
c	$2\theta^s$	c	$2\theta^r$
$\cdots$	$\cdots$	$\cdots$	$\cdots$
n	$(n-1)\theta^s$	m	$(m-1)\theta^r$

The explicit forms of Eqs. (11-8) will be the expressions

$[L_{nm}{}^{sr}] =$

$$M^{sr} \begin{bmatrix} \cos\varphi & \cos(\varphi + \theta^r) & \cdots & \cos[\varphi + (m-1)\theta^r] \\ \cos(\varphi - \theta^s) & \cos(\varphi + \theta^r - \theta^s) & \cdots & \cos[\varphi + (m-1)\theta^r - \theta^s] \\ \cos(\varphi - 2\theta^s) & \cos(\varphi + \theta^r - 2\theta^s) & \cdots & \cos[\varphi + (m-1)\theta^r - 2\theta^s] \\ \cdots & \cdots & \cdots & \cdots \\ \cos[\varphi - (n-1)\theta^s] & \cos[\varphi + \theta^r - (n-1)\theta^s] & \cdots & \cos[\varphi + (m-1)\theta^r - (n-1)\theta^s] \end{bmatrix}$$

$[L_{mn}{}^{rs}] =$

$$M^{rs} \begin{bmatrix} \cos\varphi & \cos(\varphi - \theta^s) & \cdots & \cos[\varphi - (n-1)\theta^s] \\ \cos(\varphi + \theta^r) & \cos(\varphi + \theta^r - \theta^s) & \cdots & \cos[\varphi + \theta^r - (n-1)\theta^s] \\ \cdots & \cdots & \cdots & \cdots \\ \cos[\varphi + (m-1)\theta^r] & \cos[\varphi + (m-1)\theta^r - \theta^s] & \cdots & \cos[\varphi + (m-1)\theta^r - (n-1)\theta^s] \end{bmatrix}$$

$$(11\text{-}9)$$

Observe therefore that

$$[L^{rs}_{mn}] = [L^{sr}_{nm}]_t \qquad (11\text{-}10)$$

The complete set of parameter matrices of the n-m symmetrical machine are given by Eqs. (11-3), (11-4), and (11-9).

Now, corresponding to Eqs. (10-20) and (10-21), which specify the electrical "equations of motion" of the 2-2 winding machine, we should expect the following sets of equations:

Electrical

For the stator: $[V_n^s] = [R_n^s][I_n^s] + \dfrac{d}{dt}[L_n^s I_n^s + L_{nm}^{sr} I_m^r]$

$$(11\text{-}11)$$

For the rotor: $[V_m^r] = [R_m^r][I_m^r] + \dfrac{d}{dt}[L_m^r I_m^r + L_{mn}^{rs} I_n^s]$

Mechanical.   As an extension of Eqs. (10-21)

$$T = J\ddot{\varphi} + D\dot{\varphi} + k\varphi - \frac{1}{2}\left\{[I_n^s]_t \frac{\partial L_{nm}^{sr}}{\partial \varphi}[I_m^r] + [I_m^r]_t \frac{\partial L_{mn}^{rs}}{\partial \varphi}[I_n^s]\right.$$

$$\left. + [I_n^s]_t \frac{\partial L_n^s}{\partial \varphi}[I_n^s] + [I_m^r]_t \frac{\partial L_m^r}{\partial \varphi}[I_m^r]\right\} \quad (11\text{-}12)$$

Attention is called to the more compact form into which these expressions may be written, by defining new matrices which are composed of the foregoing components as the partitioned parts.   The new matrices are the following:

$$[V] = \begin{bmatrix} V_n^s \\ V_m^r \end{bmatrix} \qquad [I] = \begin{bmatrix} I_n^s \\ I_m^r \end{bmatrix}$$

$$[R] = \begin{bmatrix} R_n^s & \\ \hline & R_m^r \end{bmatrix} \qquad [L] = \begin{bmatrix} L_n^s & L_{nm}^{sr} \\ L_{mn}^{rs} & L_m^r \end{bmatrix} \quad (11\text{-}13)$$

In terms of these new matrices the equations become the following:

$$\begin{bmatrix} V_n^s \\ V_m^r \end{bmatrix} = \begin{bmatrix} R_n^s & 0 \\ 0 & R_m^r \end{bmatrix}\begin{bmatrix} I_n^s \\ I_m^r \end{bmatrix} + \frac{d}{dt}\begin{bmatrix} L_n^s & L_{mn}^{sr} \\ L_{mn}^{rs} & L_m^r \end{bmatrix}\begin{bmatrix} I_n^s \\ I_m^r \end{bmatrix} \quad (11\text{-}14a)$$

$$T = J\ddot{\varphi} + D\dot{\varphi} + k\varphi - \frac{1}{2}[I_n^s \mid I_m^r]\begin{bmatrix} 0 & \dfrac{\partial L_{mn}^{sr}}{\partial \varphi} \\ \dfrac{\partial L_{nm}^{rs}}{\partial \varphi} & 0 \end{bmatrix}\begin{bmatrix} I_n^s \\ I_m^r \end{bmatrix} \quad (11\text{-}14b)$$

as $[L_n^s]$ and $[L_m^r]$ are independent of φ.   These equations may be written in the following form:

$$[V] = [RI] + \frac{d}{dt}[LI]$$

$$T = J\ddot{\varphi} + D\dot{\varphi} + k\varphi - \frac{1}{2}\left[I_t \frac{\partial L}{\partial \varphi}I\right] \quad (11\text{-}15)$$

It is hardly necessary to recall, of course, that despite this very compact form these matrix equations represent a set of $n + m + 1$ differential equations, there being $n + m$ electrical equations and 1 mechanical equation.   Moreover, owing to the space-dependent factors contained in $[L_{nm}^{sr}]$ and $[L_{mn}^{rs}]$, these $n + m + 1$ differential equations are nonlinear with time-varying coefficients.   In most cases the solution to this set of differential equations cannot be effected directly, but fortunately techniques have been developed which do permit the matrices to be diagonalized and the equations thereby reduced to a set which can be solved independently. Under steady-state operating conditions, we have already seen in Chap. 10 that the equations can be reduced to forms which can be handled conveniently, at least for the 2-2 phase machine. We wish here to examine the more general problem and now wish to study the diagonalization problem.

11-2. Diagonalization by a Change of Variable. To effect the diagonalization of the parameter matrices requires that we find an appropriate set of transformation matrices. The necessary properties of the desired transformation matrices are first established.

Suppose therefore that we define two nonsingular transformation matrices $[A_i]$ and $[A_v]$ such that the transformed current and potential matrices are expressible by the expressions

$$[I'] = [A_i I] \qquad [V'] = [A_v V] \tag{11-16}$$

It follows directly, by multiplying on the left, respectively, by $[A_i]^{-1}$ and $[A_v]^{-1}$, that

$$[I] = [A_i^{-1} I'] \qquad [V] = [A_v^{-1} V'] \tag{11-17}$$

These transformations are to be applied to the first of Eqs. (11-15). Premultiply the expression

$$[V] = [RI] + \frac{d}{dt}[LI]$$

by $[A_v]$. This gives

$$[A_v V] = [V'] = [A_v RI] + \frac{d}{dt}[A_v LI]$$

Now use Eqs. (11-17) to find

$$[V'] = [A_v R A_i^{-1} I'] + \frac{d}{dt}[A_v L A_i^{-1} I']$$

which may be written as

$$[V'] = [R'I'] + \frac{d}{dt}[L'I'] \tag{11-18}$$

where, by definition,

$$[R'] = [A_v R A_i^{-1}] \\ [L'] = [A_v L A_i^{-1}] \tag{11-19}$$

As a condition on the transformation matrices, we shall require that $[R']$, the transformed R matrix, shall be diagonal. This requires that

$$[R'] = [A_v R A_i^{-1}] = R[U] \tag{11-20}$$

where $[U]$ is the unit matrix. This condition is met if

$$[A_v] = [A_i] \tag{11-21}$$

Suppose further that the symmetric properties of the stator and rotor inductance coefficient matrices are retained. This requires that

$$[A_v L A_i^{-1}] = [A_v L A_i^{-1}]_t$$

which is $$[A_v L A_i^{-1}] = [A_i^{-1}]_t [L_t][A_v]_t \qquad (11\text{-}22)$$

This imposes the added requirement that

$$[A_v]_t = [A_i^{-1}] \qquad (11\text{-}23)$$

The two requirements imposed on the transformation matrices are met if

$$[A_i]_t = [A_i^{-1}]$$
$$[A_v]_t = [A_v^{-1}] \qquad (11\text{-}24)$$

Matrices which fulfill these conditions are called *orthogonal* matrices.

It is of considerable interest to note that the transformation matrices specified by Eqs. (11-21) and (11-24) are such that the expression for the instantaneous power into the system remains invariant in the transformation. That is, begin with the expression for the instantaneous power, which is

$$p = I_a V_a + I_b V_b + \cdots + I_n V_n$$

which in matrix form is

$$p = [I_a \quad I_b \quad I_c \quad \cdots \quad I_n] \begin{bmatrix} V_a \\ \cdot \\ \cdot \\ \cdot \\ V_n \end{bmatrix}$$

or equivalently
$$p = [I]_t [V] \qquad (11\text{-}25)$$

Now apply the specified transformations, which lead to

$$p = [A_i^{-1} I']_t [A_v^{-1} V']$$

which may be written in the form

$$p = [I'_t][A_i^{-1} A_v^{-1}][V']$$

But since it has been required that

$$[A_i^{-1}]_t [A_v^{-1}] = [A_i A_v^{-1}] = [A_i A_i^{-1}] = [U]$$

then finally
$$p = [I']_t [V'] \qquad (11\text{-}26)$$

Observe that this expression relative to the transformed system is precisely of the same form as that given by Eq. (11-25) relative to the original system.

Let us also examine the effects of the transformation on the electromagnetic torque, which, by Eqs. (11-15), may be written in the form

$$T_e = \frac{1}{2}\left[I_t \frac{\partial L}{\partial \varphi} I \right] \tag{11-27}$$

Recall that all variables and parameters in this expression are real. Now by the prescribed transformations

$$T_e = \frac{1}{2}\left\{ [A_i^{-1}I']_t \frac{\partial L}{\partial \varphi} [A_i^{-1}I'] \right\}$$

which may be written as

$$T_e = \frac{1}{2}[I'_t]\left[[A_i^{-1}]_t \frac{\partial L}{\partial \varphi} A_i^{-1} \right][I'] \tag{11-28}$$

Now let us examine the expression

$$\left[[A_i^{-1}]_t \frac{\partial L}{\partial \varphi} A_i^{-1} \right] = \left[A_i \frac{\partial L}{\partial \varphi} A_i^{-1} \right]$$

which may be written as

$$\left[[A_i^{-1}]_t \frac{\partial L}{\partial \varphi} A_i^{-1} \right] = \frac{\partial}{\partial \varphi}[A_i L A_i^{-1}] = \frac{\partial L'}{\partial \varphi}$$

But Eqs. (11-22) specify that [L'] shall remain symmetric in the transformation. Hence Eq. (11-28) for the torque, which may now be written

$$T_e = \frac{1}{2}\left[I_t \frac{\partial L}{\partial \varphi} I \right] = \frac{1}{2}\left[I'_t \frac{\partial L'}{\partial \varphi} I' \right] \tag{11-29}$$

shows that the expression for torque is also invariant in the transformation.

Attention is called to the fact that the foregoing specifies the general properties which are required of the transformation matrices. However, deducing the explicit forms for such matrices is quite another matter. Considerable effort has been devoted to this problem, and a small number of transformation matrices have been found which have the desired properties.[1] The a-b d-q transformation[2] which we have already used

---

[1] For a general discussion, refer to D. C. White and H. H. Woodson, "Electromechanical Energy Conversion," chap. 4, John Wiley & Sons, Inc., New York, 1959.

[2] R. H. Park, Two Reaction Theory of Synchronous Machines, pt. I, *Trans. AIEE*, **48**: 716 (1929); pt. II, *Trans. AIEE*, **52**: 352 (1933).

in Chap. 8 is one of these. Another is the well-known symmetrical-component transformation of Fortescue.[1] A third is a real transformation and is the quadrature, or Clarke,[2] transformation. A fourth transformation, and one which we shall use later, is the complex rotating transformation of Ku.[3] The original selection of these matrices was largely trial-and-error, but they do satisfy the basic transformation properties discussed above and possess properties suitable to particular types of machine constraints.

Since in some cases the transformation matrix $[A]$ may be complex, i.e., it may contain complex elements, we may generalize the properties of such matrices to the following:

$$
\left.
\begin{array}{c}
[A_t^* A] = [U] \\
[A_t^*] = [A^{-1}] \\
[A_t^{-1*}] = [A]
\end{array}
\right\}
\qquad (11\text{-}30)
$$

or

or

Such transformation matrices are known as unitary, or Hermitian, matrices. It is observed that the conditions given by Eqs. (11-30) reduce to the appropriate forms (11-21) and (11-24) when the transformation matrix $[A]$ is real.

11-3. The Symmetrical Three-phase Machine. It is desired to examine the details of the transformations of the symmetrical three-phase asynchronous machine. While this is a limited case of the n-m machine discussed in Sec. 11-1, the method of analysis is sufficiently general to permit an understanding of the process of analysis and the results obtained are quite representative of those obtained for the n-m machine.

The transformation matrix which will be employed in this study is the symmetrical-component transformation. For the machine under survey $n = m = 3$, with

$$[A_r] = [A_i] = [A] \qquad (11\text{-}31)$$

where, specifically,

$$
[A] = \frac{1}{3}
\begin{bmatrix}
1 & 1 & 1 \\
1 & a & a^2 \\
1 & a^2 & a
\end{bmatrix}
\qquad
A^{-1} =
\begin{bmatrix}
1 & 1 & 1 \\
1 & a^2 & a \\
1 & a & a^2
\end{bmatrix}
\qquad (11\text{-}32)
$$

where

$$a = e^{j2\pi/3}$$

These expressions are the limited forms of the more general transforma-

[1] C. L. Fortescue, Method of Symmetrical Coordinates Applied to the Solution of Polyphase Networks, *Trans. AIEE*, (2)**37**: 1027 (1918).

[2] E. Clarke, "Circuit Analysis of A-C Power Systems," vol. 1, John Wiley & Sons, Inc., New York, 1943.

[3] Y. H. Ku, Transient Analysis of Rotating Machines and Stationary Networks by Means of Rotating Reference Frames, *Trans. AIEE*, (1)**70**: 943 (1951).

tion matrix

$$[A] = \frac{1}{n}\begin{bmatrix} 1 & 1 & 1 & 1 & \cdots & 1 & 1 \\ 1 & a & a^2 & a^3 & \cdots & a^{-2} & a^{-1} \\ 1 & a^2 & a^4 & a^6 & \cdots & a^{-4} & a^{-2} \\ \cdots & \cdots & \cdots & \cdots & \cdots & \cdots & \cdots \\ 1 & a^{-1} & a^{-2} & \cdots & \cdots & a^2 & a \end{bmatrix}$$

$$[A^{-1}] = \begin{bmatrix} 1 & 1 & 1 & \cdots & 1 & 1 \\ 1 & a^{-1} & a^{-2} & \cdots & a^2 & a \\ 1 & a^{-2} & a^{-4} & \cdots & a^4 & a^2 \\ \cdots & \cdots & \cdots & \cdots & \cdots & \cdots \\ 1 & a & a^2 & \cdots & a^{-2} & a^{-1} \end{bmatrix}$$

(11-33)

where

$$a = e^{j2\pi/n}$$

It is readily shown that the following properties are valid for the transformation matrices here defined:

$$\begin{aligned} [A_t] &= [A] \\ [A^*] &= \tfrac{1}{3}[A^{-1}] \\ [A_t^*] &= \tfrac{1}{3}[A^{-1}] \end{aligned}$$

(11-34)

It is now desired to effect the detailed transformation of Eq. (11-14) for the 3-3 phase machine, in the manner leading to Eqs. (11-18) and (11-29). Each of the significant transformations is examined in turn.

Potential and Current Matrices. The specified expressions are the following,

$$\begin{aligned} [V^{s'}] &= [AV^s] & [I^{s'}] &= [AI^s] \\ [V^{r'}] &= [AV^r] & [I^{r'}] &= [AI^r] \end{aligned}$$

(11-35)

from which there results

$$[V^{s'}] = \begin{bmatrix} V_0^s \\ V_1^s \\ V_2^s \end{bmatrix} = \frac{1}{3}\begin{bmatrix} 1 & 1 & 1 \\ 1 & a & a^2 \\ 1 & a^2 & a \end{bmatrix}\begin{bmatrix} V_a^s \\ V_b^s \\ V_c^s \end{bmatrix} = \frac{1}{3}\begin{bmatrix} V_a^s + V_b^s + V_c^s \\ V_a^s + aV_b^s + a^2V_c^s \\ V_a^s + a^2V_b^s + aV_c^s \end{bmatrix}$$

and similarly $\quad [V^{r'}] = \begin{bmatrix} V_0^r \\ V_1^r \\ V_2^r \end{bmatrix} = \frac{1}{3}\begin{bmatrix} V_a^r + V_b^r + V_c^r \\ V_a^r + aV_b^r + a^2V_c^r \\ V_a^r + a^2V_b^r + aV_c^r \end{bmatrix}$

$$[I^{s'}] = \frac{1}{3}\begin{bmatrix} I_a^s + I_b^s + I_c^s \\ I_a^s + aI_b^s + a^2I_c^s \\ I_a^s + a^2I_b^s + aI_c^s \end{bmatrix} \qquad [I^{r'}] = \frac{1}{3}\begin{bmatrix} I_a^r + I_b^r + I_c^r \\ I_a^r + aI_b^r + a^2I_c^r \\ I_a^r + a^2I_b^r + aI_c^r \end{bmatrix}$$

(11-36)

Resistance-parameter Matrices. These are

$$\begin{aligned} [R^{s'}] &= [AR^sA^{-1}] \\ [R^{r'}] &= [AR^rA^{-1}] \end{aligned}$$

(11-37)

Combine the known matrices to find

$$[R^{s'}] = \frac{1}{3}\begin{bmatrix} 1 & 1 & 1 \\ 1 & a & a^2 \\ 1 & a^2 & a \end{bmatrix}\begin{bmatrix} R_a^s & 0 & 0 \\ 0 & R_b^s & 0 \\ 0 & 0 & R_c^s \end{bmatrix}\begin{bmatrix} 1 & 1 & 1 \\ 1 & a^2 & a \\ 1 & a & a^2 \end{bmatrix}$$

$$[R^{s'}] = \frac{1}{3}\begin{bmatrix} R_a^s + R_b^s + R_c^s & R_a^s + a^2R_b^s + aR_c^s & R_a^s + aR_b^s + a^2R_c^s \\ R_a^s + aR_b^s + a^2R_c^s & R_a^s + R_b^s + R_c^s & R_a^s + a^2R_b^s + aR_c^s \\ R_a^s + a^2R_b^s + aR_c^s & R_a^s + aR_b^s + a^2R_c^s & R_a^s + R_b^s + R_c^s \end{bmatrix}$$

But for the balanced machine for which

$$R_a^s = R_b^s = R_c^s = R$$

the expression for $R^{s'}$ reduces to

$$[R^{s'}] = \begin{bmatrix} R^s & 0 & 0 \\ 0 & R^s & 0 \\ 0 & 0 & R^s \end{bmatrix} = R^s\begin{bmatrix} 1 & 0 & 0 \\ 0 & 1 & 0 \\ 0 & 0 & 1 \end{bmatrix} = R^s[U] \qquad (11\text{-}38)$$

In an entirely similar way, it is readily found that

$$[R^{r'}] = \begin{bmatrix} R^r & 0 & 0 \\ 0 & R^r & 0 \\ 0 & 0 & R^r \end{bmatrix} = R^r[U] \qquad (11\text{-}39)$$

Inductance Matrices. Four matrices are involved in the present considerations, and these are the submatrices which form the partitioned parts of the general inductance matrix. We consider first the stator and rotor inductance matrices. The stator matrix is found to be

$$[L_n^{s'}] = [ALA^{-1}]$$
$$= \begin{bmatrix} L_{aa}^s + L_{ab}^s + L_{ac}^s & 0 & 0 \\ 0 & L_{aa}^s + a^2L_{ab}^s + aL_{ac}^s & 0 \\ 0 & 0 & L_{aa}^s + aL_{ab}^s + a^2L_{ac}^s \end{bmatrix} \quad (11\text{-}40)$$

This matrix is conveniently written in the form

$$[L_n^{s'}] = \begin{bmatrix} L_0^s & 0 & 0 \\ 0 & L_1^s & 0 \\ 0 & 0 & L_2^s \end{bmatrix}$$

where
$$L_0^s = L_{aa}^s + L_{ab}^s + L_{ac}^s$$
$$L_1^s = L_{aa}^s + a^2L_{ab}^s + aL_{ac}^s$$
$$L_2^s = L_{aa}^s + aL_{ab}^s + a^2L_{ac}^s \qquad (11\text{-}41)$$

and where, for a balanced machine,

$$L_0^s = L^s + 2M^s$$
$$L_1^s = L^s - M^s$$
$$L_2^s = L^s - M^s$$

In a precisely similar way, it is found that the rotor inductance matrix has the form

$$[L_m{}^{r\prime}] = \begin{bmatrix} L_0{}^r & 0 & 0 \\ 0 & L_1{}^r & 0 \\ 0 & 0 & L_2{}^r \end{bmatrix} \Bigg\}$$

where, in general,

$$\begin{aligned} L_0{}^r &= L_{aa}^r + L_{ab}^r + L_{ac}^r \\ L_1{}^r &= L_{aa}^r + a^2 L_{ab}^r + a L_{ac}^r \\ L_2{}^r &= L_{aa}^r + a L_{ab}^r + a^2 L_{ac}^r \end{aligned} \Bigg\} \qquad (11\text{-}42)$$

and where, for a balanced machine,

$$\begin{aligned} L_0{}^r &= L^r + 2M^r \\ L_1{}^r &= L^r - M^r \\ L_2{}^r &= L^r - M^r \end{aligned} \Bigg/$$

We consider now the stator-rotor mutual-inductance matrices $[L_{nm}^{sr}]$ and $[L_{mn}^{rs}]$ given by Eqs. (11-9). We first examine the transformation

$$L_{nm}^{sr\prime} = [A L_{nm}^{sr} A^{-1}] \qquad (11\text{-}43)$$

For convenience in the subsequent work, the trigonometric factors in the matrix for L_{nm}^{sr} are written in exponential form. That is, the first of Eqs. (11-9) is written as

$$[L_{nm}^{sr}] = \frac{M^{sr}}{2} \begin{bmatrix} e^{j\varphi} & e^{j(\varphi+\theta^r)} & e^{j(\varphi+2\theta^r)} \\ e^{j(\varphi-\theta^s)} & e^{j(\varphi+\theta^r-\theta^s)} & e^{j(\varphi+2\theta^r-\theta^s)} \\ e^{j(\varphi-2\theta^s)} & e^{j(\varphi+\theta^r-2\theta^s)} & e^{j(\varphi+2\theta^r-2\theta^s)} \end{bmatrix}$$

$$+ \frac{M^{sr}}{2} \begin{bmatrix} e^{-j\varphi} & e^{-j(\varphi+\theta^r)} & e^{-j(\varphi+2\theta^r)} \\ e^{-j(\varphi-\theta^s)} & e^{-j(\varphi+\theta^r-\theta^s)} & e^{-j(\varphi+2\theta^r-\theta^s)} \\ e^{-j(\varphi-2\theta^s)} & e^{-j(\varphi+\theta^r-2\theta^s)} & e^{-j(\varphi+2\theta^r-2\theta^s)} \end{bmatrix} \qquad (11\text{-}44)$$

The transformed form is written as follows, using the known forms for $\theta^s = 2\pi/3$, $\theta^r = 2\pi/3$:

$$[L_{nm}^{sr\prime}] = \frac{M^{sr} e^{j\varphi}}{2 \cdot 3} \begin{bmatrix} 1 & 1 & 1 \\ 1 & a & a^2 \\ 1 & a^2 & a \end{bmatrix} \begin{bmatrix} 1 & e^{j120} & e^{j240} \\ e^{-j120} & 1 & e^{j120} \\ e^{-j240} & e^{-j120} & 1 \end{bmatrix} \begin{bmatrix} 1 & 1 & 1 \\ 1 & a^2 & a \\ 1 & a & a^2 \end{bmatrix}$$

$$+ \frac{M^{sr} e^{-j\varphi}}{2 \cdot 3} \begin{bmatrix} 1 & 1 & 1 \\ 1 & a & a^2 \\ 1 & a^2 & a \end{bmatrix} \begin{bmatrix} 1 & e^{-j120} & e^{-j240} \\ e^{j120} & 1 & e^{-j120} \\ e^{j240} & e^{j120} & 1 \end{bmatrix} \begin{bmatrix} 1 & 1 & 1 \\ 1 & a^2 & a \\ 1 & a & a^2 \end{bmatrix}$$

It is observed, however, that the angle functions arising from the θ^s's and θ^r's may also be written in terms of the function a, since $a = e^{j120}$. Upon carrying out the triple matrix products in this expression, $[L_{nm}^{sr\prime}]$ is found to reduce to the equation

$$[L_{nm}^{sr'}] = \frac{M^{sr}e^{j\varphi}}{2 \cdot 3}\begin{bmatrix} 0 & 0 & 0 \\ 0 & 9 & 0 \\ 0 & 0 & 0 \end{bmatrix} + \frac{M^{sr}e^{-j\varphi}}{2 \cdot 3}\begin{bmatrix} 0 & 0 & 0 \\ 0 & 0 & 0 \\ 0 & 0 & 9 \end{bmatrix}$$

which may be written finally in the form

$$[L_{nm}^{sr'}] = \tfrac{3}{2}M^{sr}\begin{bmatrix} 0 & 0 & 0 \\ 0 & e^{j\varphi} & 0 \\ 0 & 0 & e^{-j\varphi} \end{bmatrix} \tag{11-45}$$

Similarly, it is found that

$$[L_{mn}^{rs'}] = \tfrac{3}{2}M^{sr}\begin{bmatrix} 0 & 0 & 0 \\ 0 & e^{-j\varphi} & 0 \\ 0 & 0 & e^{j\varphi} \end{bmatrix} \tag{11-46}$$

Equations of Motion. Now, by using the transformed results, the transformed equations corresponding to Eq. (11-14a) may be written in complete form. Upon using the symbol p to denote the operator d/dt, the equations become

$$\begin{bmatrix} V_0^s \\ V_1^s \\ V_2^s \\ \hdashline V_0^r \\ V_1^r \\ V_2^r \end{bmatrix}$$

$$= \left[\begin{array}{cccc:cccc} R^s + pL_0^s & 0 & 0 & 0 & 0 & 0 \\ 0 & R^s + pL_1^s & 0 & 0 & p(\tfrac{3}{2}M^{sr}e^{j\varphi}) & 0 \\ 0 & 0 & R^s + pL_2^s & 0 & 0 & p(\tfrac{3}{2}M^{sr}e^{-j\varphi}) \\ \hdashline 0 & 0 & 0 & R^r + pL_0^r & 0 & 0 \\ 0 & p(\tfrac{3}{2}M^{sr}e^{-j\varphi}) & 0 & 0 & R^r + pL_1^r & 0 \\ 0 & 0 & p(\tfrac{3}{2}M^{sr}e^{j\varphi}) & 0 & 0 & R^r + pL_2^r \end{array}\right]$$

$$\times \begin{bmatrix} I_0^s \\ I_1^s \\ I_2^s \\ \hdashline I_0^r \\ I_1^r \\ I_2^r \end{bmatrix} \tag{11-47}$$

By expanding this matrix, the following sets of equations result:

Stator:
$$V_0^s = (R^s + pL_0^s)I_0^s$$
$$V_1^s = (R^s + pL_1^s)I_1^s + p(\tfrac{3}{2}M^{sr}e^{j\varphi}I_1^r) \tag{11-48}$$
$$V_2^s = (R^s + pL_2^s)I_2^s + p(\tfrac{3}{2}M^{sr}e^{-j\varphi}I_2^r)$$

Rotor:
$$V_0^r = (R^r + pL_0^r)I_0^r$$
$$V_1^r = (R^r + pL_1^r)I_1^r + p(\tfrac{3}{2}M^{sr}e^{-j\varphi}I_1^s) \tag{11-49}$$
$$V_2^r = (R^r + pL_2^r)I_2^r + p(\tfrac{3}{2}M^{sr}e^{j\varphi}I_2^s)$$

These results are very striking in the simplifications that have been effected.   First, it is noted that each of the three kinds of sequence quantities is independent of the other two.   Second, the stator and rotor zero-sequence systems are not coupled together.   Third, the shaft position φ does not appear in the zero-sequence equations.   Because of the lack of coupling between the stator and rotor zero-sequence systems, they do not contribute to the torque development of the machine.   It is desirable, in fact, that these currents should be made zero in order to avoid having these terms degrade the performance of the machine.

A rather interesting result is the unusual way in which the shaft position enters into the equations for the positive- and negative-sequence components.   A reasonable interpretation can be given to these terms. Specifically, consider the rotor equations given by Eqs. (11-49).   These suggest that the rotor positive and negative sequences have induced voltages of the form

$$p(\tfrac{3}{2}M^{sr}e^{-j\varphi}I_1{}^s) \qquad \text{and} \qquad p(\tfrac{3}{2}M^{sr}e^{j\varphi}I_2{}^s)$$

Suppose that $I_1{}^s$ and $I_2{}^s$ are sinusoidal excitation functions, of the form $I_1{}^s e^{j\omega t}$ and $I_2{}^s e^{j\omega t}$.   This suggests that the flux linkages of the stator with the rotor vary at frequencies $\omega_1{}^r = \omega - \dot{\varphi}$ and $\omega_2{}^r = \omega + \dot{\varphi}$.   Observe that just the opposite effect occurs in the flux linkages of the rotor with the stator i.e., the frequencies $\omega_1{}^r$ and $\omega_2{}^r$ of the rotor sequence currents are changed by the exponential terms back into the stator frequencies. The situation is then the following: Voltages are induced by the stator currents into the rotor at slip frequencies, corresponding to the combination of the stator frequency and the rotor motion.   The resulting excitation of the rotor causes voltages to be induced in the stator at the stator frequency, owing to the combination of rotor frequency and rotor motion. The two rotor excitation frequencies are $\omega_1{}^r = s\omega$ for the forward excitation and $\omega_2{}^r = (2 - s)\omega$ for the backward excitation, where s is the slip.

Since the components $V_1{}^s$, $V_2{}^s$ and $V_1{}^r$, $V_2{}^r$ include the mechanical angle φ, it is expected that these sequences should contribute to the torque or energy-conversion properties of the machine.   This will now be shown to be the case.   Consider the torque equation [Eq. (11-14b)], which will be examined in its transformed form.   Thus corresponding to the expression

$$T_e = \frac{1}{2}\left[I_t \frac{\partial L}{\partial \varphi} I \right]$$

is the transformed expression

$$T_e = \frac{1}{2}\left\{ [I_t{}^{s'}{}_{|}^{}I_t{}^{r'}] \frac{\partial}{\partial \varphi}\left[\begin{array}{c|c} L^{s'} & L_{nm}^{sr'} \\ \hline L_{mn}^{rs'} & L^{r'} \end{array} \right]\left[\begin{array}{c} I^{s'} \\ \hline I^{r'} \end{array} \right] \right\} \tag{11-50}$$

However, $[L^{s'}]$ and $[L^{r'}]$ are independent of φ, and this equation reduces to the form

$$T_e = \frac{1}{2} \left\{ [I_t^{s'} \vdots I_t^{r'}] \begin{bmatrix} 0 & \vdots & \dfrac{\partial}{\partial \varphi} L_{nm}^{sr'} \\ \hdashline \dfrac{\partial}{\partial \varphi} L_{mn}^{rs'} & \vdots & 0 \end{bmatrix} \begin{bmatrix} I^{s'} \\ \hdashline I^{r'} \end{bmatrix} \right\} \tag{11-51}$$

By performing the indicated differentiations and expanding the matrix, the following expression results:

$$T_e = \tfrac{1}{2}[I_1{}^s(\tfrac{3}{2}M^{sr}je^{j\varphi})I_1{}^r + I_2{}^s(\tfrac{3}{2}M^{sr}(-j)e^{-j\varphi})I_2{}^r$$
$$+ I_1{}^r(\tfrac{3}{2}M^{sr}(-j)e^{-j\varphi})I_1{}^s + I_2{}^r(\tfrac{3}{2}M^{sr}je^{j\varphi})I_2{}^s] \tag{11-52}$$

This expression may be written in the form

$$T_e = \tfrac{3}{4}jM^{sr}[(I_1{}^sI_1{}^r + I_2{}^rI_2{}^s)e^{j\varphi} - (I_1{}^rI_1{}^s + I_2{}^sI_2{}^r)e^{-j\varphi}] \tag{11-53}$$

Observe that the two pairs of terms within the brackets are conjugates of each other, and hence T_e is a real quantity. Moreover, as surmised above, the torque is dependent only upon the 1- and 2-sequence currents (or, equivalently, the positive- and negative-sequence components) of the stator and the 1- and 2-sequence currents of the rotor. Therefore only these sequence currents need be considered in determining the electromechanical-conversion properties of the machine.

Had we considered an n-phase stator and an m-phase rotor, it would have been found, upon making the appropriate symmetrical-component transformations of the general dynamic equations of the system, in this case by using the appropriate general forms specified by Eqs. (11-33), that there would be n-sequence equations for the stator equations and m-sequence equations for the rotor equations. The expression for the electromagnetic torque would have been precisely the same as Eq. (11-52) except that it would involve the 1- and $(n-1)$-sequence currents of the stator and the 1- and $(m-1)$-sequence currents of the rotor. But these results are identical in form with that of the two-phase smooth-air-gap machine, as specified in Eq. (10-23). Therefore, the only quantities required in a consideration of the energy-conversion properties of the n-m-phase machine are the positive- and negative-sequence currents of an equivalent two-phase machine. It is in this context that one must interpret the statement "Every balanced polyphase machine can be reduced to an equivalent two-phase machine," which is often made.

11-4. Variable-coefficient Transformation. The volt-ampere equations given by Eqs. (11-48) and (11-49) still involve nonlinear terms, owing to the factor of the form $p(e^{\pm j\varphi}I)$. In the simple case of rotation at constant speed $\dot{\varphi}$, the volt-ampere equations are linear, with time-varying coefficients, and the torque equations are nonlinear and involve quadratic functions of the currents and φ.   The general solution of such equations is virtually unknown.   However, some additional progress toward a solution is possible by introducing a new transformation function which is a function of the angle φ.   These transformations, which were introduced by Ku and which are sometimes called the forward and backward trans- formations, will remove the angular dependence from both the electrical and the torque equations but will leave the electrical equations with speed terms.   In the case when the speed is constant, it will be found that these electrical equations become linear, with constant coefficients. Hence, the transformation does not completely remove the nonlinearities, but the equations are simplified.

A further word about the Ku transformation is in order.   In Eqs. (11-49) the exponential terms in $j\varphi$ are associated with the impedances. What is now to be done is to associate the exponential terms with the currents.   By doing this, all the equations involve the same frequency, namely, that of the stator.   Moreover, this amounts to defining for the rotor a new set of currents in place of the positive- and negative-sequence currents.   These are known as the forward and backward components and involve essentially transformations of the form

$$I_f{}^r = I_1{}^r e^{j\varphi} \qquad \text{and} \qquad I_b{}^r = I_2{}^r e^{-j\varphi}$$

Note that these new currents have the same amplitude as the sequence components from which they are derived; only the frequency is changed.

The specific form of the Ku transformation is that given by the follow- ing matrix:

$$[B] = \begin{bmatrix} 1 & 0 & 0 \\ 0 & e^{j\varphi} & 0 \\ 0 & 0 & e^{-j\varphi} \end{bmatrix} \tag{11-54}$$

The inverse transformation matrix is

$$[B^{-1}] = \begin{bmatrix} 1 & 0 & 0 \\ 0 & e^{-j\varphi} & 0 \\ 0 & 0 & e^{j\varphi} \end{bmatrix} \tag{11-55}$$

Observe that for this matrix

$$\begin{aligned} [B] &= [B_t] \\ [B^{-1}] &= [B^*] \end{aligned} \tag{11-56}$$

It is now desired to transform Eq. (11-47), which is written for con- venience in the form

$$\begin{bmatrix} V^{s\prime} \\ \hline V^{r\prime} \end{bmatrix} = \left\{ \begin{bmatrix} R^{s\prime} & 0 \\ \hline 0 & R^{r\prime} \end{bmatrix} + p \begin{bmatrix} L^{s\prime} & L^{sr\prime} \\ \hline L^{rs\prime} & L^{r\prime} \end{bmatrix} \right\} \begin{bmatrix} I^{s\prime} \\ \hline I^{r\prime} \end{bmatrix} \tag{11-57}$$

The transformed quantities will be denoted with a double prime and will be of the form

$$[V^{r\prime\prime}] = [BV^{r\prime}] \qquad [V^{r\prime}] = [B^{-1}V^{r\prime\prime}]$$
$$[I^{r\prime\prime}] = [BI^{r\prime}] \qquad [I^{r\prime}] = [B^{-1}I^{r\prime\prime}] \tag{11-58}$$

Specifically, we transform Eq. (11-57) as follows:

$$\begin{bmatrix} 1 & 0 \\ 0 & B \end{bmatrix} \begin{bmatrix} V^{s\prime} \\ V^{r\prime} \end{bmatrix} = \begin{bmatrix} V^{s\prime} \\ V^{r\prime\prime} \end{bmatrix} = \begin{bmatrix} 1 & 0 \\ 0 & B \end{bmatrix} \left\{ \begin{matrix} \text{bracketed} \\ \text{term in} \\ \text{Eq. (11-57)} \end{matrix} \right\} \begin{bmatrix} 1 & 0 \\ 0 & B^{-1} \end{bmatrix} \begin{bmatrix} I^{s\prime} \\ I^{r\prime\prime} \end{bmatrix}$$

Upon expansion, there results

$$\left[\frac{V^{s\prime}}{V^{r\prime\prime}} \right] = \left\{ \left[\begin{array}{c|c} R^{s\prime} & 0 \\ \hline 0 & BR^{r\prime}B^{-1} \end{array} \right] + \left[\begin{array}{c|c} pL^{s\prime} & pL^{sr\prime}B^{-1} \\ \hline BpL^{rs\prime} & BpL^{r\prime}B^{-1} \end{array} \right] \right\} \left[\frac{I^{s\prime}}{I^{r\prime\prime}} \right] \tag{11-59}$$

But since the transformation matrix $[B]$ is indirectly a function of time, it is important to observe the location of the differentiating sign in forming the matrix products. To reduce this expression, it is noted that

$$Bp(L^{rs\prime}I^{s\prime}) = BL^{rs\prime}pI^{s\prime} + B(pL^{rs\prime})I^{s\prime} \tag{11-60}$$

But

$$pL^{rs\prime} = \tfrac{3}{2}M^{sr} \left\{ \begin{bmatrix} 0 & 0 & 0 \\ 0 & pe^{-j\varphi} & 0 \\ 0 & 0 & pe^{j\varphi} \end{bmatrix} + \begin{bmatrix} 0 & 0 & 0 \\ 0 & -j\dot{\varphi}e^{-j\varphi} & 0 \\ 0 & 0 & j\dot{\varphi}e^{j\varphi} \end{bmatrix} \right\}$$

Thus

$$Bp(L^{r\prime}I^{s\prime}) = \tfrac{3}{2}M^{sr} \begin{bmatrix} 0 & 0 & 0 \\ 0 & e^{j\varphi} & 0 \\ 0 & 0 & e^{-j\varphi} \end{bmatrix} \begin{bmatrix} 0 & 0 & 0 \\ 0 & e^{-j\varphi}(p - j\dot{\varphi}) & 0 \\ 0 & 0 & e^{j\varphi}(p + j\dot{\varphi}) \end{bmatrix} \begin{bmatrix} I_0{}^s \\ I_1{}^s \\ I_2{}^s \end{bmatrix}$$

which becomes

$$BpL^{r\prime}I^{s\prime} = \tfrac{3}{2}M^{sr} \begin{bmatrix} 0 & 0 & 0 \\ 0 & p - j\dot{\varphi} & 0 \\ 0 & 0 & p + j\dot{\varphi} \end{bmatrix} \begin{bmatrix} I_0{}^s \\ I_1{}^s \\ I_2{}^s \end{bmatrix} \tag{11-61}$$

Now we consider the expression

$$Bp(L^{r\prime}B^{-1}) = B(pL^{r\prime})B^{-1} + BL^{r\prime}(pB^{-1}) \tag{11-62}$$

But

$$pL^{r\prime} = p \begin{bmatrix} L_0{}^r & 0 & 0 \\ 0 & L_1{}^r & 0 \\ 0 & 0 & L_2{}^r \end{bmatrix} = \begin{bmatrix} L_0{}^r p & 0 & 0 \\ 0 & L_1{}^r p & 0 \\ 0 & 0 & L_2{}^r p \end{bmatrix}$$

and

$$pB^{-1} = p \begin{bmatrix} 1 & 0 & 0 \\ 0 & e^{j\varphi} & 0 \\ 0 & 0 & e^{-j\varphi} \end{bmatrix} = \begin{bmatrix} 0 & 0 & 0 \\ 0 & -j\dot{\varphi}e^{-j\varphi} & 0 \\ 0 & 0 & j\dot{\varphi}e^{j\varphi} \end{bmatrix}$$

so that

$$Bp(L^{r'}B^{-1}) = \begin{bmatrix} 1 & 0 & 0 \\ 0 & e^{j\varphi} & 0 \\ 0 & 0 & e^{-j\varphi} \end{bmatrix} \begin{bmatrix} L_0^r p & 0 & 0 \\ 0 & L_1^r(p - j\dot\varphi)e^{-j\varphi} & 0 \\ 0 & 0 & L_2^r(p + j\dot\varphi)e^{j\varphi} \end{bmatrix}$$

or $$Bp(L^{r'}B^{-1}) = \begin{bmatrix} L_0^r p & 0 & 0 \\ 0 & L_1^r(p - j\dot\varphi) & 0 \\ 0 & 0 & L_2^r(p + j\dot\varphi) \end{bmatrix} \qquad (11\text{-}63)$$

Finally, we consider the quantity

$$p(L^{sr'}B^{-1}) = (pL^{sr'})B^{-1} + L^{sr'}(pB^{-1}) \qquad (11\text{-}64)$$

From the above we may write

$$pL^{sr'}B^{-1} = \tfrac{3}{2}M^{sr} \left\{ \begin{bmatrix} 0 & 0 & 0 \\ 0 & j\dot\varphi e^{j\varphi} & 0 \\ 0 & 0 & -j\dot\varphi e^{-j\varphi} \end{bmatrix} \begin{bmatrix} 1 & 0 & 0 \\ 0 & e^{-j\varphi} & 0 \\ 0 & 0 & e^{j\varphi} \end{bmatrix} \right.$$

$$\left. + \begin{bmatrix} 1 & 0 & 0 \\ 0 & e^{-j\varphi} & 0 \\ 0 & 0 & e^{j\varphi} \end{bmatrix} \begin{bmatrix} 0 & 0 & 0 \\ 0 & -j\dot\varphi e^{-j\varphi} & 0 \\ 0 & 0 & j\dot\varphi e^{j\varphi} \end{bmatrix} \right\}$$

Upon expansion, it is found that this becomes

$$pL^{sr'}B^{-1} = 0 \qquad (11\text{-}65)$$

Equation (11-59), the transformed equations, now attains the form

$$\begin{bmatrix} V_{0^s} \\ V_{1^s} \\ V_{2^s} \\ \hline V_{0^r} \\ V_{f^r} \\ V_{b^r} \end{bmatrix}$$

$$= \begin{bmatrix} R^s + L_0^s p & 0 & 0 & 0 & 0 & 0 \\ 0 & R^s + L_1^s p & 0 & 0 & 0 & 0 \\ 0 & 0 & R^s + L_2^s p & 0 & 0 & 0 \\ \hline 0 & 0 & 0 & R^r + L_0^r p & 0 & 0 \\ 0 & \tfrac{3}{2}M^{sr}(p - j\dot\varphi) & 0 & 0 & R^r + L_1^r(p - j\dot\varphi) & 0 \\ 0 & 0 & 3M^{sr}(p + j\dot\varphi) & 0 & 0 & R^r + L_2^r(p + j\dot\varphi) \end{bmatrix}$$

$$\times \begin{bmatrix} I_{0^s} \\ I_{1^s} \\ I_{2^s} \\ \hline I_{0^r} \\ I_{f^r} \\ I_{b^r} \end{bmatrix} \qquad (11\text{-}66)$$

Observe, as noted in the introduction to this section, that the transformation has removed the angular dependence but that speed terms still remain in the equations.

Now it is observed that the excitation of the rotor circuits is ordinarily accomplished by induction from the stator. That is, no direct rotor excitation voltages are necessary in Eq. (11-66). In addition, it is convenient to divide the last two equations of this set by $(p - j\dot\varphi)/p$ and $(p + j\dot\varphi)/p$, respectively. Upon doing this, the equation set attains the form

$$
\begin{bmatrix} V_{0^s} \\ V_{1^s} \\ V_{2^s} \\ ---\\ 0 \\ 0 \\ 0 \end{bmatrix}
=
\begin{bmatrix}
R^s + L_{0^s}p & 0 & 0 & 0 & 0 & 0 \\
0 & R^s + L_{1^s}p & 0 & 0 & 0 & 0 \\
0 & 0 & R^s + L_{2^s}p & 0 & 0 & 0 \\
0 & 0 & 0 & R^r + L_{0^r}p & 0 & 0 \\
0 & \tfrac{3}{2}M^{sr} & 0 & 0 & \dfrac{R^r}{(p - j\dot\varphi)/p} + L_{1^r} & 0 \\
0 & 0 & \tfrac{3}{2}M^{sr} & 0 & 0 & \dfrac{R^r}{(p + j\dot\varphi)/p} + L_{2^r}
\end{bmatrix}
\times
\begin{bmatrix} I_{0^s} \\ I_{1^s} \\ I_{2^s} \\ --- \\ I_{0^r} \\ I_{f^r} \\ I_{b^r} \end{bmatrix} \quad (11\text{-}67)
$$

It is observed that, when the rotational velocity $\dot\varphi$ can be considered constant, Eqs. (11-66) and (11-67) become a set of linear differential equations with constant coefficients and may be solved in the general case by well-known methods.

The set of Eqs. (11-67) may be represented by a set of equivalent circuits, as given in Fig. 11-1. The corresponding form under steady-

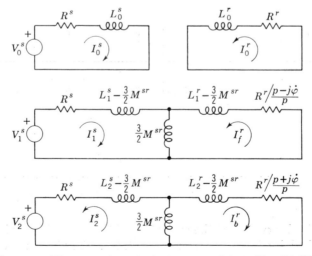

FIG. 11-1. The network equivalents appropriate to Eq. (11-67).

state sinusoidal excitation, which results by replacing p by $j\omega$ in Fig. 11-1, becomes, by a slight rearrangement, the circuits of Fig. 11-2.

The expression for the electromagnetic torque, which is given by Eq. (11-51), may also be subjected to the present transformation. In the

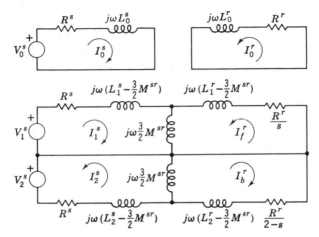

FIG. 11-2. The network equivalent under sinusoidal excitation.

present case we have the following equation, upon applying the Ku transformation:

$$T_e = \frac{1}{2}\left\{ [I_t^{s'} \mid I_t^{r''}] \left[\begin{array}{c|c} 0 & \frac{\partial}{\partial\varphi} L^{sr'}B^{-1} \\ \hline B\frac{\partial}{\partial\varphi}L^{rs'} & 0 \end{array} \right] \left[\begin{array}{c} I^{s'} \\ I^{r''} \end{array} \right] \right\} \tag{11-68}$$

But the quantities

$$B\frac{\partial}{\partial\varphi}L^{rs'} = \tfrac{3}{2}M^{sr} \begin{bmatrix} 0 & 0 & 0 \\ 0 & e^{j\varphi} & 0 \\ 0 & 0 & e^{-j\varphi} \end{bmatrix} \begin{bmatrix} 0 & 0 & 0 \\ 0 & -je^{-j\varphi} & 0 \\ 0 & 0 & je^{j\varphi} \end{bmatrix}$$

$$= \tfrac{3}{2}M^{sr} \begin{bmatrix} 0 & 0 & 0 \\ 0 & -j & 0 \\ 0 & 0 & j \end{bmatrix}$$

$$\frac{\partial}{\partial\varphi}(L^{sr'}B^{-1}) = \tfrac{3}{2}M^{sr}\frac{\partial}{\partial\varphi}\begin{bmatrix} 0 & 0 & 0 \\ 0 & 1 & 0 \\ 0 & 0 & 1 \end{bmatrix} = 0$$

Then (11-68) may be written

$$T_e = \tfrac{1}{2}[I_t^{s'} \mid I_t^{r''}]\left[\begin{array}{c|c} 0 & 0 \\ \hline \tfrac{3}{2}M^{sr}\begin{bmatrix} 0 & 0 & 0 \\ 0 & -j & 0 \\ 0 & 0 & j \end{bmatrix} & 0 \end{array} \right]\left[\begin{array}{c} I^{s'} \\ \hline I^{r''} \end{array} \right] \tag{11-69}$$

In expanded form this expression becomes

$$T_e = -\tfrac{3}{4}M^{sr}j(I_1^s I_f^r - I_2^s I_b^r) \tag{11-70}$$

This expression, as Eq. (11-53), is a quadratic function of the current variables.

11-5. Special Limiting Cases. Two important special cases of the foregoing general results are examined in detail.

Balanced Polyphase Excitation. Suppose that the machine is excited

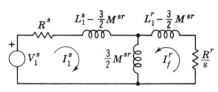

FIG. 11-3. A balanced polyphase induction machine.

from a balanced polyphase source of excitation, in which case the phasor voltages V_0^s and V_2^s are zero. Only the positive-sequence network is then excited, and the complete equivalent circuit for this case is that illustrated in Fig. 11-3. Observe that this is identically that previously given in Fig. 8-19, when the polyphase induction machine under balanced conditions was considered in detail in Sec. 8-4.

Single-phase Excitation. The single-phase motor, as already discussed in Sec. 8-6, comprises a polyphase rotor, but only a single stator phase is excited. Suppose that we designate the excited phase as a, with the remaining two phases of a three-phase machine being open-circuited, or, in the case of a single-phase machine, the extra phase windings are non-existent. In this case the sequence currents of the stator become, from Eqs. (11-36),

$$I_1^s = I_2^s = I_0^s = \frac{I_a}{\sqrt{3}} \tag{11-71}$$

and the sequence voltages are such that

$$V_1^s + V_2^s + V_0^s = \sqrt{3}\, V_a \tag{11-72}$$

The equivalent circuit now becomes that illustrated in Fig. 11-4. Attention is called to the fact that the currents in the two lines marked $\times$ are

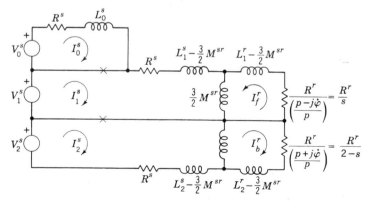

FIG. 11-4. The equivalent circuit for the single-phase induction motor.

zero, and these connections may thus be removed.   Now, by replacing the three sequence voltages by $\sqrt{3}\, V_a$, the circuit may be redrawn to the form illustrated in Fig. 11-5.

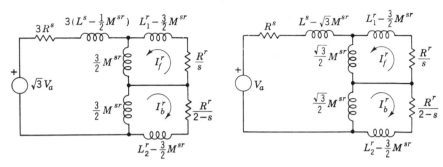

FIG. 11-5. The reduced equivalent circuit for the single-phase induction motor.

FIG. 11-6. The final equivalent circuit of the single-phase induction motor.

The equations appropriate to the manipulations in the figures essentially add the three stator equations and discard the rotor zero-sequence equation.   The resulting equations become

$$\sqrt{3}\, V_a = [3R^s + p(L_0{}^s + L_1{}^s + L_2{}^s)]\frac{I_a}{\sqrt{3}} + \tfrac{3}{2}pM^{sr}(I_f{}^r + I_b{}^r)$$

$$0 = \tfrac{3}{2}pM^{sr}\frac{I_a}{\sqrt{3}} + \left[\frac{R^r}{(p - j\dot\varphi)/p} + pL_1{}^r\right]I_f{}^r \qquad (11\text{-}73)$$

$$0 = \tfrac{3}{2}pM^{sr}\frac{I_a}{\sqrt{3}} + \left[\frac{R^r}{(p + j\dot\varphi)/p} + pL_2{}^r\right]I_b{}^r$$

By rearranging the factor $\sqrt{3}$ and replacing the factors $(p - j\dot\varphi)/p$ and $(p + j\dot\varphi)/p$ by s and $2 - s$, respectively, these equations become

$$V_a = (R^s + pL^s)I_a + \frac{\sqrt{3}}{2}pM^{sr}(I_f{}^r + I_b{}^r)$$

$$0 = \frac{\sqrt{3}}{2}pM^{sr}I_2 + (R_s{}^r + pL_1{}^r)I_f{}^r \qquad (11\text{-}74)$$

$$0 = \frac{\sqrt{3}}{2}pM^{sr}I_a + \left(\frac{R^r}{2 - s} + pL_2{}^r\right)I_b{}^r$$

This set is represented by the equivalent circuit of Fig. 11-6.   Attention is called to the fact that this equivalent circuit was introduced as Fig. 8-21 when the single-phase motor was first discussed.

PROBLEMS

11-1. In the network shown, $V_{12} = 120\underline{/0}$; $V_{23} = 120\underline{/-120}$; $V_{31} = 120\underline{/120}$.

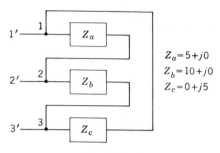

$$Z_a = 5 + j0$$
$$Z_b = 10 + j0$$
$$Z_c = 0 + j5$$

FIG. P11-1

(*a*) Use the symmetrical-component transformations, which are such that $[I] = [A^{-1}I_c]$; $[V] = [A^{-1}V_c]$, where $[A]$ and $[A^{-1}]$ are defined by Eqs. (11-32), to find the currents $I_{1'1}$, $I_{2'2}$, $I_{3'3}$.

(*b*) Solve for these currents by conventional methods, and compare with the results in (*a*).

11-2. The Clarke transformation of currents is given by

$$[I] = [C_i I_c]$$

where the $[I_c]$'s are the components of current in transformed coordinates, and where, explicitly,

$$I = \begin{bmatrix} i_a \\ i_b \\ i_c \end{bmatrix} \qquad C_i = \frac{1}{2}\begin{bmatrix} 2 & 2 & 0 \\ 2 & -1 & \sqrt{3} \\ 2 & -1 & \sqrt{3} \end{bmatrix} \qquad I_c = \begin{bmatrix} i_0 \\ i_\alpha \\ i_\beta \end{bmatrix}$$

If the power is to remain invariant in form, then it is required that

$$[I_t^* V] = [I_{ct}^* V_c]$$

It is required to find the matrix $[C_v]$ in terms of $[C_i]$ such that

$$[V] = [C_v V_c]$$

11-3. Start with the equation of motion of the generalized machine given by Eqs. (10-20) and (10-21). These equations are to be subjected to the *d-q* transformation. Choose the transformation

$$[A_{ab,dq}^{s,r}] = \begin{bmatrix} [U] & 0 \\ \hline 0 & [a_{dq}^r] \end{bmatrix} \qquad \text{where } [U] = \begin{bmatrix} 1 & 0 \\ 0 & 1 \end{bmatrix} \qquad [a_{dq}^r] = \begin{bmatrix} \cos \varphi & \sin \varphi \\ -\sin \varphi & \cos \varphi \end{bmatrix}$$

which leaves the stator variables unchanged but transforms the rotor variables. Show that under the specified transformation Eqs. (10-20) and (10-21) reduce to Eqs. (8-3) and (8-5). This will show the formal equivalence between the machine theory in Chap. 10 and that in Chap. 8.

12

Graphical Analysis of Machine Performance

In the discussions in Chaps. 7 through 11, we were concerned in some measure with deducing the speed-torque characteristics of motor systems. This involved not only the electromagnetic-torque properties of the motor but also the features of the connected load. In these considerations the complete system was described in terms of J, the inertial properties; D, the viscous damping effects of the system; and T_L, the external load torque. These factors were assumed to be constant or of known integrable form. The resulting relation was a linear differential equation with constant coefficients. The solution for the speed-time response could, in principle at least, be found by analytic methods.

It is quite possible, in the case of practical elements or loads, that some of the characteristics are nonlinear functions. In such cases the general analytic techniques of linear equations cannot be used. However, a number of special techniques have been devised for handling nonlinear equations [1], and often solutions may be found by using such techniques. In many cases computers are used to assist in the solution of such problems.

If some of the machine or load characteristics are available only in graphical form, and often pertinent information is provided only in this way by the manufacturers of machines or machine elements, the problem may again be very complicated. One can try to find the representation of such graphical results in analytical form. Often the analytical representation may not be a simple one, and the attempted resulting solution by analytic means may not be possible.

Graphical methods have been developed which permit handling a wide variety of nonlinear problems. Often, in fact, these graphical techniques allow the solution of much more complicated problems than would be possible by analytic methods. With such techniques, the solutions may not be highly accurate, but often the solutions are adequate for engineering purposes. We shall discuss such methods below.

12-1. Acceleration Time. A problem of some importance in machine analysis would be that of finding the time required to effect a change in speed from ω_1 to ω_2 of a motor having a connected load which may be time-varying, and with elements having both nonlinear and dry friction. Such a problem would not be amenable to simple analytic solution. Several graphical methods exist for handling such problems. To develop the ideas of these, we shall begin with considerations of the simple case of a motor-load system which may be expressed analytically by the torque equation

$$T_e(\omega) = J\frac{d\omega}{dt} + T_L(\omega) \qquad (12\text{-}1)$$

It is assumed that the forms of the actual functions $T_e(\omega)$ and $T_L(\omega)$ are known.

Graphical Interpretation. The physical nature of Eq. (12-1) and the process of acceleration may be illustrated graphically, as shown in Fig. 12-1. In this figure the motor and the load-torque curves are superimposed, and equilibrium occurs at that speed for which the two torques are equal in magnitude. The equilibrium speed and torque are denoted as ω_0 and T_0. At any other speed the component torques are given by the intercepts, as illustrated. Observe that the acceleration at a given speed is proportional to the horizontal distance between the two torque curves. It is large at low speeds and decreases to zero at ω_0.

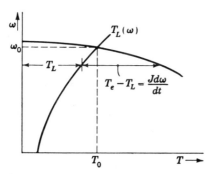

Fig. 12-1. Speed-torque curves for a motor load system.

Attention is called to the fact that $T_e(\omega)$, the electromagnetic torque, and also $T_L(\omega)$, the load torque, as used in Fig. 12-1, denote the steady-state characteristics. This means that these quantities are assumed to be operating in such a manner that the path of operation is along the curves shown. In the case of T_e this means that the transient changes must be slow enough so that the motor is in electrical equilibrium. Ordinarily this is true, since the electrical time constants are usually short compared with the mechanical time constant. For rapid accelerations for which this condition is not fulfilled, the transient process within the motor itself must be investigated.

If J is a constant and if the torque functions $T_e(\omega)$ and $T_L(\omega)$ are of integrable form, then the following expression is obtained from Eq. (12-1),

$$dt = J\frac{d\omega}{T_e(\omega) - T_L(\omega)}$$

from which, by integration,

$$t = J \int_{\omega_1}^{\omega_2} \frac{d\omega}{T_e(\omega) - T_L(\omega)} \tag{12-2}$$

This integral can, in principle at least, be evaluated.   If the speed-time curve is desired over the range from zero (the stopped state) to full operating speed, it would be necessary only to choose appropriate limits in the integration.   Correspondingly, if a curve is desired which illustrates the speed variation, the integral expression could be evaluated on an incremental basis to get successive adjacent values for the dependent variable.

Graphical Integration.   Even in those cases where the functions $T_e(\omega)$ and $T_L(\omega)$ are known and of integrable form, it is usually found more convenient to evaluate this integral graphically.   This may be done [2] by rewriting Eq. (12-2) in the form

$$t = \Sigma \, \Delta t$$

where

$$\Delta t = J \left(\frac{1}{T_e - T_L} \right)_{av} \Delta \omega \tag{12-3}$$

Here Δt is to be interpreted as the increment in time required to change the speed by the increment $\Delta \omega$.   The total time is simply the sum of these increments.   The process involved is illustrated graphically in Fig. 12-2, which is a plot of the speed-torque curve appropriate to Eq. (12-3).   Actually, the reciprocal of the accelerating torque is plotted as a function of speed, and the average value of this reciprocal is determined for each increment of speed. Note that the reciprocal of $T_e - T_L$ would become infinitely large as the speed approaches its equilibrium value, thereby leading to an infinite

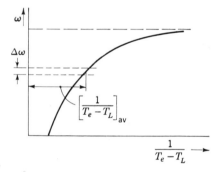

Fig.   12-2.   Graphical   integration using the speed-torque curves.

accelerating time.   To avoid this difficulty, the time would be found to reach, say, 90 or 95 per cent of the final value.

Linear Approximation.   If the torque curves of Fig. 12-1 can be approximated by straight lines, then we may write

$$T(\omega) - T_L(\omega) = k(\omega_0 - \omega) \tag{12-4}$$

The constant k has the value

$$k = \frac{T - T_L}{\Delta \omega} \tag{12-5}$$

which shows it to be the rate of change of accelerating torque with speed. In this case Eq. (12-1) may be written as

$$\frac{J}{k}\frac{d\omega}{dt} + \omega = \omega_0 \tag{12-6}$$

This is a linear equation and, in the form specified by Eq. (12-2), yields

$$t = \frac{J}{k}\int_{\omega_1}^{\omega_2}\frac{d\omega}{\omega_0 - \omega} = \frac{J}{k}\log\frac{\omega_0 - \omega_1}{\omega_0 - \omega_2} \tag{12-7}$$

The quantity J/k has the units of time; and t is the time required to accelerate the system from ω_1 to ω_2. As noted before, this time becomes infinite if ω_2 equals ω_0.

Stability. As discussed in connection with Fig. 12-1, ω_0 denotes the equilibrium speed at which the machine will operate. This does not require, of course, that ω_0 necessarily be a stable value, since the system may be such that any disturbance may cause a condition of instability. A complete discussion of the stability of the system will involve an examination of the roots of the controlling differential equation of the system. It is possible to gain considerable insight into the stability problem by examining the conditions for the system to be stable from a steady-state viewpoint. The results so obtained are useful but are not necessarily inviolate.

To examine this problem, it is supposed that the equilibrium values of torque and speed are denoted by T, T_L, and ω, and we examine the situation when these values are disturbed by amounts ΔT, ΔT_L, and $\Delta\omega$, respectively. For a small displacement from equilibrium, Eq. (12-1) becomes

$$J\frac{d\omega}{dt} + J\frac{d(\Delta\omega)}{dt} + T_L + \Delta T_L - T - \Delta T = 0 \tag{12-8}$$

Now subtract Eq. (12-1) from this expression to get

$$J\frac{d(\Delta\omega)}{dt} + \Delta T_L - \Delta T = 0 \tag{12-9}$$

It is now supposed that the deviations from the equilibrium values are small and that they may be expressed as linear functions of the change in speed, or that

$$\Delta T = \frac{\partial T}{\partial\omega}\bigg)_0 \Delta\omega \qquad \Delta T_L = \frac{\partial T_L}{\partial\omega}\bigg)_0 \Delta\omega$$

where $\partial T/\partial\omega\big)_0$ and $\partial T_L/\partial\omega\big)_0$ denote the slopes of the curves at the point of equilibrium. These expressions are combined with Eq. (12-9) to get

$$J\frac{d(\Delta\omega)}{dt} + \left[\frac{\partial T_L}{\partial\omega}\bigg)_0 - \frac{\partial T}{\partial\omega}\bigg)_0\right]\Delta\omega = 0 \tag{12-10}$$

This equation may be solved directly, the solution being

$$\Delta\omega = (\Delta\omega)_0 e^{-(1/J)[(\partial T_L/\partial\omega)_0 - \partial T/\partial\omega)_0]t} \tag{12-11}$$

In this expression $(\Delta\omega)_0$ is the initial value of the deviation in speed.

If the system is to be stable, it is necessary that the exponent in Eq. (12-11) be negative. This will ensure that the speed increment will vanish with time, so that the system will return to its equilibrium speed. But the exponent will always be negative if

$$\left.\frac{\partial T_L}{\partial\omega}\right)_0 - \left.\frac{\partial T}{\partial\omega}\right)_0 > 0 \tag{12-12}$$

This requires for stability that for a decrease in speed the motor torque must exceed the load torque; also for an increase in speed the motor torque must be less than the load torque. The general requirement for stability discussed above is illustrated in Fig. 12-3. The load torque marked T_{Ls} results in a stable operating point and that marked T_{Lu} results in an unstable situation.

Equation (12-12) as a stability criterion is useful, but it must be recognized as an approximation. If the steady-state speed-torque curves

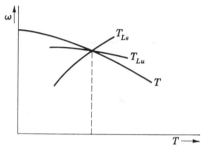

FIG. 12-3. Stability criterion applied to the speed-torque curves for motor and load.

are traversed when small disturbances cause departures from the operating point, the stability criterion is valid. However, the assumption that the system will so move is not always true.

12-2. Graphical Procedure.   A number of methods have been proposed for carrying out the detailed calculations indicated by Eq. (12-3). That proposed by Miró [3] is particularly convenient. To examine the Miró method, we alter the problem somewhat by assuming that the load is a pure inertial load, which may be written $J_L \, d\omega/dt$. Hence we consider the following equation for detailed study, rather than the equation given in Eq. (12-1),

$$T_e(\omega) = (J_L + J)\frac{d\omega}{dt} = J'\frac{d\omega}{dt} \tag{12-13}$$

where $J' = J_L + J$.   Now corresponding to Eq. (12-2) is the following equation:

$$t = J' \int_{\omega_1}^{\omega_2} \frac{d\omega}{T(\omega)} \tag{12-14}$$

Here, if J' is constant and if the torque function $T(\omega)$ is of integrable form, this expression can be evaluated. We are interested in those cases when the speed-torque curve of the motor is not described by an explicit function which makes $d\omega/T(\omega)$ easy to integrate. Often, in fact, the speed-torque curve may be given in graphical form rather than in analytic form. The procedure now is to evalue this integral graphically. This is done by writing

where
$$\left. \begin{aligned} t &= \Sigma\,\Delta t \\ \frac{\Delta t}{J'} &= \frac{\Delta\omega}{T(\omega)} \end{aligned} \right\} \qquad (12\text{-}15)$$

It is observed from Fig. 12-4 that the right-hand side of this equation is the tangent of the angle θ,

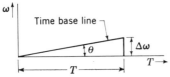

$$\tan\theta = \frac{\Delta\omega}{T(\omega)} \qquad (12\text{-}16)$$

Hence, for an arbitrarily selected value for Δt, the quantity

FIG. 12-4. Geometrical construction showing that an angle θ corresponds to a given Δt.

$$m \equiv \tan\theta = \frac{\Delta t}{J'} \qquad (12\text{-}17)$$

will be a constant, and there will be a one-to-one correspondence between the value of the angle θ and the chosen value of Δt.

Suppose that we have a motor which has a torque that is constant over a range of speeds, as illustrated in Fig. 12-5. It is assumed that the speed is ω_1 at the time t_1, and we are asked to find the motor speed at the instant $t_1 + t$, for a specified Δt. The specified Δt defines a *time base line* which has a slope specified by Eq. (12-17), as shown by the line drawn at the origin. If from ω_1 we now draw a line parallel to the time base line, and this line is referred to as a *time base parallel*, then the intersection of the time base parallel and the speed-torque curve determines the speed increment $\Delta\omega$ during the interval of time Δt. This construction thus indicates the value of

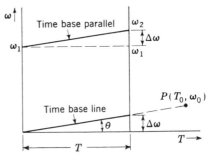

FIG. 12-5. Construction for finding the speed increment during the time interval Δt.

$\omega = \omega_2$ at the instant $t_1 + \Delta t$. This procedure can be continued to find the corresponding values of $\Delta\omega$ for successive values of Δt. Clearly, of course, if the angle θ is defined by the point $P(T_0,\omega_0)$, as illustrated, the interval of time Δt associated with this time base is

$$\Delta t = \frac{\omega_0 J'}{T_0} \qquad (12\text{-}18)$$

Example 12-2.1. A servomotor has the speed-torque curve shown in Fig. 12-2.1-1. The moment of inertia of the motor is given by $W_1R_1{}^2 = 1.2 \times 10^{-5}$ kg-m^2, and the inertial load is specified by $WR^2 = 3.2 \times 10^{-5}$ kg-m^2 and is directly coupled to the motor shaft. The motor is switched on at $t = 0$. What is the time response of the motor and coupled inertial load?

Solution. For convenience the value of Δt is chosen to be such that the time base line is defined by the origin and the point $P(0.25, 4\pi)$. Thus the value of Δt is

$$t = \frac{4\pi}{0.25} \frac{(1.2 + 3.2) \times 10^{-5}}{9.86} = 22.5 \times 10^{-5} \text{ sec}$$

The construction shown in Fig. 12-2.1-1 is now undertaken. Observe that after one

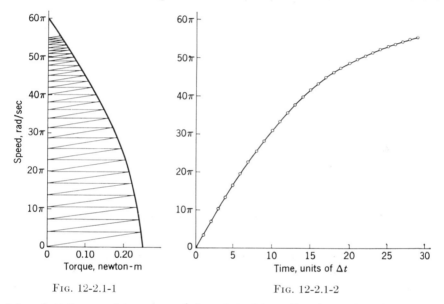

Fig. 12-2.1-1   Fig. 12-2.1-2

interval Δt the speed has changed from 0 to 3.9π radians/sec. After the second interval the speed has reached 7.1π. The successive speeds are illustrated by the points in Fig. 12-2.1-2, which is the required time-response characteristic.

Attention is called to the results obtained in Example 12-2.1 and to Eqs. (12-15), on which the development has been based. Equation (12-16) defines tan θ, but for a constant tan θ, the increments $\Delta\omega$ are constant only if $T(\omega)$ remains constant during the interval. Actually for all cases except that for which $T(\omega)$ is a constant, when the curve is parallel to the ω axis, the results are only approximate. The accuracy of the method can be increased either by decreasing the geometrical slope of the base line or by expanding the scale of the ω axis. The method can also be improved, not by considering $T(\omega)$, but by considering an average torque T_{av} in Eq. (12-15), so that

$$\frac{\Delta t}{J'} = \frac{\Delta\omega}{T_{av}} \qquad (12\text{-}19)$$

The question now arises as to how to define T_{av}. This may be done in several ways, but it appears that in all but very extreme cases of curvature the simple algebraic average of the end points is sufficient, with results within the accuracy of the plotted curves. In effect, therefore, the speed-torque curve is represented by a stepwise approximate curve composed of vertical steps, with the average T per step of the form

$$T_{av} = \frac{T_A + T_Q}{2} \tag{12-20}$$

The situation is illustrated in Fig. 12-6, which displays the two possible increments of speed, depending on the chosen values of T.

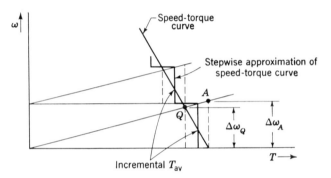

Fig. 12-6. To illustrate the ambiguity in $\Delta\omega$ when the speed-torque curve is not vertical.

12-3. Further Applications. Although the graphical method discussed above was based on Eq. (12-13), which assumed that the load was a pure inertial load, this load characteristic is not an inherent requirement in the construction procedures outlined. We wish now to consider the procedure to be followed when the load torque has other properties.

Suppose that a load torque $T_L(\omega)$ is present. This is the situation discussed in Sec. 12-1 and is illustrated in Fig. 12-1. The available torque for accelerating purposes is $T_e - T_L$, and the problem suggests making a plot of $T_e - T_L$ in terms of ω and then applying the graphical procedure given above. If the accuracy requirements are not too severe, a somewhat simpler procedure involving the individual curves for T_e and T_L may be employed. The two alternative approaches are given in Fig. 12-7.

Suppose that in addition to the external load torque $T_L(\omega)$, there exists both viscous damping and dry friction. In this case the controlling differential equation of the system would be written

$$T_e(\omega) = J\frac{d\omega}{dt} + T_L(\omega) + D\omega + T_\mu \tag{12-21}$$

In this equation $D\omega$ denotes the viscous damping, which is directly proportional to speed, and T_μ denotes the dry friction, which is a constant torque, independent of speed. Now the procedure calls for summing $T_L(\omega) + D\omega + T_\mu$ and using this as the equivalent T_L', which may be used precisely in the manner of Fig. 12-7. In fact, because of the nature of the procedure, the viscous friction need not be restricted to the simple

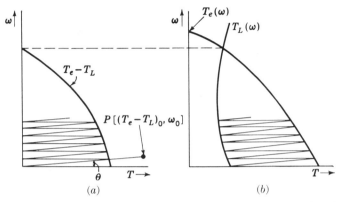

FIG. 12-7. Graphical determination of the time response of a motor for given motor torque and load torque. (a) By plotting the ω versus $T_e - T_L$ curve; (b) by using the ω versus T_e and the ω versus T_L curves.

linear speed-dependent form, nor need the dry-friction damping be a constant. It is necessary only that the form of the variations be known, either in analytical or in graphical form. One needs merely to find the appropriate T_L' and then employ the specified procedure.

If, in addition to the load torque, viscous friction, and dry friction, there is a time-varying inertial load, then the controlling differential equation now becomes

$$T_e(\omega) = [J + J_L(t)]\frac{d\omega}{dt}$$
$$+ T_L(\omega) + D\omega + T_\mu \quad (12\text{-}22)$$

The procedure in finding the motor response still proceeds as before, but now, because

$$\tan\theta = \frac{\Delta\omega}{T_e - T_L'} = \frac{\Delta t}{J + J_L(t)} \quad (12\text{-}23)$$

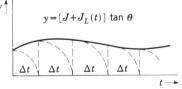

FIG. 12-8. The time increment Δt associated with an angle θ changes with time, if the moment of inertia is time-varying.

corresponding to a determined increment in speed $\Delta\omega$ at any time t, the value of the time-varying Δt must be found. This necessitates that, in addition to a construction of the type illustrated in Fig. 12-7, use must be made of a curve such as that of Fig. 12-8, which gives the value of Δt to be used as a function of time.

A further possible complication exists if $T_L(\omega)$ is also a function of time, so that now, to be precise, we should write $T_L(\omega,t)$. The situation is readily handled if the appropriate curves $T_L(\omega,t_0), T_L(\omega,t_1), T_L(\omega,t_2), \ldots$ at the times $t_0, t_1, t_2, \ldots$ are known, as in Fig. 12-9. Now the construction proceeds as in Fig. 12-7, except that the proper T_L curve must be used at each instant of time. That is, once Δt has been chosen, and therefore the time base slope has been established, a step-by-step procedure of the usual type is undertaken. Thus, at the instant t_0, the resultant torque for acceleration purposes is $T_e(0) - T_L(0)$, and after

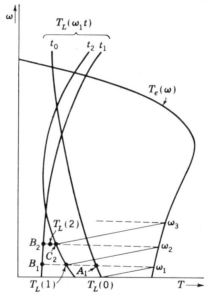

FIG. 12-9. The geometrical construction for the case of a time-varying torque load.

the time interval Δt the speed will be ω_1. For the next step, the torque for acceleration is $T_e(\omega_1) - T_L(1)$, where $T_L(1)$ is the torque that has been obtained by interpolation between the curves for T_L at times t_1 and t_2, respectively, and the torques are denoted A_1 and B_1 in the figure. That is,

$$\text{dis } [T_L(1)A_1] = \frac{\text{dis } [B_1A_1]}{t_1 - t_0} \Delta t$$

where dis $[T_L(1)A_1]$ denotes the distance from points $T_L(1)$ to A_1, with a similar interpretation for the term dis $[B_1A_1]$.

Example 12-3.1. A three-point automatic starter is used to start a motor with its connected load. Upon start, resistors $R_1 + R_2 + R_3$ are inserted in the motor armature line. When the machine has reached a speed ω_1, R_1 is automatically removed from the line. Then in a prescribed time sequence R_2 and later R_3 are removed, when the motor is connected directly to the lines. Let this timing sequence be 0.5 and 1.0 sec after speed ω_1 has been reached.   Determine the motor time response and also the maximum available accelerating torque.

Solution.   Draw the curves of the motor torque with the different values of series resistance, and the load torque, on a single sheet.   Choose a reasonable time base slope.   A convenient value would be $\Delta t = 0.1$ sec.   Carry out the graphical construction for time response starting at 0 until $\omega = \omega_1$.   Switching now occurs, with action for five intervals Δt, until the total time 0.5 sec is reached, as illustrated.   The

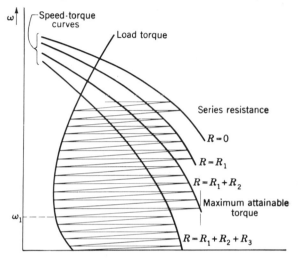

FIG. 12-3.1-1

construction is repeated for the next 0.5 sec, when the next switching operation occurs, and when the appropriate change in the construction must be made.   The results are given in the figure.

REFERENCES

1. Cunningham, W. J.: "Introduction to Nonlinear Analysis," McGraw-Hill Book Company, Inc., New York, 1958.
   Andronow, A. A., and C. E. Chaikin: "Theory & Oscillations," Princeton University Press, Princeton, N.J., 1949.
   Minorsky, N.: "Introduction to Nonlinear Mechanics," J. W. Edwards, Publisher, Inc., Ann Arbor, Mich., 1947.
   Stoker, J. J.: "Nonlinear Vibrations," Interscience Publishers, Inc., New York, 1950.
2. Jones, R. W.: "Electric Control Systems," 3d ed., John Wiley & Sons, Inc., New York, 1953.
3. Miró, J.: *Trans. AIEE (Application and Industry)*, no. 52, pp. 542–546, January, 1961.

PROBLEMS

12-1. A d-c shunt motor is to accelerate a large flywheel to a speed of 5 rps.   The combined inertia of the motor armature and flywheel is 7.5×10^5 kg-m².   A motor drive is provided which maintains the armature and field currents constant so that the motor accelerates with constant torque at a value corresponding to 150 hp at 5 rps.

(a) How long does it take to accelerate the flywheel?

(b) Suppose that upon the removal of the power the system is to be stopped from its full speed at a uniform rate in 5 sec. How much braking torque at the motor shaft would be required?

12-2. A motor has a synchronous speed of 20 rps, and its rotational inertia is 5 kg-m^2. The developed torque-slip curve of the motor T_e and the torque-slip required by the load and friction and windage T_L are shown in the accompanying figure. Determine the speed-time curve.

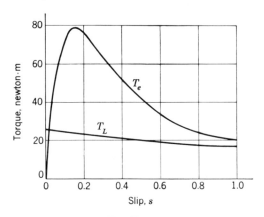

Fig. P12-2

12-3. The approximate speed-torque characteristic of a 30-hp four-pole 60-cps induction motor under balanced excitation is given by the tabulation:

Speed, p.u............	1.00	0.95	0.50	0
Torque, p.u...........	0	3.00	1.50	1.50

Unit speed is synchronous speed; unit torque is rated torque. The total inertia of the motor and load is 50 kg-m^2.

(a) What is the motor speed when operating at rated power?

(b) The motor is driving a constant-torque load of 950 newton-m when the circuit breaker opens and the motor speed begins to fall. The breaker recloses shortly thereafter. How long can the breaker remain open for the machine to regain its previous speed?

12-4. A class D high-starting-torque high-slip induction motor has the following characteristics under balanced excitation:

Speed, p.u.......	1.00	0.94	0.85	0.66	0.40	0.20	0
Torque, p.u.....	0	1.00	2.00	3.00	3.30	3.20	3.00

The motor is coupled to a device that requires rated torque, independent of speed. The inertia of motor plus load is such that it requires 1.2 sec to bring them to rated speed with constant accelerating torque equal to rated torque.

The motor is driving the load under normal steady conditions when the potential suddenly drops to 50 per cent of its rated value. It remains at this reduced potential for 0.6 sec, when full voltage is again applied. Will the motor stop? If not, what is its lowest speed? How long will be required for the motor to resume full speed?

12-5. The speed-torque curve of a 5-hp four-pole 60-cps polyphase induction motor is given in the tabulation:

Speed, p.u........	1.00	0.97	0.93	0.88	0.83	0.78	0.60	0.30	0
Torque, p.u.......	0	1.00	2.00	2.70	3.00	3.10	2.90	2.55	2.20

(a) Use the method of Sec. 12-1 to find the acceleration time of the machine for a total inertia of 45 kg-m², using the specified curve.

(b) Repeat the calculations, using a piecewise linear approximation to the speed-torque curve.

(c) Repeat (a), using the Miró method.

Appendix A

Matrices

The physical systems that are under survey in this book are of the broad general class which often is called "linear systems." A mathematical tool that is particularly well suited to the study of such linear systems is linear algebra, certain aspects of the theory of matrices being very well adapted to the analyses under consideration. It is the purpose of this appendix to present an introductory account of matrices and matrix algebra that will be suitable to our needs.

A-1. Matrices. In the limited use of matrix methods for our subsequent needs, it is convenient to consider the matrix technique as a kind of shorthand that enables us to write the algebraic or the differential equations involving systems of simultaneous equations in a very compact and convenient form. In fact, because of the compactness and the systematization that are inherent in its form, the significance of certain operations is often more easily visualized than might otherwise be possible. Ordinarily matrix methods provide no short cuts when numerical calculations are to be made, but they do provide a very useful tool for facilitating analytical manipulations.

Consider the following set of linear algebraic equations:

$$
\begin{aligned}
a_{11}x_1 + a_{12}x_2 + \cdots + a_{1n}x_n &= y_1 \\
a_{21}x_1 + a_{22}x_2 + \cdots + a_{2n}x_n &= y_2 \\
\cdots\cdots\cdots\cdots\cdots\cdots\cdots\cdots\cdots\cdots \\
a_{m1}x_1 + a_{m2}x_2 + \cdots + a_{mn}x_n &= y_m
\end{aligned}
\tag{A-1}
$$

This set of equations is written in the following matrix form:

$$
\begin{bmatrix}
a_{11} & a_{12} & a_{13} & \cdots & a_{1n} \\
a_{21} & a_{22} & & \cdots & a_{2n} \\
\cdots & \cdots & \cdots & \cdots & \cdots \\
a_{m1} & a_{m2} & & \cdots & a_{mn}
\end{bmatrix}
\begin{bmatrix}
x_1 \\
x_2 \\
\cdots \\
x_n
\end{bmatrix}
=
\begin{bmatrix}
y_1 \\
y_2 \\
\cdots \\
y_m
\end{bmatrix}
\tag{A-2}
$$

It is written more simply as

$$
[A][X] = [Y]
\tag{A-3}
$$

where $[A]$, $[X]$, and $[Y]$ are the matrices

$$
[A] =
\begin{bmatrix}
a_{11} & a_{12} & \cdots & a_{1n} \\
\cdots & \cdots & \cdots & \cdots \\
a_{m1} & \cdots & \cdots & a_{mn}
\end{bmatrix}
\qquad
[X] =
\begin{bmatrix}
x_1 \\
x_2 \\
\cdots \\
x_n
\end{bmatrix}
\qquad
[Y] =
\begin{bmatrix}
y_1 \\
y_2 \\
\cdots \\
y_m
\end{bmatrix}
\tag{A-4}
$$

Attention is called to the fact that these matrices are just arrays of coefficients. Consider matrix $[A]$ specifically, and note that the coefficients a_{ij} are just the coefficients in the same order relative to their positions in rows and columns as they appear in the defining equations (A-2). This is, the element a_{ij} belongs to the ith row and jth

319

column. Observe that, since a matrix is merely the ensemble of elements, no numerical value is associated with the array (this is to be contrasted with a determinant, which is a rational function of its elements and possesses a definite numerical value for given values of the elements).

Matrices may be square; i.e., they may contain as many rows as columns. The column matrices above are examples of nonsquare matrices. More will be said about the important types of matrices in what follows.

A-2. Definitions. It is convenient to define matrices according to the character of the array, the elements of the array, or some other special properties of the array. Some of the important types are defined below.

Order of a Matrix. A matrix with m rows and n columns is said to be of order $m \times n$.

Square Matrix. A matrix of order $m \times m$,

$$\begin{bmatrix} a_{11} & \cdots & \cdots & a_{1m} \\ \cdots & \cdots & \cdots & \cdots \\ a_{m1} & \cdots & \cdots & a_{mm} \end{bmatrix}$$

Column Matrix. A matrix containing only one column. The order is $m \times 1$.

$$\begin{bmatrix} a_{11} \\ \cdot \\ \cdot \\ \cdot \\ a_{m1} \end{bmatrix}$$

Row Matrix. A matrix containing only one row. The order is $1 \times n$.

$$[a_{11} \quad \cdots \quad \cdots \quad a_{1n}]$$

Based on the properties of the elements, the following definitions are clear:

Real Matrix. A matrix all elements of which are real.

Complex Matrix. A matrix some of whose elements are complex.

Zero, or Null, Matrix. A matrix all of whose elements are zero.

Diagonal Matrix. A square matrix all of whose elements are zero except those along the main diagonal,

$$[A] = \begin{bmatrix} a_{11} & 0 & \cdots & 0 & 0 \\ 0 & a_{22} & \cdots & 0 & 0 \\ \cdots & \cdots & \cdots & \cdots & \cdots \\ 0 & 0 & \cdots & 0 & a_{nn} \end{bmatrix}$$

Scalar Matrix. A diagonal matrix whose diagonal elements are all equal,

$$[k] = \begin{bmatrix} k & 0 & \cdots & 0 & 0 \\ 0 & k & \cdots & 0 & 0 \\ \cdots & \cdots & \cdots & \cdots & \cdots \\ 0 & 0 & \cdots & 0 & k \end{bmatrix}$$

Unit Matrix. A scalar matrix whose diagonal terms are unity,

$$[U] = \begin{bmatrix} 1 & 0 & \cdots & 0 & 0 \\ 0 & 1 & \cdots & 0 & 0 \\ \cdots & \cdots & \cdots & \cdots & \cdots \\ 0 & 0 & \cdots & 0 & 1 \end{bmatrix}$$

Transposed Matrix. The transpose of a matrix $[A]$ is a new matrix $[A]_t$, the rows of $[A]$ being the columns of $[A]_t$ (that is, rows and columns are interchanged). Thus, since $[A] = [a_{ij}]$, then $[A]_t = [a_{ji}]$. As an example,

$$[A] = \begin{bmatrix} a_{11} & a_{12} \\ a_{21} & a_{22} \\ a_{31} & a_{32} \end{bmatrix} \qquad [A]_t = \begin{bmatrix} a_{11} & a_{21} & a_{31} \\ a_{12} & a_{22} & a_{32} \end{bmatrix}$$

Symmetrical Matrix. A matrix which remains unaltered in a transposition, whence $[A] = [A]_t$. An example is

$$\begin{bmatrix} 1 & a & a^2 \\ a & a^2 & 1 \\ a^2 & 1 & a \end{bmatrix}$$

Skew-symmetrical Matrix. A matrix which changes sign in a transposition but is otherwise unchanged, so that $[a_{ji}] = [-a_{ij}]$. An example follows:

$$\begin{bmatrix} 0 & a & b \\ -a & 0 & c \\ -b & -c & 0 \end{bmatrix}$$

In a skew-symmetrical matrix, the diagonal elements are necessarily zero. Moreover, symmetrical and skew-symmetrical matrices are necessarily square.

Complex Conjugate of a Matrix. To form the complex conjugate of a matrix, each element of $[A^*]$ must be the complex conjugate of the corresponding element of $[A]$. An example follows:

$$[A] = \begin{bmatrix} a_1 + ja_2 & b_1 + jb_2 \\ c_1 + jc_2 & d_1 + jd_2 \end{bmatrix} \qquad [A^*] = \begin{bmatrix} a_1 - ja_2 & b_1 - jb_2 \\ c_1 - jc_2 & d_1 - jd_2 \end{bmatrix}$$

Hermitian Matrix. A complex matrix which satisfies the condition $[A] = [A^*]_t$, or correspondingly $[a_{ji}] = [a_{ij}^*]$. An example follows:

$$\begin{bmatrix} 1 & 2 + j3 & 1 - j6 \\ 2 - j3 & 3 & 0 \\ 1 + j6 & 0 & 5 \end{bmatrix}$$

Attention is called to the fact that in the last two cases it has been necessary to use the properties of "equality of matrices." By definition: Two matrices are equal if and only if *all* their corresponding elements are equal. This definition requires, as a necessary condition, that for the equality of two matrices both must have the same number of rows and the same number of columns.

A-3. Matrix Algebra. Some of the more important algebraic operations involving matrices are now to be examined.

1. Addition of matrices. Let $[A]$ and $[B]$ be two matrices of the same order, $m \times n$. The matrix sum $[A] + [B]$ is defined by the relation

$$[A + B]_{ij} = [A_{ij}] + [B_{ij}] \qquad i = 1, \ldots, m; j = 1, \ldots, n \qquad \text{(A-5)}$$

That is, the corresponding elements are added. Observe that, when $[A]$ and $[B]$ are not of the same order, $[A] + [B]$ is not defined.

2. Subtraction of matrices. If $[A]$ and $[B]$ are two matrices of the same order, then there exists a unique matrix $[X]$ of the same order as $[A]$ and $[B]$, such that $[A] + [X] = [B]$, or $[X] = [B] - [A]$, from which

$$[B - A]_{ij} = [B_{ij}] - [A_{ij}] \qquad \text{(A-6)}$$

3. Matrix multiplication. By definition, the product of an $m \times n$ matrix $[A]$ by a scalar matrix $[r]$ is a new matrix, every element of which is r times that of the original

matrix. Thus, if

$$[A] = [A_{ij}] \qquad \text{then} \qquad [r][A] = [rA_{ij}]$$

The order of the matrix r must be such as to make the designated multiplication possible. Evidently, it follows that

$$[r][A] = [A][r] \tag{A-7}$$

Now consider the product of two matrices $[A]$ and $[B]$, where $[A]$ is a matrix of order $m \times n$ and $[B]$ is a matrix of order $n \times p$. The result, which is a natural extension of the results indicated in Eqs. (A-1) and (A-2), is expressed by the product matrix $[C]$, given by

$$[C] = [A][B]$$

the general term of the product matrix $[C]$ being given by

$$c_{ij} = \sum_{k=1}^{n} a_{ik}b_{kj} \qquad i = 1, \ldots, m; j = 1, \ldots, p \tag{A-8}$$

As an example, consider the product of the matrices indicated,

$$\begin{bmatrix} a_{11} & a_{12} & a_{13} \\ a_{21} & a_{22} & a_{23} \\ a_{31} & a_{32} & a_{33} \end{bmatrix} \begin{bmatrix} b_{11} & b_{12} \\ b_{21} & b_{22} \\ b_{31} & b_{32} \end{bmatrix} = \begin{bmatrix} a_{11}b_{11} + a_{12}b_{21} + a_{13}b_{31} \\ a_{21}b_{11} + a_{22}b_{21} + a_{23}b_{31} \\ a_{31}b_{11} + a_{32}b_{21} + a_{33}b_{31} \end{bmatrix} \begin{bmatrix} a_{11}b_{12} + a_{12}b_{22} + a_{13}b_{32} \\ a_{21}b_{12} + a_{22}b_{22} + a_{23}b_{32} \\ a_{31}b_{12} + a_{32}b_{22} + a_{33}b_{32} \end{bmatrix}$$

Attention is called to the requirement that the number of rows of matrix $[A]$ must equal the number of columns of matrix $[B]$; otherwise the product is not defined. When the product $[AB]$ is defined, the matrices are said to be *conformable*. Also, in the product $[AB]$, $[A]$ is said to premultiply $[B]$, or, conversely, $[B]$ is said to postmultiply $[A]$.

Note that in general $[AB] \neq [BA]$. In the above example $[AB]$ is defined, whereas $[BA]$ is not defined. Two matrices which satisfy the relation

$$[AB] = [BA] \tag{A-9}$$

are said to be commuting matrices.

When matrices have a large number of rows and columns, it may be desirable to *partition* them into smaller sections, called submatrices. To understand the process of partitioning, consider the matrix product shown,

$$\begin{bmatrix} b_{11} & b_{12} \\ b_{21} & b_{22} \\ \hline b_{31} & b_{32} \end{bmatrix} \begin{bmatrix} a_{11} & a_{12} & a_{13} & a_{14} \\ a_{21} & a_{22} & a_{23} & a_{24} \end{bmatrix}$$

$$= \begin{bmatrix} b_{11}a_{11} + b_{12}a_{21} & b_{11}a_{12} + b_{12}a_{22} & b_{11}a_{13} + b_{12}a_{23} & b_{11}a_{14} + b_{12}a_{24} \\ b_{21}a_{11} + b_{22}a_{21} & b_{21}a_{12} + b_{22}a_{22} & b_{21}a_{13} + b_{22}a_{23} & b_{21}a_{14} + b_{22}a_{24} \\ \hline b_{31}a_{11} + b_{32}a_{21} & b_{31}a_{12} + b_{32}a_{22} & b_{31}a_{13} + b_{32}a_{23} & b_{31}a_{14} + b_{32}a_{24} \end{bmatrix}$$

Suppose now that the matrix $[B]$ is partitioned into two parts, in accordance with the dashed line; also matrix $[A]$ is partitioned into three parts, as shown. The resulting situation is written in the form

$$\begin{bmatrix} B_1 \\ B_2 \end{bmatrix} [A_1 \mid A_2 \mid A_3] = \begin{bmatrix} B_1A_1 & B_1A_2 & B_1A_3 \\ B_2A_1 & B_2A_2 & B_2A_3 \end{bmatrix}$$

Observe therefore that the product $[BA]$ may be evaluated as though the submatrices were ordinary matrix elements. In order to effect the partitioning, it is necessary, of course, that the submatrices be conformable; that is, $[B_1]$ must be conformable with $[A_1]$, $[A_2]$, and $[A_3]$. The same requirement is imposed on $[B_2]$.

It is now desired to examine what is meant by the "inverse" of a matrix. This is conveniently done by referring again to the set of linear algebraic equations of Eqs. (A-1). These equations express the x's in terms of the y's. Since these are algebraic equations, they may be solved to yield the y's in terms of the x's. The results will be of the form

$$b_{11}y_1 + b_{12}y_2 + \cdots + b_{1n}y_n = x_1$$
$$\cdots\cdots\cdots\cdots\cdots\cdots\cdots\cdots\cdots\cdots \tag{A-10}$$
$$b_{n1}y_1 + b_{n2}y_2 + \cdots + b_{nn}y_n = x_n$$

where
$$b_{ij} = \frac{\Delta_{ji}}{\Delta}$$

with Δ_{ji} denoting the cofactor of the element a_{ji} in the determinant Δ. Equations (A-10) may be written in matrix form as

$$[B][Y] = [X]$$

If the matrix $[B]$ exists, it is called the "inverse of matrix $[A]$" and it is ordinarily written in the form

$$[B] = [A^{-1}]$$

To examine the situation further, it is noted that

$$[B][Y] = [A^{-1}][Y] = [A^{-1}][A][X]$$

This requires that

$$[A^{-1}A] = [U]$$

Similarly, by proceeding from Eq. (A-3),

$$[AX] = [A][A^{-1}Y] = [AA^{-1}][Y] = [Y]$$

It follows from these expressions that

$$[AA^{-1}] = [A^{-1}A] = [U] \tag{A-11}$$

It follows from the foregoing that the inverse of a matrix exists if the matrix is square and its determinant is not zero. Such a matrix is called a nonsingular matrix; thus only a nonsingular matrix will possess an inverse.

The foregoing discussion permits an explicit form to be written for the inverse matrix. Consider the square nonsingular matrix $[A]$ and the corresponding cofactor matrix $[\Delta_{ij}]$. Each element of $[\Delta_{ij}]$ is obtained by computing the cofactor corresponding to the element A_{ij} of the determinant $|A|$. This requires that in the determinant the ith row and the jth column be deleted and the value of the resulting determinant be computed. This value, when multiplied by the factor $(-1)^{i+j}$ to yield the appropriate sign for each term, gives one term of the inverse matrix. The complete result is seen to be

$$[A^{-1}] = \frac{1}{|A|}[\Delta_{ij}]_t \tag{A-12}$$

To find the inverse of the product of two matrices $[A]$ and $[B]$, each of which is nonsingular, it is noted first that

$$[AB][AB]^{-1} = [U]$$

Now consider the expression

$$[AB][B^{-1}A^{-1}] = [A][BB^{-1}][A^{-1}] = [AA^{-1}] = [U]$$

Thus it is seen that

$$[AB]^{-1} = [B^{-1}A^{-1}] \tag{A-13}$$

This shows that the inverse of the product of two matrices is the product of the inverse matrices in reverse order.

A somewhat similar form exists for the transpose of the product of two matrices. Consider the two conformable matrices $[A]$ and $[B]$. The term in the ith row and jth column of the transpose of their product is

$$[(AB)_{ij}]_t = [AB]_{ji} = \sum_k A_{jk}B_{ki}$$

which is now written

$$[(AB)_{ij}]_t = [AB]_{ji} = \sum_k B_{ik_t}A_{kj_t}$$

$$= [B_tA_t]_{ij}$$

Thus it is seen that

$$[AB]_t = [B_tA_t] \tag{A-14}$$

This shows that the transpose of the product of two matrices is the product of the transposed matrices in reverse order.

A-4. Orthogonal Matrices. We wish to examine the properties of *orthogonal* matrices, since these prove to be of particular interest in our work. A matrix $[A]$ is an orthogonal matrix if it is real, nonsingular, and such that

$$[A_tA] = [U] \tag{A-15}$$

It follows therefore that for orthogonal matrices

$$[A_t] = [A^{-1}] \tag{A-16}$$

Because of these conditions, the following three basic properties apply for orthogonal matrices:

1. A unit matrix is an orthogonal matrix.
2. The inverse of an orthogonal matrix is also an orthogonal matrix.
3. The product of two orthogonal matrices of the same order is also an orthogonal matrix. This requires that

$$[AB]_t[AB] = [U] \qquad \text{if } [B_tB] = [A_tA] = [U]$$

This is valid because

$$[AB]_t[AB] = [B_tA_t][AB] = [B_tA_tAB] = [U]$$

A problem of considerable interest in our work is to find transformations $[S]$ such that, if a so-called canonic transformation is applied to a given symmetric matrix $[A]$, the resultant matrix remains symmetric. In this case for a given symmetric matrix $[A]$, it is required to find $[S]$ such that $[B] = [S^{-1}AS]$ remains symmetric. Transformations of this type arise in the symmetrical-component transformations which are of importance in the analysis of rotating machinery and in power-system analysis. Other transformations having these general properties are also introduced in our studies. The general properties of $[S]$ may be deduced by forming

$$[B_t] = [S^{-1}AS]_t = [S_tA_tS_t^{-1}] = [S_tA_tS_t^{-1}]$$

But in order that $[S_tAS_t^{-1}]$ may be equal to $[B]$, it is required that $[S^t] = [S^{-1}]$, which requires that $[S]$ be an orthogonal matrix.

A transformation that is of importance in our study of rotating machinery is the so-called *a-b d-q* transformation, which is introduced in Chap. 8. This transformation and its inverse are given,

$$[S] = \begin{bmatrix} \cos\varphi & \sin\varphi \\ -\sin\varphi & \cos\varphi \end{bmatrix} \qquad [S^{-1}] = \begin{bmatrix} \cos\varphi & -\sin\varphi \\ \sin\varphi & \cos\varphi \end{bmatrix}$$

Note that this satisfies condition (A-16) and hence is an orthogonal matrix.

Appendix B
Maxwell's Equations

Many of the problems to be discussed in this book are formulated in terms of the electric and magnetic fields which have been generated in certain specified regions of space. The starting point for this work is the Maxwell equations, which describe the sources and the field vectors in the broad fields of electrostatics, magnetostatics, and electromagnetic induction. It is with these equations that the interesting and important phenomena of electromagnetic wave motion and radiation are discussed. Likewise some of the results will be used in the analysis of such classical devices as transformers and rotating machinery.

B-1. The Maxwell Equations. The Maxwell equations contain a complete description of static and dynamic electric and magnetic fields when the dielectric mediums or the magnetic mediums are at rest. These equations supply us with a statement of the space and time variations of $\mathbf{E}$ and $\mathbf{H}$ at all points in the electromagnetic field. Consequently, if a set of initial values of $\mathbf{E}$ and $\mathbf{H}$ at all points in the electromagnetic field are given, their values at all future times may be found. Also, if values of $\mathbf{E}$ and $\mathbf{H}$ are specified as a function of time over any surface (for example, the surface of a radio antenna or the surface of a transformer core), it is possible to find their values at all other points in the field.

The Maxwell equations are the following set of four differential equations, which express point statements concerning the field quantities. These equations contain a description of all ordinary electromagnetic-field phenomena. The names of those scientists who developed the basic equations in the set are also included.

$$\nabla \cdot D = \rho \qquad \text{Gauss} \qquad \text{(B-1}a\text{)}$$
$$\nabla \cdot B = 0 \qquad \qquad \text{(B-1}b\text{)}$$
$$\nabla \times \mathbf{H} = \mathbf{J}_c + \frac{\partial D}{\partial t} \qquad \text{Ampère, Maxwell} \qquad \text{(B-1}c\text{)}$$
$$\nabla \times \mathbf{E} = -\frac{\partial \mathbf{B}}{\partial t} \qquad \text{Faraday} \qquad \text{(B-1}d\text{)}$$

To these are often added several auxiliary equations, including

$$\nabla \cdot \mathbf{J}_c + \frac{\partial \rho}{\partial t} = 0 \qquad \text{continuity equation} \qquad \text{(B-2)}$$

$$\mathbf{D} = \epsilon\mathbf{E} \qquad \mathbf{B} = \mu\mathbf{H} \qquad \mathbf{J} = \gamma\mathbf{E} \qquad \text{constitutive equations} \qquad \text{(B-3)}$$

These equations specify relations which are valid at each point in space.

A feature of Ampère's law [Eq. (B-1c)] that is worthy of special mention follows from the incompleteness of the magnetic-circuit law for the time-varying case. This, in fact, was one of the important contributions of Maxwell. The initial problem is made evident by reference to Fig. B-1, which represents a portion of a circuit containing a capacitor in which a current is assumed to flow. To evaluate Ampère's circuital law, $\oint \mathbf{H} \cdot d\mathbf{l}$, requires that the line integral taken around the contour of any circuit L is to be related to the total current through a cap with the contour as its

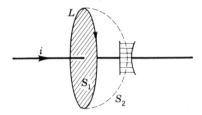

FIG. B-1. To demonstrate the incompleteness of Ampère's law.

edge. For the cap specified by the surface S_1 the total current is i, and in this case, if the law is correct,

$$\oint_L \mathbf{H} \cdot d\mathbf{l} = i$$

Now consider the cap specified by the surface S_2, which is so chosen that it passes between the plates of the capacitor. Clearly, in this case, a perfect dielectric being assumed, no conduction current passes through the surface S_2, and it appears that

$$\oint_L \mathbf{H} \cdot d\mathbf{l} = 0$$

unless the circuital law itself undergoes some change when it goes from the static case to the time-varying case. This is contrary to reason, since if a unique solution exists it cannot possibly be a function of the choice of the cap with L as perimeter. The introduction of the postulate of the displacement current by Maxwell avoided this inconsistency and permitted the generalization of the Ampère law to the form

$$\nabla \times \mathbf{H} = \mathbf{J}_c + \frac{\partial \mathbf{D}}{\partial t} \tag{B-4}$$

As known from our past studies, for each of the equations in Eqs. (B-1) which specifies derivatives of the field quantities at a point in space, there is a corresponding statement which applies for a finite region of space. Although the point statement was obtained from considerations of the integral statement, it is not inconsistent to state that the integral statement may be obtained from the point statement. This is done by performing an integration over a surface or a volume and then transforming the integrals by an application of the divergence theorem or Stokes's theorem, as pertinent. The integral forms corresponding to the differential equations in Eqs. (B-1) as modified by Eq. (B-4) are the following:

$$\oiint \mathbf{D} \cdot \mathbf{n} \, dA = \int_\tau \rho \, d\tau$$

$$\oiint \mathbf{B} \cdot \mathbf{n} \, dA = 0$$

$$\oint \mathbf{H} \cdot d\mathbf{l} = \int_A \left(\mathbf{J}_c + \frac{\partial \mathbf{D}}{\partial t} \right) \cdot \mathbf{n} \, dA$$

$$\oint \mathbf{E} \cdot d\mathbf{l} = - \int_A \frac{\partial \mathbf{B}}{\partial t} \cdot \mathbf{n} \, dA$$

$$\tag{B-5}$$

Before extending the Maxwell equations to the general problems of electromagnetic waves, some comments concerning the several equations of Eqs. (B-1) are in order. Consider the third equation of the group, which expresses Ampère's law in the extended form given in Eq. (B-4), containing the displacement current as well as the conduction current densities. The divergence of this expression is examined. This is

$$\nabla \cdot (\nabla \times \mathbf{H}) = \nabla \cdot \mathbf{J}_c + \nabla \cdot \left(\frac{\partial \mathbf{D}}{\partial t}\right)$$

But as may be readily shown by performing the indicated operations, div (curl $\mathbf{A}$) $\equiv 0$ for any vector; then

$$\nabla \cdot \left(\frac{\partial \mathbf{D}}{\partial t}\right) + \nabla \cdot \mathbf{J}_c = 0 \tag{B-6}$$

By combining this expression with the continuity equation [Eq. (B-2)] there results

$$\nabla \cdot \left(\frac{\partial \mathbf{D}}{\partial t}\right) - \frac{\partial \rho}{\partial t} = 0$$

An interchange of the order of partial differentiation yields the expression

$$\frac{\partial}{\partial t} (\nabla \cdot \mathbf{D} - \rho) = 0$$

which is always satisfied if, in general,

$$\nabla \cdot \mathbf{D} = \rho \tag{B-7}$$

This expression is known to hold for static fields. It now appears as a general expression, as implied by Eqs. (B-1c) and (B-2), although Eq. (B-6) merely requires that the quantity $\nabla \cdot \mathbf{D} - \rho$ be independent of time and, in general, a constant. However, a situation is possible in which both ρ and $\nabla \cdot \mathbf{D}$ are zero in a region of space so that $\nabla \cdot D - \rho = 0$ in the region. Equation (B-6) then specifies that this relationship must be independent of time, when Eq. (B-7) follows.

There is no direct proof that the Maxwell generalization of Ampère's law is valid, but there is very convincing indirect proof of its validity. In fact, it is only through the existence of the displacement current that Maxwell showed there should be electromagnetic fields capable of being propagated through space as waves. The velocity and other characteristics of the waves were predictable from the field equations. Subsequently Hertz in the 1890s showed the experimental existence of electromagnetic waves which possessed all the properties predicted by Maxwell. It is now known, of course, that radio and light waves are Maxwell electromagnetic waves.

Another interesting feature of the postulate of displacement current is the symmetry that is added to the laws of electromagnetism. The generalized Ampère law indicates that an electric displacement current (a time-changing electric field) produces a magnetic field. Correspondingly, Faraday's law [Eq. (B-1d)] specifies that a time-changing magnetic field produces an electric field. In fact, by comparing Eqs. (B-1c) and (B-1d), it is clear that $-\partial \mathbf{B}/\partial t$ behaves like a magnetic-displacement current density. However, magnetic conduction currents do not exist in nature because there are no free magnetic poles.

It is of some interest to consider finally Faraday's law, specified in Eq. (B-1d). Proceeding as above, by taking the divergence of both sides of this equation and noting again that div (curl $\mathbf{A}$) $\equiv 0$ for any vector, then it is required that

$$\nabla \cdot (\nabla \times \mathbf{E}) = -\nabla \cdot \left(\frac{\partial \mathbf{B}}{\partial t}\right) \equiv 0$$

The order of the partial derivative is changed without affecting the results and yields

$$\frac{\partial}{\partial t}(\nabla \cdot \mathbf{B}) = 0 \qquad \text{(B-8)}$$

This expression states that the quantity $\nabla \cdot \mathbf{B}$ is a constant, in general, independent of time. But the $\mathbf{B}$ function may actually be a function of time. Moreover, a non-zero value of the divergence of $\mathbf{B}$ has never been found in nature, and it is postulated therefore that the constant is zero. Equation (B-8) requires that $\nabla \cdot \mathbf{B}$ remain zero and, in fact, that it has always been zero. The deduction made from Eq. (B-8) is that everywhere and always

$$\nabla \cdot \mathbf{B} = 0 \qquad \text{(B-9)}$$

From the present viewpoint, if Eq. (B-1d) is postulated, then Eq. (B-1b) follows as a deduction. However, Eq. (B-1b) is so important that it is usually listed as one of the Maxwell equations.

B-2. Poynting's Vector. It is known from our prior work in electric and magnetic fields (see the discussion in Chap. 2) that the energy associated with a given configuration of charge can be expressed in two forms, one involving the field vectors and the other involving capacitance, namely,

$$W_e = \tfrac{1}{2} \int_{\text{space}} \mathbf{E} \cdot \mathbf{D} \, d\tau = \tfrac{1}{2}CV^2 \qquad \text{joules} \qquad \text{(B-10)}$$

Similarly, the energy associated with a system of rigid current circuits is expressible in terms of the appropriate magnetic-field vectors or in terms involving inductance, namely,

$$W_m = \tfrac{1}{2} \int_{\text{space}} \mathbf{B} \cdot \mathbf{H} \, d\tau = \tfrac{1}{2}LI^2 \qquad \text{joules} \qquad \text{(B-11)}$$

It is expected, therefore, that the total energy stored in a volume of any electromagnetic field in which all field vectors exist may be taken as

$$W = W_e + W_m = \tfrac{1}{2} \int_{\text{space}} (\mathbf{D} \cdot \mathbf{E} + \mathbf{B} \cdot \mathbf{H}) \, d\tau \qquad \text{(B-12)}$$

Moreover, the time rate of decrease of stored energy gives the available instantaneous power and may be written as

$$P(t) = -\frac{\partial}{\partial t}\left[\tfrac{1}{2} \int_{\tau} (\mathbf{D} \cdot \mathbf{E} + \mathbf{B} \cdot \mathbf{H}) \, d\tau \right] \qquad \text{(B-13)}$$

But by the conservation of energy this power may be changed to thermal form, or it may leave through the surface that encloses τ. This condition is written

$$P(t) = \int_{\tau} \mathbf{J} \cdot \mathbf{E} \, d\tau + \oint \mathbf{S} \cdot \mathbf{n} \, dA \qquad \text{(B-14)}$$

where the first term denotes the Joule heat that is developed in the volume element and the second term denotes a vector whose magnitude expresses the power flow per unit area through the surface and whose direction is in the direction of maximum flow. It is desired to find an explicit form for the power-flow density vector $\mathbf{S}$.

To find the form for $\mathbf{S}$, it is noted that Eq. (B-13) may be written in the form

$$P(t) = -\int_{\tau} \left(\mathbf{E} \cdot \frac{\partial \mathbf{D}}{\partial t} + \mathbf{H} \cdot \frac{\partial \mathbf{B}}{\partial t} \right) d\tau \qquad \text{(B-15)}$$

Combine this expression with Maxwell's equations to find

$$P(t) = - \int_\tau (\mathbf{E} \cdot \nabla \times \mathbf{H} - \mathbf{E} \cdot \mathbf{J} - \mathbf{H} \cdot \nabla \times \mathbf{E}) \, d\tau$$

which is

$$P(t) = \int_\tau \mathbf{E} \cdot \mathbf{J} \, d\tau + \int_\tau (\mathbf{H} \cdot \nabla \times \mathbf{E} - \mathbf{E} \cdot \nabla \times \mathbf{H}) \, d\tau$$

Use is now made of the vector identity

$$\text{div} (\mathbf{A} \times \mathbf{B}) = \mathbf{B} \cdot \nabla \times \mathbf{A} - \mathbf{A} \cdot \nabla \times \mathbf{B} \qquad \text{(B-16)}$$

which permits writing $P(t)$ in the form

$$P(t) = \int_\tau \mathbf{E} \cdot \mathbf{J} \, d\tau + \int_\tau \nabla \cdot (\mathbf{E} \times \mathbf{H}) \, d\tau \qquad \text{(B-17)}$$

This is in the general form expected and was written originally in Eq. (B-14). For equivalence, it is required that the following expressions be related:

$$\oint \mathbf{S} \cdot \mathbf{n} \, dA = \int_\tau \nabla \cdot (\mathbf{E} \times \mathbf{H}) \, d\tau \qquad \text{(B-18)}$$

By applying the divergence theorem to the integral on the right, then

$$\int_\tau \nabla \cdot (\mathbf{E} \times \mathbf{H}) \, d\tau = \oint \mathbf{n} \cdot (\mathbf{E} \times \mathbf{H}) \, dA$$

which therefore permits identifying the vector $\mathbf{S}$ with

$$\mathbf{S} = \mathbf{E} \times \mathbf{H} \qquad \text{(B-19)}$$

The vector $\mathbf{S}$ is called the Poynting vector.

The Poynting vector $\mathbf{S}$ specifies the instantaneous direction and magnitude of energy flow density at any point in the medium, and from Eq. (B-18) it may be interpreted as the flux of power per unit area. From Eq. (B-19) it is seen that $\mathbf{S}$ is always perpendicular to the plane determined by $\mathbf{E}$ and $\mathbf{H}$. For example, if $\mathbf{E}$ and $\mathbf{H}$ are perpendicular to each other, which is the situation with plane, linearly polarized waves in space, then $\mathbf{S}$ is in the direction of propagation of the wave, which is perpendicular to the plane of $\mathbf{E}$ and $\mathbf{H}$.

Index